Electrical and Electronic Principles

Noel M Morris

Principal Lecturer
North Staffordshire Polytechnic

Longman
Scientific &
Technical

Longman Scientific & Technical
Longman Group UK Limited,
Longman House, Burnt Mill, Harlow,
Essex CM20 2JE, England
and Associated Companies throughout the world

First published in Great Britain by Pitman Publishing Limited 1980
Reprinted 1983, 1984, 1985
Reprinted by Longman Scientific & Technical 1986, 1988

ISBN 0-582-98851-9

Produced by Longman Singapore Publishers (Pte) Ltd.
Printed in Singapore.

Contents

Preface

The purpose of this book is to provide a sound introduction to electrical and electronic engineering principles. The treatment of the subject matter is such that it should appeal not only to students preparing for examinations, both for professional and technician qualifications, but also to the reader who is studying the subject as a supplementary topic.

Engineers and technicians who wish to refresh their knowledge of the subject will find the information presented in an easily digestible form. Problems (with answers) are provided at the end of each chapter; this feature will make the book doubly valuable to the reader studying on his own.

The book is developed in a logical form, commencing with a chapter on the fundamentals of electricity, which reflects modern thinking on the subject. Chapters 2, 3 and 4 are devoted to a discussion and analysis of electrical circuits, including Ohm's law, series and parallel circuits, and Kirchhoff's laws. These, as with other chapters, are liberally supported by worked examples.

There follow three chapters on the principles of magnetic circuits, electromagnetism and electrostatics. A knowledge of these topics is vital to the understanding of electrical and electronic devices. Chapter 8 deals with transients occurring in electrical circuits when they are either connected to, or disconnected from, a d.c. supply; this chapter is placed in its logical position in the book, since its understanding implies a knowledge of the principles of electromagnetism and electrostatics.

Chapter 9 introduces alternating current (both single-phase and three-phase). The transformer, which is an alternating current device, is dealt with in chapter 10. Finally, in chapter 11, a range of basic test instruments including moving-coil meters, moving-iron meters, dynamometer instruments, the d.c. potentiometer and the Wheatstone bridge are described and analysed. This chapter is placed at the end of the book because, for the reader to fully appreciate the principles both of direct current and alternating current measurements, a knowledge of the work in earlier sections of the book is necessary. However in the case of, say, direct current measurements, the reader may study relevant parts of the final chapter at any appropriate time. The final chapter also includes a section on the use of digital multimeters.

I would like to thank AVO Limited, Salford Electrical Instruments Limited, and Welwyn Electric Limited for permission to reproduce photographs and technical information. Thanks are also due to the electrical and electronics industry at large for supplying other information used in the book.

I am indebted to my wife for her assistance in completing the book, and also for her patience with my preoccupation whilst it was being written.

Noel M. Morris

1 Fundamentals of Electricity

1.1 Electrons and Protons

All solids, liquids and gases are principally made up of two basic types of particles known as electrons and protons. The electron is the smaller of the two; the proton is 1840 times more massive than the electron.

The **electron** carries a **negative** electrical charge.

The **proton** carries an equal and opposite **positive** charge.

When a material is in an uncharged state, it contains as many protons as it does electrons. However, if we remove some electrons from the material, the net positive charge on it exceeds the remaining negative charge so that the material exhibits a net positive charge. This phenomenon can be experienced by anyone wearing clothes manufactured from man-made fibre; while the garment is being worn, some electrons transfer to the wearer, and the static charge built up in this way may cause the wearer to experience an electrical shock during removal of the garment.

1.2 Basic Atomic Structure

All atoms have broadly the same type of structure, with the heavier protons forming the nucleus, around which the electrons orbit (see figure 1.1). The electrons orbit in distinct layers or **shells.** The radius of the orbit depends on the balance between two forces: the mechanical outward force on the electron due to its motion, and the inward electrostatic pull between the positive charge on the nucleus and the negative charge on the electron. The shell in which an electron finds itself depends on its energy; a high-energy electron orbits in a shell further away from the nucleus than does a low-energy electron.

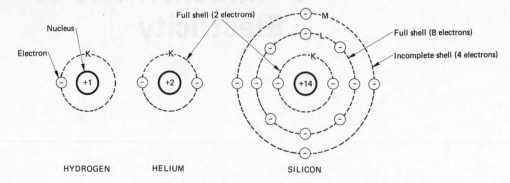

Fig. 1.1 Structure of hydrogen, helium and silicon atoms

Scientists have lettered the shells alphabetically, beginning with the K-shell (which is the shell nearest to the nucleus). Each shell can also be given a number (K = 1, L = 2, M = 3, etc) and it has been shown that the maximum number of electrons which can orbit in any shell is $2n^2$, where n is the "number" of the shell. The maximum number of electrons which may orbit in shells K to N is given in Table 1.1.

Table 1.1

Shell	Shell number	Maximum number of electrons in orbit
K	1	2
L	2	8
M	3	18
N	4	32

Examples of atomic structure are shown in figure 1.1. In the hydrogen atom, the K-shell contains only one electron, and the shell is said to be an **incomplete shell**. Like hydrogen, neon has only one shell (the K-shell) but, since it contains two electrons, it is described as a **full shell**. Silicon, with fourteen protons, has fourteen electrons in orbit, which completely fill the K-shell and L-shell and partially fill the M-shell. In a complex structure like silicon, the electrons in the inner shells are **tightly bound** to the nucleus due to the electrostatic force involved. Electrons farthest away from the nucleus (those in the M-shell in silicon) can be detached from the atom more easily and are said to be **loosely bound**. The gaps between the shells are regions where electrons cannot orbit, and are described as **forbidden energy gaps**.

It is the electrons in the outermost shell which are of particular interest to electrical and electronic engineers, since these dictate many properties of the substance. The outermost shell is known as the **valence shell**, and the electrons in this shell are known as **valence electrons**.

1.3 Atomic Bonds

When atoms combine, they do so by attempting to empty the outer shell by **losing electrons**, or by attempting to fill the outer shell by **gaining electrons**, or alternatively they **share electrons** with other atoms in order to give the appearance of a full shell. The latter method is of particular interest to electronic engineers, since this is the way in which some of the most useful semiconductor materials bond together. In the sharing process, each valence electron forms an orbit around two atoms including the parent atom and one other atom, forming what is known as a **covalent bond** between the atoms.

1.4 Ionization and Excitation

Since an individual atom contains as many electrons as it does protons, it is electrically neutral in its normal state. However, the addition of an electron gives it a net negative charge; and the removal of an electron gives it a net positive charge. The process of adding or removing electrons was first mentioned in section 1.1. When an atom carries either a negative or a positive charge it is known as an **ion**, and the process of producing this charge is known as **ionization**.

When an electron receives energy from an external source, such as heat or light, the extra energy allows it to move to a higher orbit. This process is known as **excitation**. Similarly, when an electron gives up energy, it falls from a higher orbit to a lower one. This loss of energy from the electron may appear in the form of heat or light; an example of the latter occurs in the *light-emitting diode* (led).

1.5 Holes and Electrons

When an atom loses an electron (why this occurs need not concern us here), the electrical charge balance is upset and the atom takes on a net positive charge. This positive charge is described as an electronic **hole**, and can be regarded as the absence of an electron where one would normally be found. Thus a hole is regarded as a **positive charge carrier**, much as an electron is a negative charge carrier.

1.6 Current and Charge

When the electrical circuit between a generator and an electrical load such as a lamp or heater is complete, electric current flows round the circuit. Electric current is simply the movement of electrical charge carriers (such as electrons) around the circuit. Consider now the movement of electrons; when the circuit is complete, the electrons are attracted from the negative pole of the supply and flow via the load to the positive pole of the supply. Since electrons cannot "accumulate" at any point in the circuit, they must complete the return path inside the generator to return to the negative pole. Current (symbol I) has the unit of the **ampere** (symbol A).

Certain devices such as cells and capacitors (see chapter 7) have the ability to store a quantity of electricity. Electrical **quantity** or electrical **charge** (symbol Q) is the capacity of a piece of electrical apparatus to store (or to discharge for that matter) a certain current for a given length of time. For example, the storage capacity of an accumulator is stated as a certain number of ampere-hours (unit symbol Ah). Thus an accumulator with a storage capacity of 40 Ah can discharge electricity at the rate of 1 A for 40 hours or 2 A for 20 hours. However, the hour is a long period of time, and we normally specify quantity or charge in ampere seconds or **coulombs** (unit symbol C). Thus

$$\text{Quantity} = \text{current} \times \text{time}$$

or in symbols

$$Q = It \text{ coulombs (C)} \qquad (1.1)$$

where the current is in amperes and time is in seconds.

An electron is a charge carrier whose electrical charge is

$$e = -1.6 \times 10^{-19} \text{ C}$$

That is, a current of 1 A flows in a circuit when

$$1/1.6 \times 10^{-19} = 6.25 \times 10^{18} \text{ electrons}$$

pass through each point in the circuit in one second. Strictly speaking we should talk of "rate of flow of charge" rather than current flow, but the latter is more conventional.

EXAMPLE 1.1

If a current of 3 A flows in a circuit for 120 ms, calculate the quantity of electricity which is involved.

Solution $I = 3$ A; $t = 120$ ms $= 120 \times 10^{-3}$ s $= 0.12$ s.
  From eqn. (1.1)

$$Q = It = 3 \times 0.12 = 0.36 \text{ C} \quad (Ans.)$$

EXAMPLE 1.2

If a charge of 8 C moves past a given point in a circuit in 0.2 s, calculate the current in the circuit.

Solution $Q = 8$ C; $t = 0.2$ s.

$$I = Q/t = 8/0.2 = 40 \text{ A} \quad (Ans.)$$

EXAMPLE 1.3

If an insulated conductor is charged to 3 C, how many additional electrons has it acquired?

Solution $Q = 3$ C; negative charge on an electron $= 1.6 \times 10^{-19}$ C.

$$\text{Number of electrons} = 3/(1.6 \times 10^{-19})$$
$$= 1.875 \times 10^{19} \text{ electrons} \quad (Ans.)$$

1.7 Potential Difference (p.d.) and Electromotive Force (e.m.f.)

Potential energy is the potential to do work. The potential energy of an electrical circuit infers that the circuit has the ability to move an electric charge around the circuit; that is, to cause current to flow. The difference in electrical potential between two points is known as the **potential difference** (symbol E) between the points, and the unit of p.d. is the **volt** (unit symbol V). Voltage is defined as

$$\text{Voltage} = \frac{\text{energy or work (joules)}}{\text{charge (coulombs)}}$$

or in symbols

$$E = \frac{W}{Q} \text{ volts (V)} \qquad (1.2)$$

In some cases the letter V is used where we use E above (i.e.

$V = W/Q$), and on the continent of Europe the letter U is used in place of E.

When discussing a voltage source such as a cell or a generator, we refer to the **electromotive force** (abbreviated to **e.m.f.**—symbol E) of the source. The e.m.f. of the source is a measure of its ability to cause a current to flow in an electrical circuit; e.m.f. is also measured in volts. When a number of cells are connected together so as to increase the available e.m.f., the combination of cells is called a **battery**.

1.8 Resistance of an Electrical Circuit

Resistance is the word used to describe the opposition of a circuit to the flow of current. Metals are usually good **conductors** of electricity and exhibit a low resistance. Materials known as **insulators** (which include glass and many plastics) are poor conductors and exhibit a very high resistance to current flow. A range of materials exist known as **semiconductors** (which include such materials as silicon, germanium and gallium arsenide) whose resistance lies between that of conductors and that of insulators. Certain properties of semiconductors make them useful in transistors and integrated circuits.

In general we can say that metals are good conductors and that non-metallic materials are poor conductors. These terms are relative, of course, and a "perfect" conductor and a "perfect" insulator do not exist in reality.

Metals have a low resistance because the outer orbits of their atoms overlap with one another to some extent, so that it is relatively easy for an electron to move from one atom to another.

Insulators, on the other hand, have a high resistance because this overlap does not occur between their atoms. Consequently, the transfer of electrons from one atom to another is relatively difficult.

1.9 The Unit of Resistance

Electrical resistance (symbol R) has the unit of the **ohm** (symbol Ω—pronounced omega) and is defined as follows:

When a current of 1 A flows through a circuit having a resistance of 1 Ω, the p.d. between the ends of the circuit is 1 V.

Fig. 1.2 (*a*) Wirewound resistor (*b*) and (*c*) circuit symbols. *Courtesy of Welwyn Electric Limited)*

Table 1.2 Resistance multiples in common use

Multiple name	Symbol	Multiple
milliohm	$m\Omega$	$\times 10^{-3}$ ($\times 0.001$)
kilohm	$k\Omega$	$\times 10^{3}$ ($\times 1000$)
megohm	$M\Omega$	$\times 10^{6}$ ($\times 1\,000\,000$)

One form of resistor known as a **wirewound resistor** consists of many turns of resistance wire wrapped around an insulating support (see figure 1.2*a*). The preferred circuit symbol for the resistor is shown in figure 1.2*b*, diagram *c* representing an alternative circuit symbol.

In some cases, such as in the measurement of resistance of conductors having a large cross-sectional area, the unit of the ohm is too large. In other cases, such as in electronic circuits, the ohm is much too small. A list of the multiples of resistance in common use is given in Table 1.2.

1.10 The Effect of Temperature Change on Resistance

Due to the nature of the materials used for conductors (i.e. copper and aluminium), their resistance rises as the temperature increases; it also falls with temperature reduction. The amount by which the resistance changes is related to a factor known as the **temperature coefficient of resistance** (symbol α) in the way described below.

In the following discussion we will concern ourselves with the effect of temperature change on normal types of conductor material. A graph showing the change in resistance of a conductor with temperature is illustrated in figure 1.3. At $0°$ C its resistance is R_0, at temperature θ_1 it is R_1, and at temperature θ_2 it is R_2. The graph relating resistance and temperature

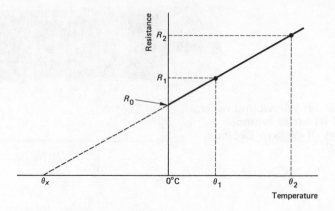

Fig. 1.3 Graph showing the change of resistance of a conductor with temperature

is, in fact, a straight line, so that its slope at all points is the same as that between θ_1 and θ_2. That is

$$\text{Slope} = \frac{R_2 - R_1}{\theta_2 - \theta_1} \, \Omega/^\circ C$$

The slope gives the increase in resistance for a given temperature rise. The **temperature coefficient of resistance referred to temperature θ_1** is given the symbol α_1, where

$$\alpha_1 = \frac{\text{slope of the resistance/temperature graph}}{R_1}$$

$$= \frac{R_2 - R_1}{(\theta_2 - \theta_1)R_1} \, (^\circ C)^{-1} \tag{1.3}$$

Since the above equation has dimensions of

$$\text{resistance}/(\text{temperature} \times \text{resistance})$$

the effective dimensions of α are

$$1/\text{temperature} \quad \text{or} \quad (\text{temperature})^{-1} \quad \text{i.e. } (^\circ C)^{-1}$$

$(^\circ C)^{-1}$ can be read as "per degree C".

The temperature coefficient of resistance referred to θ_2 is described as α_2, where

$$\alpha_2 = \frac{\text{slope of the resistance/temperature graph}}{R_2}$$

$$= \frac{R_2 - R_1}{(\theta_2 - \theta_1)R_2} \tag{1.4}$$

Alternatively, the slope may be calculated between θ_0 and θ_1 as follows

$$\text{Slope} = \frac{R_1 - R_0}{\theta_1 - \theta_0} = \frac{R_1 - R_0}{\theta_1 - 0} = \frac{R_1 - R_0}{\theta_1} \, \Omega/^{\circ}\text{C}$$

Hence the **temperature coefficient of resistance referred to 0° C** is

$$\alpha_0 = \frac{R_1 - R_0}{\theta_1 R_0} \, (^{\circ}\text{C})^{-1} \tag{1.5}$$

The value of α_0 for annealed copper is typically 0.004 264 $(^{\circ}\text{C})^{-1}$. We can re-arrange eqn. (1.5) as follows:

$$\alpha_0 \theta_1 R_0 = R_1 - R_0$$

or

$$R_1 = R_0(1 + \alpha_0 \theta_1) \tag{1.6}$$

Also, since the slope of the resistance/temperature graph is $(R_2 - R_0)/\theta_2$, we can show that

$$R_2 = R_0(1 + \alpha_0 \theta_2) \tag{1.7}$$

A useful equation is obtained by dividing eqn. (1.6) by eqn. (1.7) as follows:

$$\frac{R_1}{R_2} = \frac{1 + \alpha_0 \theta_1}{1 + \alpha_0 \theta_2} \tag{1.8}$$

Assuming that the graph is linear down to zero resistance, we will find that it cuts the zero resistance line at temperature θ_x (see figure 1.3). The slope of the graph between 0° C and θ_x is

$$(R_0 - 0)/(0 - \theta_x) = R_0/(-\theta_x)$$

Using our definition of temperature coefficient of resistance, we see that the value of α_0 is

$$\alpha_0 = \frac{\text{slope of resistance/temperature graph}}{R_0}$$

$$= \frac{R_0}{-\theta_x} \times \frac{1}{R_0} = \frac{1}{-\theta_x}$$

Table 1.3 Temperature coefficients of resistance

Material	α_0 (°C)$^{-1}$	Material	α_0 (°C)$^{-1}$
Aluminium	0.004	Manganin	
		(Cu, Mn, Ni alloy)	0.0 (average)
Carbon	−0.0003	Nickel	0.005
Constantan		Nichrome	
(Cu–Ni alloy)	0.0 (average)	(Ni, Fe, Cr alloy)	0.0002
Copper	0.004	Silver	0.004
Gold	0.004	Tungsten	0.005
Iron	0.006		

Measurements show that, for annealed copper wire, the value of θ_x is about −234.5° C; hence for annealed copper wire

$$\alpha_0 = \frac{1}{-(-234.5)} = 0.004\ 264\ (°C)^{-1}$$

A list of the approximate temperature coefficients of resistance for a number of materials is provided in Table 1.3.

There are certain alloys such as constantan, eureka and manganin, which show very little change in resistance with temperature. These materials are used in the construction of accurate resistance elements for laboratory use, in which the resistance must remain constant over a wide temperature variation.

In other materials such as semiconductors and insulators, the resistance reduces as the temperature increases, and vice versa.

EXAMPLE 1.4

The resistance of a length of iron wire is 20 Ω at 18° C. Calculate its resistance if a) it is cooled to 0° C, b) it is heated to 60° C.

Solution $R_1 = 20\ \Omega$, $\theta_1 = 18°$ C.
   From Table 1.3, α_0 for iron is 0.006 per °C.
a) From eqn. (1.6)

$$R_1 = R_0(1 + \alpha_0\theta_1)$$

hence

$$R_0 = R_1/(1 + \alpha_0\theta_1) = 20/(1 + [0.006 \times 18])$$
$$= 18.05\ \Omega \quad (Ans.)$$

b) $R_1 = 20\ \Omega$, $\theta_1 = 18°$ C, $\theta_2 = 60°$ C.
From eqn. (1.8)

$$\frac{R_1}{R_2} = \frac{1 + \alpha_0\theta_1}{1 + \alpha_0\theta_2}$$

hence

$$R_2 = R_1(1 + \alpha_0\theta_2)/(1 + \alpha_0\theta_1)$$
$$= 20(1 + [0.006 \times 60])/(1 + [0.006 \times 18])$$
$$= 24.55\,\Omega \quad (Ans.)$$

Note The value of R_2 obtained in *b*) above could also be calculated from eqn. (1.7) as follows

$$R_2 = R_0(1 + \alpha_0\theta_2)$$
$$= 18.05(1 + [0.006 \times 60]) = 24.55\,\Omega$$

1.11 Resistivity

The **resistivity**, symbol ρ (pronounced rho), of a material is an important property since it relates the electrical resistance of a conductor to its physical size, i.e. it relates the resistance to the length and area of the conductor.

Clearly, if we double the length of a conductor and leave the cross-sectional area unchanged, the resistance of the conductor to the flow of current is doubled. This is analogous in hydraulics to doubling the length of piping through which fluid flows in a hydraulic circuit; the net effect is a doubling of the resistance to fluid flow. Thus

Resistance $\propto$ length l of the conductor

If we double the cross-sectional area through which the current flows and leave the conductor length unchanged, we halve the resistance to current flow (which is analogous in hydraulics to doubling the cross-sectional area of the pipe). Hence

Resistance α $\dfrac{1}{\text{area } a}$

The relationship between the resistance and the length, area and resistivity of a material is given by the following equation.

$$\text{Resistance} = \text{resistivity} \times \frac{\text{length}}{\text{area}}$$

or in symbols

$$R = \rho\frac{l}{a}\ \text{ohms}\ (\Omega) \tag{1.9}$$

hence

$$\rho = Ra/l$$

From the above expression, the dimensions of resistivity are

Resistance × area/length = resistance × (length × length)/length
$$= \text{resistance} \times \text{length}$$
$$= \text{ohm metre } (\Omega \, \text{m})$$

In the case of good conductors, resistivity is given in microhm metres ($\mu\Omega$ m). Typical values are
for copper 0.0173 $\mu\Omega$ m (1.73×10^{-8} Ω m)
and for aluminium 0.0283 $\mu\Omega$ m (2.83×10^{-8} Ω m).

EXAMPLE 1.5

Determine the resistance of a 100 m length of aluminium wire of diameter 2 mm. The resistivity of aluminium is 0.0283 $\mu\Omega$ m.

Solution $r = 1 \, \text{mm} = 10^{-3} \, \text{m}$, $l = 100 \, \text{m}$, $\rho = 0.0283 \times 10^{-6} \, \Omega \, \text{m}$.

Area of wire $= \pi r^2 = \pi \times (10^{-3})^2 = 3.142 \times 10^{-6} \, \text{m}^2$
$R = \rho l/a = 0.0283 \times 10^{-6} \, (\Omega \, \text{m}) \times 100 \, (\text{m})/3.142 \times 10^{-6} \, (\text{m}^2)$
$= 0.9 \, \Omega$ (*Ans.*)

Note that the basic SI units are used in equations, i.e. Ω, m and m^2 rather than $\mu\Omega$ and mm, etc. Dimensions *must* be converted into the basic SI values before being inserted into equations.

EXAMPLE 1.6

A length of copper wire of diameter 4 mm has a resistance of 0.069 Ω. If the resistivity of copper is 0.0173 $\mu\Omega$ m, determine the length of the wire.

Solution $r = 2 \, \text{mm} = 2 \times 10^{-3} \, \text{m}$, $R = 0.069 \, \Omega$, $\rho = 0.0173 \times 10^{-6} \, \Omega \, \text{m}$.
Since $R = \rho l/a$, then

$l = Ra/\rho$
$= 0.069 \, (\Omega) \times \pi \times (2 \times 10^{-3})^2 (\text{m}^2)/0.0173 \times 10^{-6} \, (\Omega \, \text{m})$
$= 50.12 \, \text{m}$ (*Ans.*)

1.12 Conductance and Conductivity

Conductance, symbol G, is the reciprocal of resistance and has the unit of the **siemens** (unit symbol S). Hence

$$G = \frac{1}{R} \tag{1.10}$$

Thus a resistance of 100 Ω is equivalent to a conductance of 0.01 S.

Conductivity, symbol σ (pronounced sigma), is the reciprocal of resistivity. Replacing ρ in eqn. (1.9) by $1/\sigma$ gives

$$R = \frac{1}{\sigma a} \qquad (1.11)$$

or, alternatively, since $R = 1/G$ then

$$G = \frac{\sigma a}{l} \qquad (1.12)$$

The dimensions of conductivity are $(\Omega\,m)^{-1}$.

EXAMPLE 1.7

Calculate the area of a copper conductor of length 120 m whose conductance is 0.38 S and whose conductivity is $57.8 \times 10^6\,(\Omega\,m)^{-1}$.

Solution $l = 120$ m, $G = 0.38$ S, $\sigma = 57.8 \times 10^6\,(\Omega\,m)^{-1}$.
  From eqn. (1.13), $G = \sigma a / l$, hence

$$\begin{aligned}
a &= Gl/\sigma \\
&= 0.38\,(S) \times 120\,(m)/57.8 \times 10^6\,(\Omega\,m)^{-1} \\
&= 0.789 \times 10^{-6}\,m^2 \text{ or } 0.789\,mm^2 \quad (Ans.)
\end{aligned}$$

1.13   Preferred Values of Resistance

In order to provide coverage of a wide range of resistor values using only a limited number of resistors, a "preferred" range of values of resistances is used. Since nothing in real life is perfect, we would not expect every resistor having a nominal value of 100 Ω to have a resistance of 100.000 Ω. Manufacturers produce components within a selected **tolerance** band; if this band is ± 10 per cent, then a 100 Ω (nominal) resistance would have a resistance in the range from

$$(100\,\Omega - 10\%) = 90\,\Omega \quad \text{to} \quad (100\,\Omega + 10\%) = 110\,\Omega$$

A five per cent tolerance range means that a resistance of 100 Ω (nominal) resistor lies in the range 95–105 Ω. For general-purpose use in electronic circuits, the tolerance range of resistors is usually ± 10 per cent and ± 5 per cent. Closer tolerance values i.e. ± 2 per cent, or wider tolerance values, i.e. ± 20 per cent, are also available. The accuracy of the resistor is usually reflected in its cost.

Preferred values are chosen so that the upper value of one resistor is either equal to or just overlaps with the lower value of the next higher resistor. This is illustrated in Table 1.4 for three preferred values within the 10 per cent tolerance range.

Table 1.4

Nominal value	Lower value	Upper value
27 Ω		29.7 Ω
33 Ω	29.7 Ω	36.3 Ω
39 Ω	35.1 Ω	

We see that, within a 10 per cent tolerance range, the lowest value of the 33 Ω range is equal to the upper value of the 27 Ω range, and the upper value of the 33 Ω range overlaps with the lowest value of the 39 Ω range. A list of nominal values together with their tolerances is given in Table 1.5.

Table 1.5 Nominal resistance values and their tolerances

20%	10%	5%	20%	10%	5%
10	10	10	33	33	33
		11			36
	12	12		39	39
		13			43
15	15	15	47	47	47
		16			51
	18	18		56	56
		20			62
22	22	22	68	68	68
		24			75
	27	27		82	82
		30			91

1.14 Resistor Colour Code

Resistors with power ratings less than about 2 W used in electronic circuits are colour-coded according to an international standard. The method of coding resistors with axial leads is shown in figure 1.4. The colour code used is listed in Table 1.6, and can be remembered by means of the mnemonic

Bye **B**ye **R**osie **O**ff **Y**ou **G**o, **B**ristol **V**ia **G**reat **W**estern

The first letter of each word gives the first letter of the colour associated with its value in the colour code: Black = 0, Brown = 1, Red = 2, etc. (Great Western refers to the defunct British railway line that ran to Bristol.) Two examples of colour coding are given in Table 1.7.

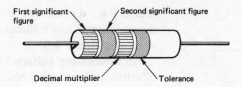

First significant figure
Second significant figure
Decimal multiplier
Tolerance

Fig. 1.4 Resistor colour code

Table 1.6 Resistor colour code

Colour	Significant value	Decimal multiplier	Tolerance (per cent)
no band			20
silver		0.01	10
gold		0.1	5
black	0	1	
brown	1	10	
red	2	10^2 (×100)	2
orange	3	10^3 (×1000)	
yellow	4	10^4 (×10 000)	
green	5	10^5 (×100 000)	
blue	6	10^6 (×1 000 000)	
violet	7	10^7 (×10 000 000)	
grey	8	10^8 (×100 000 000)	
white	9	10^9 (×1 000 000 000)	

Table 1.7 Two colour-coding examples

1st *band*	2nd *band*	3rd *band*	4th *band*	Value	Tolerance
orange	white	orange	silver	39 kΩ	10%
yellow	violet	red	gold	4700 Ω	5%

1.15 Direct and Alternating Voltage and Current

When we measure the instantaneous output voltage from a battery, we find that one terminal is always positive with respect to the other terminal. A voltage source of this kind is known as a **direct voltage source** or as a **unidirectional voltage source**. When a resistor is connected to this voltage source, a current flows through the resistor in one direction only; this is known as **direct current** (abbreviated to d.c). The abbreviation is sometimes used as a descriptive adjective to describe equip-

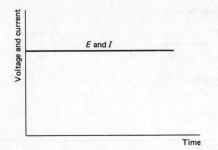

Fig. 1.5 Direct voltage and current

ment, e.g., d.c. motor, d.c. circuit, etc. A graph showing a direct voltage and a direct current plotted to a base of time is shown in figure 1.5.

An **alternating voltage** is one which periodically reverses or alternates about zero volts. That is to say, the voltage of the "live" wire is positive for a period of time, followed by another period during which it is negative. When such a voltage is connected to a resistor, it causes an **alternating current** to flow in the resistor. (Alternating current is sometimes abbreviated to a.c.)

A simple alternating voltage source is shown in figure 1.6*a*, and comprises two batteries of equal voltage. The common connection C of the batteries is connected to the centre-tap of a potentiometer. When the sliding contact (also known as the *wiper*) of the potentiometer is in position A, the live wire is positive with respect to the common line. When the slider is moved to position B, the live wire becomes negative with respect to the common line. Since the common line is connected to ground, it is often referred to as the **neutral wire** or neutral line.

If the slider is moved up and down the potentiometer, so that its displacement varies sinusoidally with time, then the voltage of the live wire varies sinusoidally with time as shown

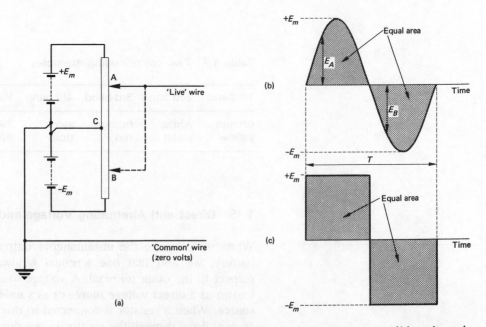

Fig. 1.6 (*a*) A simple alternating voltage source, (*b*) a sinusoidal voltage waveform, and (*c*) a rectangular wave or square wave

in figure 1.6*b*. The **peak positive voltage** $+E_m$ occurs when the slider is at the top of the potentiometer; the **peak negative voltage** $-E_m$ occurs when the slider is at the bottom of the potentiometer.

An alternating waveform is one whose area under the graph in the positive half-cycle is equal to the area under the graph in the negative half-cycle. Both waveforms in figure 1.6 satisfy this condition.

The total time taken to complete the alternating waveform is known as the **periodic time** T (see figure 1.6*b*).

The **frequency** f of the waveform is the number of complete cycles which occur every second, so that

$$\text{Frequency } f = \frac{1}{T} \text{ cycles per second or hertz (Hz)}$$

where T is measured in seconds. If the periodic time is 1 ms, the frequency is

$$f = 1/(1 \times 10^{-3}) = 10^3 \text{ Hz or } 1 \text{ k Hz}$$

Alternating waveforms may take many forms, an example being the *square wave* or *rectangular wave* in figure 1.6*c*. This waveform is generated by suddenly moving the slider of the potentiometer in figure 1.6*a* from one end to the other, the wiper remaining either at the top or at the bottom of the potentiometer for a time equal to one-half of the periodic time.

Exercises

1.1 In connection with electrical circuits, explain what is meant by *a*) an electron, *b*) shells in an atomic structure, *c*) a proton, *d*) an incomplete shell, *e*) a loosely bound electron, *f*) a forbidden energy gap, *g*) a valence electron, *h*) a hole.

1.2 A battery discharges a current of 2.5 A for 5 hours. Calculate the quantity of electricity discharged into the circuit *a*) in coulombs, *b*) in ampere-hours.
[*a*) 45 000 C; *b*) 12.5 Ah]

1.3 Calculate the voltage applied to an electrical machine if it does 36 MJ of work when 180 000 C of electricity flow through it. Ignore the effects of power loss in the machine.
[200 V]

1.4 Express the resistance of a 1.2 kΩ resistor in *a*) megohms, *b*) ohms, *c*) milliohms.
[*a*) 0.0012 MΩ; *b*) 1200 Ω; *c*) 1.2×10^6 mΩ]

1.5 At 0° C a length of copper wire has a resistance of 1.4 Ω. Determine its resistance at *a*) 20° C, *b*) −10° C. The temperature coefficient of resistance of copper at 0° C is 0.004 (°C)$^{-1}$.
[*a*) 1.512 Ω; *b*) 1.344 Ω]

1.6 If, at 25° C, the temperature coefficient of resistance of a material is 0.0045 (°C)$^{-1}$, determine its value at 0° C.
[0.0051 (°C)$^{-1}$]

1.7 At 0° C the temperature coefficient of resistance of copper is 0.0042 $(°C)^{-1}$). Determine its value at 30° C.

[0.00373 $(°C)^{-1}$]

1.8 A length of aluminium wire of temperature coefficient of resistance referred to 20° C of 0.0039 $(°C)^{-1}$, has a resistance of 25 Ω at 50° C. Determine its resistance at 20° C.

[22.39 Ω]

1.9 The resistance of a length of wire at 20° C is 5 Ω and is 6 Ω at 90° C. Determine the temperature coefficient of resistance referred to 0° C of the material from which the wire is formed. What is the resistance of the wire at 40° C?

[0.003 $(°C)^{-1}$; 5.28 Ω]

1.10 Calculate the resistance of each core of a cable whose cross-sectional area is 30 mm^2 and whose length is 100 m. The resistivity of the conductor material is 0.028 $\mu\Omega$ m.

[0.093 Ω]

1.11 A coaxial cable used in a data transmission system is surrounded by a flexible copper braid screen. The average cross-sectional area of the screen is 10 mm^2 and the length of the cable is 50 m. Calculate the resistance of the screen if its resistivity is 25 $\mu\Omega$ mm.

[0.125 Ω]

1.12 A coil for an electrical machine has 500 turns of wire made from a material whose resistivity is 0.017 $\mu\Omega$ m. If the mean length per turn is 200 mm and the resistance of the coil is 4 Ω, determine the cross-sectional area of the wire.

[0.425 mm^2]

1.13 The resistance of a length of wire of 5 mm^2 cross-sectional area and length 32.3 m is found to be 0.12 Ω at 0° C. When the temperature of the wire is raised to 50° C its resistance is 0.144 Ω. Determine a) the temperature coefficient of resistance of the wire referred to 0° C and b) the resistivity of the wire at 0° C.

[a) 0.004 $(°C)^{-1}$; b) 0.0186 $\mu\Omega$ m]

1.14 Determine the conductance of the length of wire in problem 1.13 a) at 0° C and b) at 50° C. Calculate also the conductivity of the wire at 0° C.

[a) 8.33 S; b) 6.94 S; 53.76 × 10^6 $(\Omega$ m)$^{-1}$]

1.15 Give the colour code bands for the following resistance values: 1 MΩ, 82 kΩ, 3300 Ω, 150 Ω, 47 Ω and 2.2 Ω.

1.16 The colour code bands (commencing at the most significant value) on a resistor are: yellow, violet, orange, gold. State the values of the resistor and its tolerance.

[47 kΩ±5%]

1.17 Explain how two 1 kΩ, 1 W rated resistors are connected to form a) a 2 kΩ, 2 W rated circuit, b) a 500 Ω, 2 W rated circuit. Calculate the value of the voltage which must be applied to each circuit in order to dissipate 2 W.

[a) 63.24 V; b) 31.62 V]

2 Ohm's Law, Power, and Energy

Ohm's law (named after the scientist George Simon Ohm) gives the relationship in an electrical circuit between the current I in amperes, the e.m.f. (or p.d.) E in volts, and the resistance R in ohms. One form of the equation is

$$I = \frac{E}{R} \qquad (2.1)$$

that is

$$\text{Amperes} = \frac{\text{volts}}{\text{ohms}}$$

A ghoulish reminder of this form of the equation is

Interment = Earth over Remains

The flow of current in an electrical circuit is analogous to the flow of water through pipes in a hydraulic system as follows: the water flow is equivalent to current flow in an electrical circuit, the pump pressure is analogous to the applied voltage, and the resistance of the hydraulic circuit is analogous to electrical resistance.

2.1 The Linear Relationship between Current and Electromotive Force in a Resistor

To illustrate the above formulae, consider what happens in a circuit when a fixed resistor of $10\,\Omega$ is connected to a d.c.

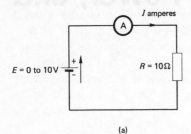

(a)

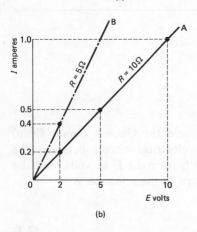

(b)

Fig. 2.1 The linear relationship between *I* and *E* in a purely resistive circuit

supply voltage which can be varied from zero to 10 V as shown in figure 2.1*a*. The current and voltage notation adopted in figure 2.1 is explained as follows:

> *a)* The current is assumed to flow *out* of the positive pole of the battery and *into* the negative pole. The arrow indicating the direction of flow of the current is drawn *on the branch* in which the current flows. In figure 2.1*a* there is only one branch.
>
> *b)* A voltage (potential) arrow is drawn *by the side* of the battery, the arrow pointing from the negative pole to the positive pole.

The above notation is important since it shows the "direction" of action both of the voltage and the current. More will be said about this later.

When the supply voltage is zero, the current in the circuit is also zero, since without an e.m.f. there can be no current. Increasing the supply voltage to 2 V (see graph A in figure 2.1*b*) results in a current of

$$I = \frac{E}{R} = \frac{2\,\text{V}}{10\,\Omega} = 0.2\,\text{A}$$

An e.m.f. of 5 V gives a current of

$$I = \frac{E}{R} = \frac{5\,\text{V}}{10\,\Omega} = 0.5\,\text{A}$$

and an e.m.f. of 10 V gives a current of 1 A. Note that the graph relating the current and voltage is a straight line passing through the origin; that is, the current is proportional to the applied voltage.

If the resistor is replaced by one having a resistance of 5 Ω, then when the supply voltage is 2 V (see graph B in figure 2.1*b*) the current is

$$I = \frac{E}{R} = \frac{2}{5} = 0.4\,\text{A}$$

That is, the current is doubled (at the same value of voltage) when compared to the circuit having a resistance of 10 Ω.

In an electrical power circuit such as may be found in the home and in industry, resistance values are fairly low and current values are high. For example, if a 20 Ω resistor is connected to a 240 V mains supply, the current drawn is

$$I = \frac{E}{R} = \frac{240}{20} = 12\,\text{A}$$

In heavy engineering industry, the current drawn by a large item of electrical equipment may be many hundreds of amperes, some equipment consuming several thousand amperes.

In electronic circuits, resistor values are usually high and (in many cases) the supply voltage is low. For example the current flowing in a part of a transistor amplifier may be as low as a few microamperes (remember, $1\,\mu A = 10^{-6}\,A = 0.000\,001\,A$) or even smaller.

When using Ohm's law it is VERY IMPORTANT TO REMEMBER to convert all values to the BASIC UNITS of amperes, volts and ohms before using them in equations. Failure to do this may result in errors arising in the calculation.

EXAMPLE 2.1

A voltage of 1200 mV is applied to a resistor of 5.6 kΩ. Calculate the value of the current in the resistor.

Solution

$$E = 1200\,\text{mV} = 1200 \times 10^{-3}\,\text{V} = 1.2\,\text{V}$$

$$R = 5.6\,\text{k}\Omega = 5.6 \times 10^{3}\,\Omega = 5600\,\Omega$$

$$I = \frac{E}{R} = \frac{1.2}{5600} = 0.000\,214\,\text{A}$$
$$= 0.214 \times 10^{-3}\,\text{A} = 0.214\,\text{mA} \quad (Ans.)$$

A point to remember is to **round** the calculated value to a practical value. For example, in the above example the calculated value of $0.214\,285\,71\ldots$ mA has been rounded to 0.214 mA, since the latter value could be read on an instrument of reasonable accuracy. The "rounding" operation may result in some small errors in calculations, but provided that common sense is applied the results will be within acceptable engineering limits.

2.2 Voltage and Ohm's Law

If we re-arrange equation (2.1) we get

$$E = IR \tag{2.2}$$

or

$$\text{Volts} = \text{amperes} \times \text{ohms}$$

EXAMPLE 2.2

Calculate the voltage developed across a 15 Ω resistor when a current of 6.3 A flows in it.

Solution $I = 6.3$ A, $R = 15$ Ω.

$$E = IR = 6.3 \times 15 = 94.5 \text{ V} \quad (Ans.)$$

EXAMPLE 2.3

A current of 8 μA flows in a resistor of resistance 10 kΩ. Calculate the p.d. across the resistor.

Solution $I = 8 \mu A = 8 \times 10^{-6}$ A, $R = 10$ kΩ $= 10 \times 10^3$ Ω.

$$E = IR = (8 \times 10^{-6}) \times (10 \times 10^3)$$
$$= 80 \times 10^{-3} \text{ V or } 80 \text{ mV} \quad (Ans.)$$

2.3   Resistance and Ohm's Law

Re-arranging eq. (2.1) once more gives

$$R = \frac{E}{I} \qquad\qquad (2.3)$$

or

$$\text{Ohms} = \frac{\text{volts}}{\text{amperes}}$$

EXAMPLE 2.4

A constant value of current is supplied through each of two resistors R_1 and R_2. If the p.d. across R_1 is 10 V and that across R_2 is 2.3 V, calculate the values of R_1 and R_2.

Solution $I = 2$ mA $= 0.002$ A, $E_1 = 10$ V, $E_2 = 2.3$ V.

$$R_1 = \frac{E_1}{I} = \frac{10}{0.002} = 5000 \text{ Ω or } 5 \text{ kΩ} \quad (Ans.)$$

$$R_2 = \frac{E_2}{I} = \frac{2.3}{0.002} = 1150 \text{ Ω or } 1.15 \text{ kΩ} \quad (Ans.)$$

2.4   Aiding and Opposing Voltages

In many electrical circuits we find a number of voltage sources which may either aid or oppose one another. In this section we develop a method which is useful when dealing with more complex circuits later in the book. We consider the two circuits in figure 2.2. The circuit notation used here is that outlined earlier, namely a) the current arrow is drawn on the branch in which it flows and points in conventional direction of current flow and b) the potential arrow associated with each battery points from the negative pole to the positive pole of the battery.

Series aiding voltages (figure 2.2a)

To determine the voltage of point X with respect to point W, we adopt the following procedure. Proceeding from point W (our starting point) and moving towards X (our finishing point), we *give each e.m.f. a positive sign if it points in the direction in which we move around the circuit* (which it does for both batteries). Hence

Potential of X relative to W is $E_{XW} = E_1 + E_2$

Since W is our starting point we refer to it as the **reference point** (which may be regarded as the "zero voltage point" in the circuit). The idea of starting points and finishing points is very useful in more complex d.c. circuits and in a.c. circuits.

Series opposing voltages (figure 2.2b)

In this case we need to determine the potential of point Z with respect to point Y. In this case our starting (reference) point is Y, and proceeding to Z we find that e.m.f. arrow E_1 *opposes* our movement around the circuit, so that we write this voltage down as $-E_1$. E.m.f. arrow E_2 points in the direction of movement around the circuit, hence

Potential of Z relative to Y is $E_{ZY} = -E_1 + E_2$

If $E_1 = 10$ V, $E_2 = 20$ V and $R = 5\ \Omega$, then

$$E_{ZY} = -10 + 20 = +10\ V$$

i.e. Z is positive with respect to Y, and

$$I = E/R = 10/5 = 2\ A$$

flowing away from Z and entering Y.

However, if $E_1 = 30$ V and $E_2 = 10$ V, then

$$E_{ZY} = -30 + 20 = -10\ V$$

i.e. Z is negative with respect to Y, and

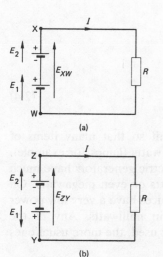

Fig. 2.2 A circuit with e.m.f.s which are (*a*) series aiding, (*b*) series opposing

$$I = E/R = -10/5 = -2 \text{ A}$$

corresponding to a current of 2 A flowing away from Y and entering Z.

2.5 Electrical Power

In a d.c. circuit the relationship between the power P in watts, the voltage V in volts, and the current I in amperes is

$$P = EI \text{ watts (W)}$$

or in symbols

$$\text{Watts} = \text{volts} \times \text{amperes} \qquad (2.4)$$

The watt is a practical size of unit so that many items of equipment can be rated directly in watts (lamps for example). However, other devices such as electric generators have much higher power ratings, often kilowatts or even megawatts. On the other hand, many electronic devices have a very low power consumption, and may be rated in milliwatts. Any of the multiples given in chapter 1 may be used, the more usual ones being given below.

$$1 \text{ MW} = 1 \text{ megawatt} = 10^6 \text{ W} = 1\,000\,000 \text{ W}$$
$$1 \text{ kW} = 1 \text{ kilowatt} = 10^3 \text{ W} = \qquad 1\,000 \text{ W}$$
$$1 \text{ mW} = 1 \text{ milliwatt} = 10^{-3} \text{ W} = \qquad 0.001 \text{ W}$$

Thus

power in megawatts = power in watts/1 000 000

power in kilowatts = power in watts/1000

power in milliwatts = power in watts × 1000

If the power consumed is 5863 W, it corresponds to 0.005 863 MW, or 5.863 kW or 5 863 000 mW.

Equation (2.4) may also be re-arranged as follows

$$E = \frac{P}{I} \quad \text{or} \quad I = \frac{P}{E}$$

EXAMPLE 2.5

Calculate the power generated by a d.c. generator when its terminal voltage is 120 V and the output current is 12.6 A.

Solution $E = 120$ V, $I = 12.6$ A.

$$P = EI = 120 \times 12.6 = 1512 \text{ W} \quad (Ans.)$$

EXAMPLE 2.6

A battery whose terminal voltage is 9 V supplies an electronic circuit with a current of 12.5 mA. Calculate the power consumed by the circuit.

Solution $E = 9$ V, $I = 12.5$ mA $= 12.5 \times 10^{-3}$ A.

$$P = EI = 9 \times 12.5 \times 10^{-3}$$

$$= 0.1125 \text{ W or } 112.5 \text{ mW} \quad (Ans.)$$

EXAMPLE 2.7

A load consumes a current of 289 A at a voltage of 10 kV. Calculate the power consumed by the load.

Solution $E = 10$ kV $= 10\,000$ V, $I = 289$ A.

$$P = EI = 10\,000 \times 289$$

$$= 2\,890\,000 \text{ W or } 2.89 \text{ MW} \quad (Ans.)$$

2.6   Power and Ohm's Law

Combining Ohm's law with the expression for power (eqn. (2.4)) we get

$$P = EI = (IR)I = I^2 R \tag{2.5}$$

and

$$P = EI = E\left(\frac{E}{R}\right) = \frac{E^2}{R} \tag{2.6}$$

EXAMPLE 2.8

If the power consumed by a resistance of 4.7 kΩ is 350 mW, determine the current in the circuit.

Solution $R = 4.7$ kΩ $= 4700$ Ω, $P = 350$ mW $= 0.35$ W.
   Re-arranging eqn. (2.5) gives

$$I^2 = P/R$$

$$I = \sqrt{(P/R)} = \sqrt{(0.35/4700)}$$

$$= 0.008\,63 \text{ A or } 8.63 \text{ mA} \quad (Ans.)$$

EXAMPLE 2.9

An electrical circuit having a resistance of 2.5 Ω consumes 100 kW. Calculate the value of the supply voltage.

Solution $R = 2.5\ \Omega$, $P = 100\ \text{kW} = 100\,000\ \text{W}$.
Re-arranging eqn. (2.6) gives

$$E^2 = PR$$

$$E = \sqrt{(PR)} = \sqrt{(100\,000 \times 2.5)} = 500\ \text{V} \quad (Ans.)$$

2.7 Circuit Notation for Power Generation and Power Consumption

In the examples dealt with above, we referred to both power *production* (by a generator or battery) and power *consumption* (by an electrical load which could be a resistor, a motor, an electronic circuit, or a battery which is on charge, etc.) We must therefore be able to identify the two types of element, a generator or a load on the circuit diagram. It is not, for example, easy to say if a battery is discharging (generating power) or is charging (consuming power). In this section we develop a circuit notation which allows us to identify which circuit element is acting as a generator and which as a load.

Consider the circuit in figure 2.3. The battery E_1 is the source of power and is quite clearly the *generator* in the circuit. The resistor R is consuming power and is therefore a *load*. If we inspect the current and potential arrows on the circuit, we see that

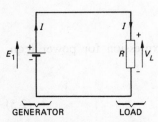

Fig. 2.3 A circuit notation for power generation and for power consumption

1 In the case of the *generator*, the direction of the e.m.f. arrow E_1 *acts in the same direction* as that of the current arrow I.
2 In the case of a *load*, the direction of the p.d. arrow V_L acts *in the opposite direction* to that of the current arrow I. [Remember that the current *inside* the resistor flows from a point of high potential (i.e. more positive) to a point of low potential.]

The above notation is particularly useful when dealing with more complex circuits than the kind in figure 2.3.

2.8 Electrical Energy

Whenever current flows in an electrical circuit having resistance, energy is consumed. The equation for electrical energy is

Energy in joules (J) or watt-seconds = power × time (2.7)

where the power is in watts, and time is in seconds. That is

$$\text{Joules} = \text{watts} \times \text{seconds}$$

Any of the equations used earlier for power may be used in eqn. (2.7) so that

$$W = Pt = EIt = I^2 Rt = \frac{E^2}{R} t \text{ joules (J)} \qquad (2.8)$$

Moreover since $W = E(It)$, and from chapter 1, $Q = It$, then

$$W = EQ \text{ joules (J)} \qquad (2.9)$$

EXAMPLE 2.10

Calculate the energy consumed when a resistor of $10\,\Omega$ is connected to a 20 V supply for 2 hours.

Solution $R = 10\,\Omega$, $E = 20$ V, $t = 2\,\text{h} = 2 \times 60 \times 60\,\text{s} = 7200\,\text{s}$.

$$W = \frac{E^2}{R} t = \frac{20^2}{10} \times 7200 = 288\,000\,\text{J} \quad (Ans.)$$

EXAMPLE 2.11

A microcomputer system consumes a current of 1.6 A at a supply voltage of 5 V. Calculate the daily energy consumption if it operates 24 hours per day.

Solution $E = 5$ V, $I = 1.6$ A, $t = 24\,\text{h} = 24 \times 60 \times 60\,\text{s} = 86\,400\,\text{s}$.

$$W = EIt = 5 \times 1.6 \times 86\,400 = 691\,200\,\text{J} \quad (Ans.)$$

2.9 The Kilowatt Hour

The joule is an impractically small unit of energy, illustrated by the above examples. A much larger unit is used by the electrical supply authority. This unit is the kilowatt hour (kW h) or 1000 watt hour. The unit is

$$1\,\text{kW h} = 1\,\text{kW} \times 1\,\text{h} = 1000\,\text{W} \times (60 \times 60)\text{s}$$
$$= 3\,600\,000\,\text{J or } 3.6\,\text{MJ}$$

For example, in the first of the examples in section 2.8, the energy consumed in kW h is

$$288\,000/3.6 \times 10^6 = 0.08 \text{ kW h}$$

The energy in kW h can be calculated from the equation

Energy in kW h = power in kW × time in h

EXAMPLE 2.12

Calculate the energy consumed in kW h when a current of 15 A flows through a circuit for 4 h, the supply voltage being 220 V.

Solution $E = 220$ V, $I = 15$ A, $t = 4$ h.

$$\text{Power in kW} = \frac{EI}{1000} = \frac{220 \times 15}{1000} = 3.3 \text{ kW}$$

$$\text{Energy in kW h} = 3.3 \times 4 = 13.2 \text{ kW h} \quad (\textit{Ans.})$$

2.10 Non-linear Resistors

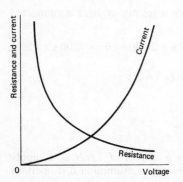

Fig. 2.4 The characteristic of a non-linear resistor

In the great majority of resistors used in electrical engineering and in electronics, the current and the voltage obey Ohm's law, that is the current is proportional to the applied voltage. There are certain electrical materials, however, which do not obey Ohm's law and in which the relationship between current and voltage is non-linear. That is the current/voltage graph is not a straight line. A graph showing this type of relationship is illustrated in figure 2.4.

A device having the characteristic shown has high resistance at low values of voltage; its resistance reduces rapidly in value as the applied voltage increases. A non-linear resistor of this kind can be connected in parallel with other items of equipment for use as a voltage surge diverter (for example, to protect a telephone from voltage surges due to lightning). At normal values of applied voltage, its resistance is very high and it shunts very little current away from the circuit it is protecting. When a high voltage surge occurs on the supply lines (due to lightning, for example), the resistance of the non-linear resistor falls to a low value. When this occurs it bypasses the majority of the surge current, thereby protecting the circuit with which it is connected in parallel. When used in this way it is described as a *surge diverter*.

Exercises

2.1 A 30 Ω resistor is connected to the terminals of a 15 V d.c. supply. Calculate the current in the resistor.
[0.5 A]

2.2 A current of 6.8 A flows in a circuit of resistance 80 Ω. Determine the p.d. across the circuit.
[544 V]

2.3 The current drawn by an electric lamp when it is illuminated is 0.5 A, the supply voltage being 240 V. Determine the "hot" resistance of the lamp.
[480 Ω]

2.4 A 4.7 kΩ resistor is used in a transistor amplifier circuit. If the p.d. at one end of the resistor relative to the chassis is 10 V, and at the other end is 0.8 V, calculate the current in the resistor.
[1.96 mA]

2.5 An incandescent lamp rated at 60 W, 50 V, is used in a portable hand lamp. Calculate a) the current drawn by the lamp and b) the "hot" resistance of the lamp.
[a) 1.2 A; b) 41.7 Ω]

2.6 A two-core cable carries a direct current of 15 A to a consumers premises. If the resistance of each core of the cable is 0.1 Ω, calculate a) the power loss in the cable and b) the total potential drop in the cable.
[a) 45 W; b) 3 V]

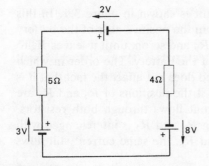

Fig. 2.5

2.7 Calculate the current in the circuit in figure 2.5.
[1 A]

2.8 Calculate the power consumed in examples 2.1 to 2.4, inclusive.
[7.5 W; 3 699.2 W; 120 W; 18.05 mW]

2.9 A generator supplies 100 kW of power to a load at a voltage of 6.6 kV. Calculate a) the current drawn by the load and b) the resistance of the load.
[a) 15.15 A; b) 435.6 Ω]

2.10 A current of 15 A flows for 3 hours through a 5 Ω resistance. Calculate a) the p.d. across the resistance, b) the power consumed, and c) the energy consumed i) in kW h, ii) in MJ.
[a) 75 V; b) 1.125 kW; c) i) 16.875 kW h, ii) 60.75 MJ]

2.11 A test on a non-linear resistor gave the following readings

V (volts)	0	10	20	30	40
I (milliamperes)	0	15	52	217	487

Calculate the resistance of the resistor at each value of voltage in the table. Determine the power consumed when the applied voltage is 40 V.
[Commencing at 10 V: 666.7 Ω, 384.6 Ω, 138.2 Ω, 82.1 Ω; 19.48 W]

3 Series and Parallel Circuits containing Resistors

3.1 The Meaning of a Series Circuit

> **A series circuit is one in which the same current flows through every part of the circuit.**

An example of a series circuit is shown in figure 3.1. In this circuit the current I flows from the positive pole of the battery to resistor R_1, then through R_2 and so on, until it leaves R_8 to return to the negative pole of the battery. The order in which the components are connected does not affect the fact that it is a series circuit; for example, if the positions of R_3 and R_4 are interchanged, the same current flows through both resistors. Also if the branch containing R_1 and R_2 is interchanged with the branch containing R_5 and R_6, the same current still flows through both branches.

When a number of resistors are connected in series they are sometimes described as a **string** of resistors.

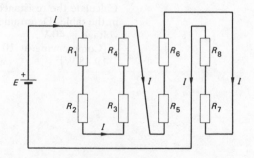

Fig. 3.1 A series circuit

3.2 The Equivalent Resistance of a Series Circuit

In the following we show how a number of series-connected resistors can be replaced by a single "equivalent" resistance. The concept of an equivalent resistance is useful when analysing series circuits.

In the series circuit in figure 3.2a, current I flows through each resistor. The p.d. across R_1 is, by Ohm's law, $V_1 = IR_1$, across R_2 it is $V_2 = IR_2$, and across R_3 it is $V_3 = IR_3$. However, the sum of these p.d.s must be equal to the supply voltage. That is

$$E = IR_1 + IR_2 + IR_3 = I(R_1 + R_2 + R_3) \qquad (3.1)$$

Suppose that we replace the circuit in figure 3.2a by the circuit in figure 3.2b containing the single resistor R_S, the value of this resistor being selected so that the current flowing in both circuits is the same; that is, the resistance of the circuit in figure 3.2b is equivalent to that in figure 3.2a. In the case of figure 3.2b, the circuit equation is

$$E = IR_S \qquad (3.2)$$

where R_S is the **equivalent resistance of the series circuit**. Since the resistance of the circuit in figure 3.2b is equivalent to that in figure 3.2a, then eqns. (3.1) and (3.2) are also equivalent, hence

$$IR_S = I(R_1 + R_2 + R_3)$$

or

$$R_S = R_1 + R_2 + R_3 \qquad (3.3)$$

If the circuit contains n resistors (where n is an integer) R_1, R_2, $R_3, \ldots, R_n$ in series, the equivalent resistance of the circuit is

$$R_S = R_1 + R_2 + R_3 + \ldots + R_n \qquad (3.4)$$

That is to say,

The equivalent resistance of a series circuit is equal to the sum of the individual resistances in the circuit.

Also, the series connection results in an equivalent resistance which is *greater than the value of the highest individual resistance* in the series circuit.

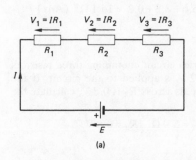

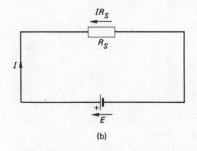

Fig. 3.2 Equivalent resistance of a series circuit

EXAMPLE 3.1

Determine the equivalent resistance of a series circuit containing four resistors whose values are $2\,\Omega$, $5.6\,\Omega$, $8.3\,\Omega$ and $0.2\,\Omega$.

Solution $R_1 = 2\,\Omega$, $R_2 = 5.6\,\Omega$, $R_3 = 8.3\,\Omega$, $R_4 = 0.2\,\Omega$.
The equivalent resistance is given by

$$R_S = R_1 + R_2 + R_3 + R_4 = 2 + 5.6 + 8.3 + 0.2 = 16.1\,\Omega \quad (Ans.)$$

EXAMPLE 3.2

The current flowing through a series circuit containing three resistors R_1, R_2 and R_3 is $0.8\,A$ when $12\,V$ is applied to the circuit. If the resistance of R_1 is $5.9\,\Omega$ and the p.d. across R_2 is $0.8\,V$, calculate the resistance of R_2 and of R_3.

Solution $E = 12\,V$, $I = 0.8\,A$, $R_1 = 5.9\,\Omega$, $IR_2 = 0.8\,V$.
From eqn. (3.2) $E = IR_S$

$$R_S = E/I = 12/0.8 = 15\,\Omega$$

but $R_S = R_1 + R_2 + R_3$ hence

$$15 = 5.9 + R_2 + R_3$$

$$R_2 + R_3 = 15 - 5.9 = 9.1\,\Omega \qquad\qquad\qquad (3.5)$$

Now $IR_2 = 0.8\,V$

$$R_2 = 0.8\,V/0.8\,A = 1\,\Omega \quad (Ans.)$$

From eqn. (3.5)

$$R_3 = 9.1 - R_2 = 9.1 - 1 = 8.1\,\Omega \quad (Ans.)$$

EXAMPLE 3.3

A series circuit containing three resistors R_1, R_2 and R_3 dissipate $10\,mW$ when connected to a $10\,V$ supply. Calculate the p.d. across R_1 given that R_2 dissipates $5\,mW$ and that the resistance of R_3 is $2\,k\Omega$.

Solution $E = 10\,V$, $P_S = 10 \times 10^{-3}\,W$, $P_2 = 5 \times 10^{-3}\,W$, $R_3 = 2\,k\Omega = 2000\,\Omega$.
The power dissipated by the series circuit whose equivalent resistance is R_S is

$$P_S = E^2/R_S$$

hence

$$R_S = E^2/P_S = 10^2/10 \times 10^{-3} = 10\,000\,\Omega$$

Also $IR_S = E$

$$I = E/R_S = 10/10\,000 = 0.001\,A$$

Now $I^2 R_2 = 5 \times 10^{-3}\,W$

$$R_2 = 5 \times 10^{-3}/0.001^2 = 5000\,\Omega$$

Now, since $R_S = R_1 + R_2 + R_3$, then

$$R_1 = R_S - (R_2 + R_3) = 10\,000 - (5000 + 2000) = 3000\,\Omega$$

therefore

$$IR_1 = 0.001 \times 3000 = 3\,V \quad (Ans.)$$

3.3 Voltage Division between Series-connected Resistors

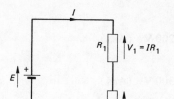

Fig. 3.3 Potential drops in a series circuit

When current I flows in the series circuit in figure 3.3, the p.d. across R_1 is given by $V_1 = IR_1$ and that across R_2 is $V_2 = IR_2$. Also the applied voltage is given by $E = IR_S$, where R_S is the equivalent resistance of the series circuit. From the above relationships we see that

$$I = \frac{E}{R_S} = \frac{V_1}{R_1} = \frac{V_2}{R_2} \tag{3.6}$$

From the first part of eqn. (3.6) we see that

$$\frac{E}{R_S} = \frac{V_1}{R_1}$$

that is

$$V_1 = E \times \frac{R_1}{R_S} = E \times \frac{R_1}{R_1 + R_2} \tag{3.7}$$

$$= \text{applied voltage} \times \frac{R_1}{\substack{\text{equivalent resistance} \\ \text{of the series circuit}}}$$

The relationship $E/R_S = V_2/R_2$ of eqn. (3.6) gives

$$V_2 = E \times \frac{R_2}{R_S} = E \times \frac{R_2}{R_1 + R_2}$$

In the general case where the circuit contains n resistors in series, the p.d. across resistor n is $V_n = IR_n$, hence

$$\frac{E}{R_S} = \frac{V_n}{R_n}$$

and

$$V_n = E \times \frac{R_n}{R_S} = E \times \frac{R_n}{R_1 + R_2 + \ldots + R_n} \tag{3.8}$$

EXAMPLE 3.4

Three resistors having resistance of $100\,\Omega$, $200\,\Omega$ and $300\,\Omega$ are connected in series with a $600\,V$ d.c. supply. Calculate a) the p.d. across each resistor, b) the current in the circuit, c) the power consumed by i) the $200\,\Omega$ resistor and ii) the whole circuit.

Solution $R_1 = 100\,\Omega$, $R_2 = 200\,\Omega$, $R_3 = 300\,\Omega$, $E = 600\,V$.
 From the above data,

$$R_S = R_1 + R_2 + R_3 = 100 + 200 + 300 = 600\,\Omega$$

a) From eqn. (3.8) (putting $n = 1$)

$$V_1 = ER_1/R_S = 600 \times 100/600 = 100 \text{ V} \quad (Ans.)$$

also

$$V_2 = ER_2/R_S = 600 \times 200/600 = 200 \text{ V} \quad (Ans.)$$

and

$$V_3 = ER_3/R_S = 600 \times 300/600 = 300 \text{ V} \quad (Ans.)$$

Note The above results can be checked, since

$$E = V_1 + V_2 + V_3 = 100 + 200 + 300 = 600 \text{ V}$$

b) $I = E/R_S = 600/600 = 1 \text{ A} \quad (Ans.)$

c) i) We may calculate the power consumed by R_2 either from $P_2 = I^2 R_2$ or from $P_2 = V_2^2/R_2$. Choosing the former gives

$$P_2 = I^2 R_2 = 1^2 \times 200 = 200 \text{ W} \quad (Ans.)$$

ii) The total power, P_T may be calculated either from $P_T = I^2 R_S$ or from $P_T = E^2/R_S$. Choosing the latter gives

$$P_T = 600^2/600 = 600 \text{ W} \quad (Ans.)$$

EXAMPLE 3.5

A circuit in a transistor amplifier consists of two resistors in series with one another. If the supply voltage is 9 V, and the value of one resistor is 82 kΩ, calculate the value of the second resistor if a voltage of 1.7 V is developed across it.

Solution $E = 9 \text{ V}$, $R_1 = 82 \text{ k}\Omega$, $V_2 = 1.7 \text{ V}$.
Since $E = V_1 + V_2$ then the p.d. developed across R_1 is

$$V_1 = E - V_2 = 9 - 1.7 = 7.3 \text{ V}$$

Now $V_1 = IR_1$, hence

$$I = V_1/R_1 = 7.3/(82 \times 10^3) = 0.089 \times 10^{-3} \text{ A}$$

Also $V_2 = IR_2$, therefore

$$R_2 = V_2/I = 1.7/(0.089 \times 10^{-3}) = 19\,101 \ \Omega \text{ or } 19.101 \text{ k}\Omega \quad (Ans.)$$

Check $V_2 = ER_2/R_S = 9 \times 19\,101/(82\,000 + 19\,101) = 1.7 \text{ V}$

3.4 Effect of an Open-circuit and of a Short-circuit in a Series Circuit

An **open-circuit** is simply a break in the circuit wiring (see figure 3.4). Since the circuit is broken, its resistance is infinity, and the current is zero ($I = E/R = E/\infty = 0$). In this case the p.d. across each of the series resistors ($= IR$) is zero. It follows therefore that the whole of the supply voltage appears across the open-circuit.

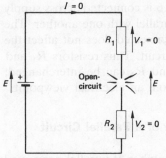

Fig. 3.4 The effect of an open-circuit in a series circuit

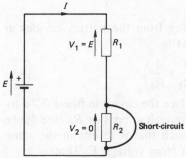

Fig. 3.5 The effect of a short-circuit in a series circuit

If, for example, R_1 and R_2 are filament lamps and one of the filaments "burns out", then the circuit is opened at that point. In a series circuit of this kind, all the lamps will be extinguished since the current is zero for this type of fault (a not uncommon fault in Xmas tree lights!).

Open-circuits can arise in practice from a number of causes including broken wiring, oxidized connections, faulty components, etc.

A component or part of a circuit is said to be **short-circuited** when it is bridged by a path of zero resistance, as shown in the case of R_2 in figure 3.5.

If, in figure 3.5, $E = 10$ V, $R_1 = 2\,\Omega$ and $R_2 = 8\,\Omega$, then prior to the short-circuit being applied to R_2 the current is

$$I = E/(R_1 + R_2) = 1 \text{ A}$$

After R_2 has been short-circuited, the total resistance of the circuit is reduced to $2\,\Omega$ and the current is

$$I = E/R_1 = 10/2 = 5 \text{ A}$$

Thus the short-circuit causes the current in the circuit to increase. As a result, the power dissipated by R_1 increases (in this case by a factor of 25 times) when compared with the normal circuit condition. This fact may well lead to R_1 developing a fault (which may be either an open-circuit or a short-circuit, depending on the type of component).

If R_1 and R_2 in figure 3.5 are filament lamps, then a short-circuit in one of them leads to an increase in the current in the remaining lamp; this may be sufficient to cause it to overheat and fail.

The above can be summarized as follows.

An OPEN-CIRCUIT in a series circuit results, firstly, in the current falling to zero and, secondly, in the voltage across the open-circuit being equal to the supply voltage.

A SHORT-CIRCUIT across a section of a series circuit results, firstly, in an increase in the current, secondly in the voltage across the short-circuited component(s) being zero, and thirdly in an increase in the power dissipated in the "healthy" components.

3.5 The Meaning of a Parallel Circuit

Components are said to be connected in parallel with one another when they have the same voltage across them.

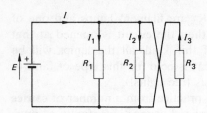

Fig. 3.6 A parallel circuit

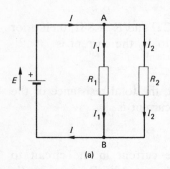

(a)

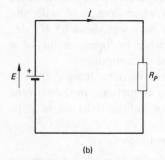

(b)

Fig. 3.7 Equivalent resistance of a parallel circuit

Each of the resistors in figure 3.6 is connected across supply E, hence they are connected in parallel with one another. The order in which the resistors are connected does not affect the fact that figure 3.6 is a parallel circuit. Thus resistors R_1 and R_3 can be interchanged, or R_2 and R_3 can be interchanged, etc, without altering the circuit from an electrical viewpoint.

3.6 The Equivalent Resistance of a Parallel Circuit

In the following we show how a number of parallel-connected resistors can be replaced by a single equivalent resistance.

In the parallel circuit in figure 3.7a, the applied voltage E appears across each resistor so that

$$I_1 = \frac{E}{R_1} \quad \text{and} \quad I_2 = \frac{E}{R_2}$$

Now, the total current I flowing from the battery divides at junction A into I_1 and I_2. That is

$$I = I_1 + I_2 = \frac{E}{R_1} + \frac{E}{R_2} = E\left(\frac{1}{R_1} + \frac{1}{R_2}\right) \quad (3.9)$$

Let us suppose that we can replace the circuit in figure 3.7a by the circuit containing a single equivalent resistor R_P (see figure 3.7b), the value of R_P being such that it results in the same value of current I to be drawn from voltage E. That is

$$I = \frac{E}{R_P} \quad (3.10)$$

where R_P is the **equivalent resistance of the parallel circuit**.

Since the circuit in diagram a is equivalent to that in b, then eqns. (3.9) and (3.10) are equivalent. That is

$$\frac{E}{R_P} = E\left(\frac{1}{R_1} + \frac{1}{R_2}\right)$$

or

$$\frac{1}{R_P} = \frac{1}{R_1} + \frac{1}{R_2} \quad (3.10)$$

The above argument can be extended to meet the case where there are n resistors $(R_1, R_2, R_3, \ldots, R_n)$ in parallel with one another to give the general expression for the equivalent resistance of a parallel circuit, which is

$$\frac{1}{R_P} = \frac{1}{R_1} + \frac{1}{R_2} + \frac{1}{R_3} + \ldots + \frac{1}{R_n} \quad (3.11)$$

Hence,

The reciprocal of the equivalent resistance of a parallel circuit is equal to the sum of the reciprocals of the resistances of each of the parallel-connected branches.

As will be seen from the examples below, the parallel connection of resistors results in an equivalent resistance whose value is *less than that of the lowest individual resistance* in the circuit.

In the special case of two resistors in parallel (see figure 3.7*a*), the resistance of the circuit (from eqn. (3.10)) is

$$R_P = \frac{R_1 R_2}{R_1 + R_2}$$
(3.12)

EXAMPLE 3.6

Calculate the equivalent resistance of two parallel-connected resistors of value $8\,\Omega$ and $10\,\Omega$.

Solution $R_1 = 8\,\Omega$, $R_2 = 10\,\Omega$.
   From eqn. (3.10)

$$\frac{1}{R_P} = \frac{1}{8} + \frac{1}{10} = 0.125 + 0.1 = 0.225 \text{ S or } (\Omega)^{-1}$$

hence

$$R_P = 1/0.225 = 4.444\,\Omega \quad (Ans.)$$

Note that the value of R_P is less than the lowest individual resistance in the parallel circuit.

EXAMPLE 3.7

The current drawn by three parallel-connected resistors R_1, R_2 and R_3, when connected to a 20 V supply is 2 A. If the value of R_1 is $100\,\Omega$ and the current in R_2 is 1 A, determine the value of R_3. Calculate the total power consumed by the parallel circuit.

Solution $E = 20$ V, $I = 2$ A, $R_1 = 100\,\Omega$, $I_2 = 1$ A.
   The equivalent resistance R_P of the parallel circuit is

$$R_P = \frac{E}{I} = \frac{20}{2} = 10\,\Omega$$

Now $E = I_2 R_2$

$$R_2 = E/I_2 = 20/1 = 20\,\Omega$$

From eqn. (3.11)

$$\frac{1}{R_P} = \frac{1}{R_1} + \frac{1}{R_2} + \frac{1}{R_3}$$

or

$$\frac{1}{R_3} = \frac{1}{R_P} - \frac{1}{R_1} - \frac{1}{R_2} = \frac{1}{10} - \frac{1}{100} - \frac{1}{20} = 0.04\,\text{S}$$

Therefore $R_3 = 1/0.04 = 25\,\Omega$ (*Ans.*)

The power consumption can be calculated either from $P = EI$ or $P = I^2 R_P$ or $P = E^2/R_P$. Using the first gives

$$P = EI = 20 \times 2 = 40\,\text{W} \quad (Ans.)$$

EXAMPLE 3.8

An electrical motor is supplied at a voltage of 250 V and consumes a current of 50 A. An electrical heater rated at 2 kW is also supplied from the same source. Connected in parallel with the above loads is a 3 kW lighting load. Calculate *a*) the equivalent resistance of the connected load, *b*) the current drawn from the supply, and *c*) the current in each branch of the load.

Solution The loads are

motor   50 A, 250 V

heater   2 kW, 250 V

lighting 3 kW, 250 V

a) The power consumed by the motor is

$$50\,\text{A} \times 250\,\text{V} = 12\,500\,\text{W or } 12.5\,\text{kW}$$

Total power consumed is

$$(12.5 + 2 + 3)\,\text{kW} = 17.5\,\text{kW} = E^2/R_P$$

hence

$$R_P = E^2/17\,500\,\text{W} = 250^2/17\,500 = 3.57\,\Omega \quad (Ans.)$$

b) The total power consumed by the load $= 17\,500\,\text{W} = EI$ where I is the total current drawn by the three parallel-connected branches. Hence

$$I = 17\,500/250 = 70\,\text{A} \quad (Ans.)$$

c) From $P = EI$

Heater current = heater power$/E = 2000/250 = 8\,\text{A}$ (*Ans.*)

Lighting current = lighting power$/E = 3000/250 = 12\,\text{A}$ (*Ans.*)

Motor current = 50 A (given in question)

Note The answer to part *b*) can be checked from the above values as follows.

$I =$ motor current + heater current + lighting current

$$= 50 + 8 + 12 = 70\,\text{A}$$

3.7 Current-sharing between Parallel Branches

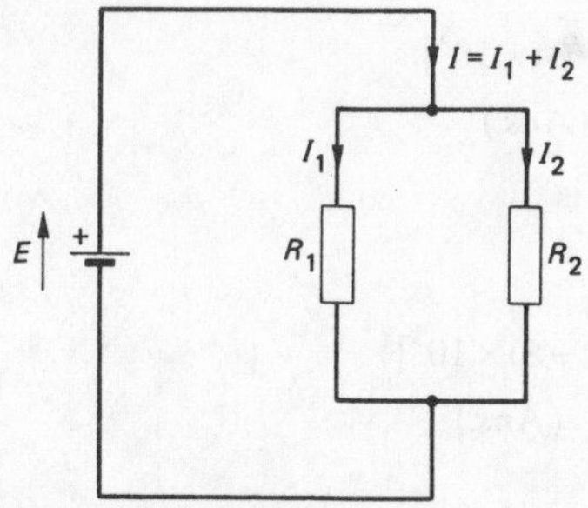

Fig. 3.8 Current division between parallel branches

In a number of applications we need to determine how the current I flowing from the supply (see figure 3.8) divides between parallel-connected branches.

Since the p.d. across each branch of a parallel circuit has the same value, and if the equivalent resistance of the parallel circuit is R_P, then

$$E = IR_P = I_1 R_1 = I_2 R_2$$

Extracting the first two terms of the above expression gives

$$IR_P = I_1 R_1$$

hence

$$I_1 = \frac{IR_P}{R_1} \tag{3.13}$$

Now $R_P = R_1 R_2/(R_1 + R_2)$, therefore

$$I_1 = \frac{I}{R_1} \times \frac{R_1 R_2}{(R_1 + R_2)} = \frac{IR_2}{R_1 + R_2} \tag{3.14}$$

Applying a similar technique to the branch containing R_2 gives

$$I_2 = \frac{IR_P}{R_2} \tag{3.15}$$

$$= \frac{IR_1}{R_1 + R_2} \tag{3.16}$$

Note that eqns. (3.13) and (3.15) are generally similar to one another. If we extend the above argument to the general case when the circuit has n parallel branches each containing one of the resistors $R_1, R_2, R_3, \ldots, R_n$, then the current in the gth branch, I_g, containing resistor R_g is

$$I_g = \frac{IR_P}{R_g} \tag{3.17}$$

$$= E/R_g \tag{3.18}$$

EXAMPLE 3.9

Two resistors of value $10\,\text{k}\Omega$ and $8\,\text{k}\Omega$ are connected in parallel with one another, and the combination draws a current of $15\,\text{mA}$ from the supply. Determine a) the current in each resistor, b) the p.d. across the parallel circuit, and c) the power consumed by each resistor.

Solution $R_1 = 10\,\text{k}\Omega$, $R_2 = 8\,\text{k}\Omega$, $I = 15\,\text{mA} = 15 \times 10^{-3}\,\text{A}$

a) From eqn. (3.14) the current in the $10\,\text{k}\Omega$ resistor is

$$I_1 = IR_2/(R_1 + R_2)$$
$$= (15 \times 10^{-3}) \times (8 \times 10^3)/[(10 + 8) \times 10^3]$$
$$= 6.7 \times 10^{-3}\,\text{A or } 6.67\,\text{mA} \quad (Ans.)$$

From eqn. (3.16) the current in R_2 is

$$I_2 = IR_1/(R_1 + R_2)$$
$$= (15 \times 10^{-3}) \times (10 \times 10^3)/[(10 + 8) \times 10^3]$$
$$= 8.33 \times 10^{-3}\,\text{A or } 8.33\,\text{mA} \quad (Ans.)$$

Note $I_1 + I_2 = 15\,\text{mA} = I$

b) The p.d. across the circuit is calculated from

$$E = I_1 R_1 = (6.67 \times 10^{-3}) \times (10 \times 10^{-3}) = 66.7\,\text{V} \quad (Ans.)$$

c) The power consumed by R_1 is

$$P_1 = I_1^2 R_1 = (6.67 \times 10^{-3})^2 \times (10 \times 10^3) = 0.445\,\text{W} \quad (Ans.)$$

and the power consumed by R_2 is

$$P_2 = I_2^2 R_2 = (8.33 \times 10^{-3})^2 \times (8 \times 10^3) = 0.555\,\text{W} \quad (Ans.)$$

EXAMPLE 3.10

Three parallel-connected resistors R_1, R_2 and R_3 consume a total power of 10 kW when connected to a 100 V supply. If the value of R_1 is $10\,\Omega$, and the power consumed by R_2 is 5 kW, determine a) the current drawn from the supply, b) the value of R_2 and of R_3, and c) the current flowing in each branch of the circuit.

Solution   Total power consumed $P_T = 10\,000\,\text{W}$, $E = 100\,\text{V}$, $R_1 = 10\,\Omega$, power consumed by $R_2 = 5000\,\text{W}$.
a) Since $P_T = EI$, then

$$I = P_T/E = 10\,000/100 = 100\,\text{A} \quad (Ans.)$$

b) The total power consumed is given by $P_T = E^2/R_P$, where R_P is the equivalent resistance of the parallel circuit, hence

$$R_P = E^2/P_T = 100^2/10\,000 = 1\,\Omega$$

The power consumed by R_2 is $P_2 = E^2/R_2$, hence

$$R_2 = E^2/P_2 = 100^2/5000 = 2\,\Omega \quad (Ans.)$$

The equation for the reciprocal of the equivalent resistance of the parallel circuit is

$$\frac{1}{R_P} = \frac{1}{R_1} + \frac{1}{R_2} + \frac{1}{R_3}$$

hence

$$\frac{1}{R_3} = \frac{1}{R_P} - \frac{1}{R_1} - \frac{1}{R_2} = \frac{1}{1} - \frac{1}{10} - \frac{1}{2} = 1 - 0.1 - 0.5 = 0.4\,\text{S}$$

or $R_3 = 2.5\,\Omega$ (*Ans.*)

c) Now $I_1 = E/R_1 = 100\,\text{V}/10\,\Omega = 10\,\text{A}$ (*Ans.*)

Also $P_2 = EI_2$, therefore

$$I_2 = P_2/E = 5000/100 = 50\,\text{A}\quad (\textit{Ans.})$$

and $I_3 = E/R_3 = 100/2.5 = 40\,\text{A}$ (*Ans.*)

3.8 Parallel Circuit Calculations using Conductance

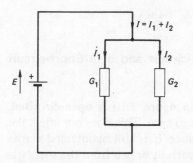

Fig. 3.9 Parallel circuit calculations using conductance values

Since the **conductance** G of a circuit is given by $G = 1/R$, then the circuit in figure 3.8 can be replaced by that in figure 3.9 where

$$I_1 = EG_1 \quad \text{and} \quad I_2 = EG_2$$

If we replace the parallel circuit in figure 3.9 by one having an equivalent conductance G_P which draws current I when connected to voltage E, then

$$I = EG_P$$

But in figure 3.9, $I = I_1 + I_2$ or

$$EG_P = EG_1 + EG_2 = E(G_1 + G_2)$$

That is the **equivalent conductance** of a parallel circuit with two branches is

$$G_P = G_1 + G_2 \tag{3.19}$$

Also since $E = I/G_P = I_1/G_1 = I_2/G_2$, then

$$I_1 = I \times \frac{G_1}{G_P} \tag{3.20}$$

$$I_2 = I \times \frac{G_2}{G_P} \tag{3.21}$$

EXAMPLE 3.11

A resistance of $10\,\Omega$ is connected in parallel with a conductance of $0.4\,\text{S}$. Calculate the equivalent conductance of the parallel circuit. If the circuit is connected to a $10\,\text{V}$ supply, determine the total current drawn from the supply and also the current in each branch of the circuit.

Solution $G_1 = 1/R_1 = 1/10 = 0.1$ S, $G_2 = 0.4$ S, $E = 10$ V

From eqn. (3.19)

$$G_P = G_1 + G_2 = 0.1 + 0.4 = 0.5 \text{ S} \quad (Ans.)$$

Now

$$I = EG_P = 10 \times 0.5 = 5 \text{ A} \quad (Ans.)$$

From eqn. (3.20)

$$I_1 = IG_1/G_P = 5 \times 0.1/0.5 = 1 \text{ A} \quad (Ans.)$$

and from eqn. (3.21)

$$I_2 = IG_2/G_P = 5 \times 0.4/0.5 = 4 \text{ A} \quad (Ans.)$$

3.9 The Effect of an Open-circuit and of a Short-circuit on a Parallel Circuit

If the branch containing R_1 in figure 3.10 is **open-circuited**, the current in that branch falls to zero. This does not affect the current in the other branch, since E is still maintained across R_2. The net result is that the current drawn from the supply is reduced to I_2. Thus if R_1 and R_2 are electric lamps, the effect of an open-circuit in one branch is to cause the lamp in that branch to be extinguished, the brilliance of the other lamp being unchanged.

In the event of a **short-circuit** across one of the resistors in figure 3.10, the resistance of that branch and also that of the equivalent resistance of the parallel circuit falls to zero. As a result, the current drawn from the supply rises to a very high value (limited only by the resistance of the wiring and the internal resistance of the battery); moreover, the voltage across the parallel circuit falls to zero.

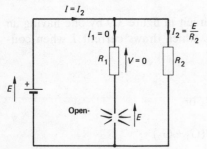

Fig. 3.10 The effect of an open-circuit in one branch

3.10 Series-Parallel Circuits

Many practical circuits have more-or-less complex current paths which cannot be described as being either a pure series circuit or a pure parallel circuit.

An example of a series-parallel circuit is shown in figure 3.11. Here current I_1 flows through R_1, after which it divides at junction A into two branches, one carrying current I_2 and the other carrying I_3. Thus resistor R_1 is in series with the parallel circuit between junctions A and B. Note that the voltage V_{AB} between junctions A and B is common to the two branches in which currents I_2 and I_3 flow; these branches are therefore in parallel with one another. Moreover, since I_2

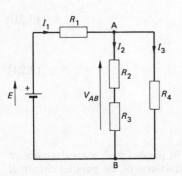

Fig. 3.11 A series-parallel circuit

flows in both R_2 and R_3, then R_2 and R_3 form a series branch within the parallel circuit.

The series-parallel circuit is solved using the knowledge gained earlier in this chapter. The general procedure is

> **1** *Reduce the series-parallel circuit to a number of identifiable pure-series and pure-parallel circuits.*
> **2** *Calculate the equivalent resistance of each of the pure-series and pure-parallel circuits.*
> **3** *Combine the values calculated in* **2** *above to give the equivalent resistance R_T of the series-parallel circuit.*
> **4** *Use R_T to determine the current in the circuit.*

The above procedure may, of course, be varied by the conditions set in the problem. We will now consider the solution of a number of series-parallel circuits.

3.11 Series-connected Parallel Banks of Resistors

Figure 3.12a illustrates a circuit containing series-connected parallel banks of resistors. Here the voltage V_X appears across R_1 and R_2, so that R_1 and R_2 are in parallel with one another. Similarly, R_3 and R_4 are in parallel with one another, and each has voltage V_Y across it. Also, since the current I flows not only to junction L but also to junction M, then the parallel combination R_1–R_2 is in series with the parallel combination R_3–R_4.

The circuit in figure 3.12a is analysed as follows. The equivalent resistance R_{P1} of the parallel combination R_1 and R_2 is determined as follows (see also figure 3.12b).

$$R_{P1} = \frac{R_1 R_2}{R_1 + R_2} = \frac{10 \times 20}{10 + 20} = 6.667\ \Omega$$

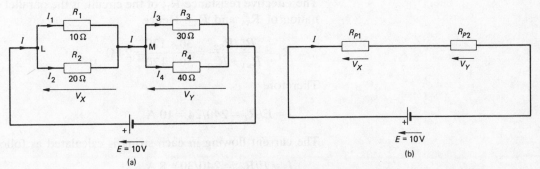

Fig. 3.12 (a) Parallel bank R_1 and R_2 is in series with parallel bank R_3 and R_4, (b) equivalent circuit

The equivalent resistance R_{P2} of the parallel combination R_3–R_4 is

$$R_{P2} = \frac{R_3 R_4}{R_3 + R_4} = \frac{30 \times 40}{30 + 40} = 17.143 \ \Omega$$

R_{P1} and R_{P2} are then combined in series, as shown in figure 3.12b to give an effective circuit resistance R_T of

$$R_T = R_{P1} + R_{P2} = 6.667 + 17.143 = 23.81 \ \Omega$$

The current I drawn by the circuit is calculated from Ohm's law

$$I = E/R_T = 10/23.81 = 0.42 \ \text{A}$$

Using the equations for current division in parallel circuits [eqns. (3.14) and (3.16)] gives $I_1 = 0.28$ A, $I_2 = 0.14$ A, $I_3 = 0.24$ A, and $I_4 = 0.18$ A.

3.12 Parallel-connected Strings of Resistors

Figure 3.13a shows a typical circuit in which two strings of resistors are connected in parallel with one another. In this case resistor string R_1–R_2 is connected in parallel with resistor string R_3–R_4–R_5. The equivalent circuit is shown in figure 3.13b in which R_{S1} is the equivalent resistance of R_1 and R_2 in series, that is

$$R_{S1} = R_1 + R_2$$

Resistor R_{S2} in figure 3.13b is the equivalent resistance of the resistor string R_3–R_4–R_5, where

$$R_{S2} = R_3 + R_4 + R_5$$

With the values given in figure 3.13a,

$$R_{S1} = 10 + 20 = 30 \ \Omega$$
$$R_{S2} = 30 + 40 + 50 = 120 \ \Omega$$

The effective resistance R_T, of the circuit, is the parallel combination of R_{S1} and R_{S2}. Hence

$$R_T = \frac{R_{S1} R_{S2}}{R_{S1} + R_{S2}} = \frac{30 \times 120}{30 + 120} = 24 \ \Omega$$

Therefore

$$I = E/R_T = 240/24 = 10 \ \text{A}$$

The current flowing in each string is calculated as follows.

$$I_1 = E/R_{S1} = 240/30 = 8 \ \text{A}$$
$$I_2 = E/R_{S2} = 240/120 = 2 \ \text{A}$$

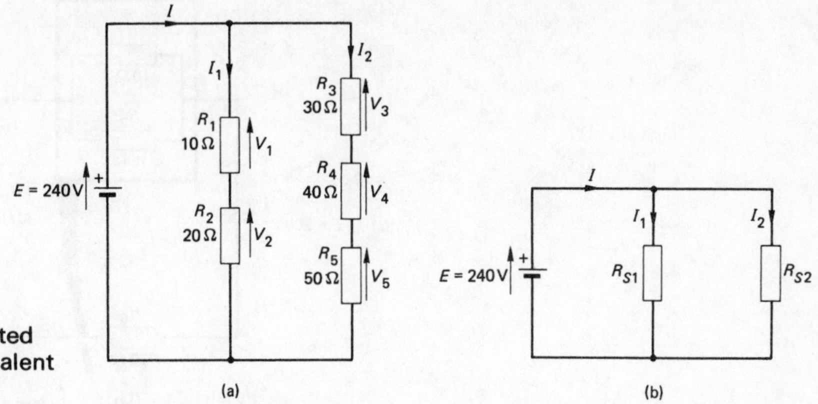

Fig. 3.13 (*a*) Parallel-connected strings of resistors, (*b*) equivalent circuit

The p.d. across each resistor in figure 3.13*a* can be calculated from Ohm's law ($E = IR$) to give $V_1 = 80$ V, $V_2 = 160$ V, $V_3 = 60$ V, $V_4 = 80$ V, and $V_5 = 100$ V.

EXAMPLE 3.12

The following values refer to a circuit similar to that in figure 3.13 (*a*): $E = 10$ V, $R_2 = 500 \,\Omega$, $V_3 = 2.5$ V, the power consumed by the complete circuit is 100 mW, the power consumed by the branch containing R_1 and R_2 is 25 mW, and the power consumed by R_4 is 28.125 mW. Determine the value of each resistor in the circuit.

Solution $E = 10$ V; $R_2 = 500 \,\Omega$; $V_3 = 2.5$ V; total power $P = 100 \times 10^{-3}$ W; $P_1 + P_2 = 25 \times 10^{-3}$ W; $P_4 = 28.125 \times 10^{-3}$ W.
For the string containing R_1 and R_2

$$\text{Power} = 25 \times 10^{-3} = E^2/(R_1 + R_2) = 10^2/(R_1 + R_2)$$

hence $R_1 + R_2 = 100/25 \times 10^{-3} = 4000 \,\Omega$
therefore

$$R_1 = 4000 - R_2 = 4000 - 500 = 3500 \,\Omega \quad (Ans.)$$

For the string containing R_3, R_4 and R_5

$$\text{Power consumed} = P - (P_1 + P_2) = 100 \times 10^{-3} - 25 \times 10^{-3}$$
$$= 75 \times 10^{-3} \text{ W}$$

but   Power consumed by R_3, R_4 and $R_5 = EI_2$
hence

$$I_2 = \text{power consumed}/E = 75 \times 10^{-3}/10 = 7.5 \times 10^{-3} \text{ A}$$

From Ohm's law

$$R_3 = V_3/I_2 = 2.5/7.5 \times 10^{-3} = 333.3 \,\Omega \quad (Ans.)$$

Now $P_4 = I_2^2 R_4$ or

$$R_4 = P_4/I_2^2 = 28.125 \times 10^{-3}/(7.5 \times 10^{-3})^2 = 500 \,\Omega \quad (Ans.)$$

For the complete string R_3, R_4, R_5, the total resistance is

$$R_3 + R_4 + R_5 = E/I_2 = 10/7.5 \times 10^{-3} = 1333.3 \,\Omega$$

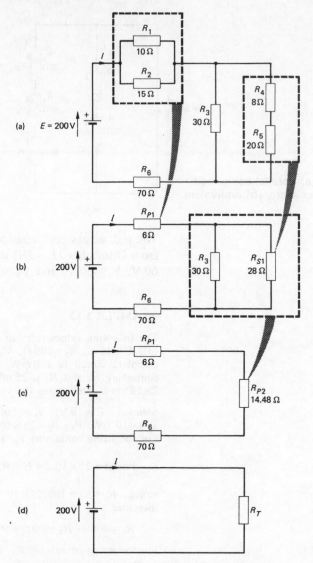

Fig. 3.14 Analysis of a series-parallel circuit

hence
$$R_5 = 1333.3 - (R_3 + R_4) = 1333.3 - (333.3 + 500)$$
$$= 500\ \Omega \quad (Ans.)$$
Therefore
$$R_1 = 3500\ \Omega,\ R_2 = 500\ \Omega,\ R_3 = 333.3\ \Omega,\ R_4 = 500\ \Omega,\ R_5 = 500\ \Omega$$

3.13   Analysis of a Series-Parallel Circuit

A practical circuit may contain a combination of series-connected and parallel-connected resistors, an example being shown in figure 3.14. It is first necessary to break down the basic circuit into simple units as follows.

First, the parallel-connected resistors R_1 and R_2 are combined into an equivalent parallel resistance R_{P1}. Next, the resistor string R_4–R_5 is combined into its equivalent series resistance R_{S1}. The result of these operations is illustrated in figure 3.14b.

The next operation is to combine R_3 and R_{S1} into an equivalent parallel combination R_{P2}, to give the circuit shown in figure 3.14c. Finally, R_{P1}, R_{P2} and R_6 are combined to give the equivalent resistance R_T of the whole circuit. The detailed calculation is given below.

$$R_{P1} = R_1R_2/(R_1+R_2) = 10 \times 15/(10+15) = 6\,\Omega$$

$$R_{S1} = R_4 + R_5 = 8 + 20 = 28\,\Omega$$

$$R_{P2} = R_3R_{S1}/(R_3+R_{S1}) = 30 \times 28/(30+28) = 14.48\,\Omega$$

$$R_T = R_{P1} + R_{P2} + R_6 = 6 + 14.48 + 70 = 90.48\,\Omega$$

and

$$I = E/R_T = 200/90.48 = 2.21\,\text{A}$$

Exercises

3.1 Four resistors connected in series have the following resistances: 1.2 kΩ, 87.2 Ω, 10 000 mΩ, 6.7×10^8 $\mu\Omega$. Calculate the resistance of the circuit in ohms.
[1967.2 Ω]

3.2 Three resistors A, B and C are connected in series. If the resistance of A is 100 Ω, the total resistance of the circuit is 500 Ω, and the p.d. across resistor C is 50 V when the current is 0.2 A, calculate a) the p.d. across resistor B, b) the resistance of resistor B, c) the voltage applied to the series circuit, and d) the power consumed by each resistor.
[a) 30 V; b) 150 Ω; c) 100 V; d) $P_A = 4$ W, $P_B = 6$ W, $P_C = 10$ W]

3.3 Two resistors A and B of resistance 20 Ω and 80 Ω, respectively, are connected in series with one another. Calculate the p.d. across each of them and the power consumed by each resistor when a 200 V d.c. supply is connected to the circuit.
[$V_A = 40$ V; $V_B = 160$ V; $P_A = 80$ W; $P_B = 320$ W]

3.4 Two resistors connected in series with one another consume a power of 100 mW when connected to a 100 V supply. If the voltage across one of the resistors is 40 V, determine the resistance of the remaining resistor.
[60 kΩ]

3.5 Five resistors, each of 100 Ω, are connected in series with one another. The circuit operates at a supply voltage of 200 V. Calculate the power consumed by each resistor. If one of the resistors develops a short-circuit, determine the power consumed by each resistor.
[16 W; 25 W]

3.6 Resistors of 5 Ω and 10 Ω are connected in parallel with one another. Determine the equivalent resistance of the circuit.
[3.33 Ω]

3.7 A resistor of $10\,\Omega$ resistance is connected in parallel with another resistor R. Determine the value of R if the equivalent resistance of the parallel circuit is $4\,\Omega$.

[$6.67\,\Omega$]

3.8 Resistor A of $10\,\Omega$ resistance is connected in parallel with resistor B and resistor C. The circuit is connected to a $10\,V$ supply, and it is found that resistor B carries a current of $2\,A$, and that resistor C consumes $12.5\,W$. Determine *a*) the resistance of resistor B and resistor C, *b*) the conductance of the parallel circuit, and *c*) the power consumed by the complete circuit.

[(a)$R_B = 5\,\Omega$, $R_C = 8\,\Omega$; b) $0.325\,S$; c) $3.25\,W$]

3.9 Resistors of $5\,\Omega$, $10\,\Omega$ and $20\,\Omega$ are connected in parallel with one another. Determine the value of resistance which must be connected in parallel with this combination to give a circuit with a conductance of $0.45\,S$.

[$10\,\Omega$]

3.10 A parallel circuit contains two resistors A and B whose values are $30\,\Omega$ and $20\,\Omega$, respectively. If the parallel combination draws a current of $100\,A$, determine the current in each resistor.

[$I_A = 40\,A$, $I_B = 60\,A$]

3.11 The power consumed by two parallel-connected resistors is $100\,mW$ when a voltage of $10\,V$ is applied. If one of the resistors has a resistance of $4000\,\Omega$, determine the current in each resistor.

[$0.0025\,A$; $0.0075\,A$]

3.12 Determine the resistance between terminals A and B of the circuits in diagrams *a* and *b* of figure 3.15.

[(a) $62\,\Omega$; b) $18.46\,\Omega$]

3.13 Due to ageing, the value of resistor R in figure 3.15b changes in value. If the new value of resistance of the complete circuit is $20\,\Omega$, calculate the new value of resistor R.

[$40\,\Omega$]

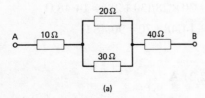

(a)

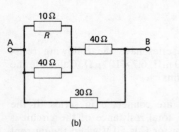

(b)

Fig. 3.15

4 Kirchhoff's Laws

4.1 Statement of Laws

Many electrical circuits are more involved than those described hitherto, and in order to determine either the current in a branch of the network or the potential between two points in the network, it is necessary to solve the equations of the network. The German physicist Gustav R. Kirchhoff laid down two basic laws which enable us to determine the network equations. These are

First law (the current law)
The algebraic sum of the current flowing towards any point in a circuit is equal to the sum of the current flowing away from the point.

Second law (the voltage law)
In any closed circuit (or mesh) the algebraic sum of the e.m.f.s and potential drops is zero.

4.2 Kirchhoff's Current Law

Kirchhoff's first law is illustrated in figure 4.1. Here, currents I_A, I_B and I_D flow *towards* junction J (a junction is also known as a **node**), and current I_C flows *away* from it. Hence

Total current flowing towards junction $J = I_A + I_B + I_D$

Total current flowing away from junction $J = I_C$

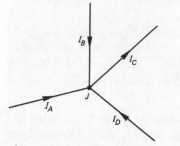

Fig. 4.1 Kirchhoff's current law

Therefore

$$I_A + I_B + I_D = I_C$$

If, for example $I_A = 10$ A, $I_B = 6$ A and $I_C = 18$ A, then

$$10 + 6 + I_D = 18 \text{ A}$$

or $I_D = 2$ A

In connection with the above, **a junction or node is usually defined as a point in a circuit where three or more wires meet** (although in some cases it is defined as a point where two or more wires meet).

Kirchhoff's current law can be illustrated by comparing it with the flow of water in a pipe system. Assuming that there is no loss of water at the junction and if the water flow is not blocked, then at any junction in the system the amount of water flowing towards the junction is equal to the amount of water flowing away from the junction.

The first law may be summarized by saying that electrical current cannot "accumulate" in the system.

4.3 Kirchhoff's Voltage Law

In any closed circuit the algebraic sum of the e.m.f.s and p.d.s is zero. Let us apply this to the closed circuit ABCDA in figure 4.2. (Remember, the finish of a *closed* circuit is also the starting point.) The general procedure to be adopted in establishing the circuit equation is as follows.

1 *By the side of each battery or generator draw a "potential" arrow pointing from the negative pole to the positive pole of the power source.*
2 *Decide in which direction the current flows, and indicate this on the circuit by an arrow.*
3 *By the side of each resistor draw a p.d. arrow pointing in the opposite direction to the current flow through the resistor.*
4 *Proceed around the loop (starting at any point, and finishing at the starting point) and write down Kirchhoff's voltage equation for the loop.*

Following the steps outlined above, we begin by drawing the potential arrows by the side of E_1 and E_2, each pointing from the negative pole of the respective battery to the positive pole. In the case considered, E_1 and E_2 oppose each other but we do not know which has the greater value. We must therefore arbitrarily select a direction in which the current is assumed to

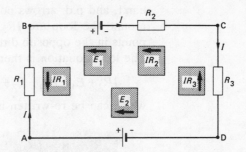

Fig. 4.2 Kirchhoff's voltage law

flow; if the selected direction is incorrect the calculated value of current will merely be negative, indicating that it flows in the opposite direction to that chosen. Let us assume that the current flows in a clockwise direction around the loop (see figure 4.2).

Having chosen the direction of current flow, we then draw the p.d. arrows (IR_1, IR_2, IR_3) pointing in the opposite direction to the current flow through the respective resistors. We can now write down Kirchhoff's voltage equation for the loop. To illustrate how this is done, let us commence at point A and proceed around the loop in the direction ABCDA

Loop ABCDA The loop equation (eqn. (4.1)) is given below and an explanation of how it is obtained follows.

$$-IR_1 - E_1 - IR_2 - IR_3 + E_2 = 0 \qquad (4.1)$$

or

$$E_2 - E_1 = IR_1 + IR_2 + IR_3 \qquad (4.2)$$

Associated with resistor R_1 is a p.d. arrow which points in the opposite direction to our direction of movement around the circuit, so that we give a negative sign to the p.d. across R_1, i.e. the p.d. becomes $-IR_1$ in the equation. The e.m.f. arrow associated with E_1 also opposes our movement around the circuit, so that it is written down as $-E_1$. Also the p.d. arrows associated with R_2 and R_3 oppose our motion around the circuit, so that these p.d.s are written down as $-IR_2$ and $-IR_3$, respectively. However, the e.m.f. arrow E_2 points in the direction of movement so that it is written down as $+E_2$. This completes the closed circuit since we have arrived back at point A. The resulting equation is given in eqn. (4.1). The equation is then re-arranged in the form given in eqn. (4.2).

Loop CBADC To illustrate that neither the starting point nor the direction of movement around the loop affects the circuit equation, we now commence at point C and proceed around the loop in an anticlockwise direction. In this case the e.m.f. and p.d. arrows pointing in the direction of movement around the loop are IR_2, E_1, IR_1 and IR_3; e.m.f. arrow E_2 points in the opposite direction to the direction of movement. The loop equation is therefore

$$IR_2 + E_1 + IR_1 - E_2 + IR_3 = 0$$

which can be re-written in the form

$$IR_1 + IR_2 + IR_3 = E_2 - E_1 \qquad (4.3)$$

Equations (4.2) and (4.3) are identical.

4.4 The Branch Current Method of Solving Circuits

In this section we solve circuits using what is known as the **branch current method** of applying Kirchhoff's laws. Using this method we *assign a current to each branch of the network*. The application of this method is illustrated in the following examples.

APPLICATION 1

Calculate the current in each branch of the network in figure 4.3.

Solution Following the general procedure, we first of all draw e.m.f. arrows by the side of each battery in the manner outlined.

Next we decide the direction of current flow *in each branch*, and indicate the current flow on the circuit. We will assume that current flows out of the positive pole of each battery (i.e. both batteries discharge into the circuit); we assign I_1 to the current leaving E_1, and I_2 to the current leaving E_2. At junction A, both currents meet and flow through resistor R_3 (remember, the total current flowing towards any junction is equal to the current flowing away from the junction). We assign current I_3 to the branch containing R_3, but since $I_1 + I_2 = I_3$ we need only calculate the values of I_1 and I_2. In general,

If there are N wires meeting at a junction, only (N−1) values of current need be known in order to calculate the remaining value of current.

In this case there are three wires meeting at junction A, so that we need to know only I_1 and I_2 in order to calculate I_3.

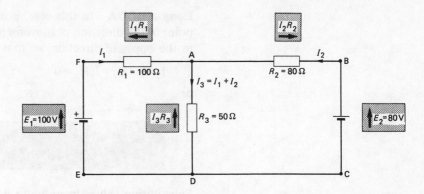

Fig. 4.3 Application 1 of the branch current method

Next we draw p.d. arrows by the side of each resistor pointing in the opposite direction to that of the current flow through the resistor.

Finally we need to obtain loop equations which will allow us to evaluate the unknown currents. We require **the same number of equations as there are unknown values of current**. In figure 4.3 there are two unknown values of current (I_3 is not unknown when we have calculated I_1 and I_2 since $I_3 = I_1 + I_2$), so that we need *two sets of independent equations* in this case, which are obtained from closed circuits within the network. There are three possible closed circuits in figure 4.3, which are ABCDEFA, ABCDA and ADEFA. Let us select the circuits ABCDEFA and ABCDA. (As shown earlier, the direction in which we proceed around each loop is immaterial.)

Loop ABCDEFA Beginning at point A and proceeding around the loop in a clockwise direction, the potential arrows pointing in the direction of movement around the loop are I_2R_2 and E_1, whilst E_2 and I_1R_1 point in the opposite direction. Hence

$$I_2R_2 - E_2 + E_1 - I_1R_1 = 0$$

or

$$-E_2 + E_1 = I_1R_1 - I_2R_2$$

Substituting values from figure 4.3 gives

$$-80 + 100 = 20 = 100I_1 - 80I_2 \tag{4.4}$$

Loop ABCDA In this case, potential arrows I_2R_2 and I_3R_3 point in the direction of movement, and e.m.f. arrow E_2 points in the opposite direction, so that

$$I_2R_2 - E_2 + I_3R_3 = 0$$

or

$$E_2 = I_2R_2 + I_3R_3$$
$$= I_2R_2 + (I_1 + I_2)R_3 = I_1R_3 + I_2(R_2 + R_3)$$

Substituting values from figure 4.3 gives

$$80 = 50I_1 + I_2(80 + 50) = 50I_1 + 130I_2 \qquad (4.5)$$

Solving the equations

Equations (4.4) and (4.5) can now be solved for I_1 and I_2

$$20 = 100I_1 - 80I_2$$
$$80 = 50I_1 + 130I_2$$

To eliminate I_1 between the above equations we multiply eqn. (4.5) by -2 and add it to eqn. (4.4) as follows

$$\begin{array}{rl} 20 = & 100I_1 - 80I_2 \\ -160 = & -100I_1 - 260I_2 \\ \hline -140 = & -340I_2 \quad \text{result of addition} \end{array}$$

Hence

$$I_2 = -140/-340 = 0.412 \text{ A}$$

The value of I_2 above is obtained by rounding the answer to a practical value, i.e. one which it is possible to read on a meter. The value of I_1 is obtained by substituting the value of I_2 into either eqn. (4.4) or eqn. (4.5). Choosing eqn. (4.4) gives

$$20 = 100I_1 - 80I_2 = 100I_1 - (80 \times 0.412)$$
$$= 100I_1 - 32.96$$

Therefore

$$I_1 = (20 + 32.96)/100 = 0.53 \text{ A}$$

The final solutions are

$$I_1 = 0.53 \text{ A}$$
$$I_2 = 0.412 \text{ A}$$
$$I_3 = I_1 + I_2 = 0.942 \text{ A}$$

Checking the solution

Whenever possible, it is advisable to make an independent check on the solution obtained. To do this, we will write down the loop equation for the third (unused) loop of the circuit (loop ADEFA), and substitute the calculated values of current as follows

Loop ADEFA   The equation is

$$-I_3 R_3 + E_1 - I_1 R_1 = 0$$

Substituting the above values gives

$$-(0.942 \times 50) + 100 - (0.53 \times 100) = -47.1 + 100 - 53$$
$$= -0.1$$

Note that the value on the right-hand side of the above equation should be zero! The value is -0.1 due to the rounding of values of current to give realistic figures. Had we taken the calculated current to many more decimal places (which we could not read on a conventional measuring instrument), the result of the calculation would have been zero. However, it is worth while commenting that, if we compare the value of 0.1 on the right-hand side of the equation with the 100 V on the left-hand side, we see that the overall error in our calculation is not greater than about 0.1 per cent.

APPLICATION 2

To illustrate a more complex circuit, we will calculate the current in each branch of figure 4.4, and also calculate the power consumed by the circuit. We will also calculate the potential of point C with respect to point $F(V_{CF} = I_3 R_3)$.

Solution   To determine the current in each branch, we follow the steps outlined earlier. Firstly we draw an e.m.f. arrow by the side of battery E_1 pointing from its negative pole to its positive pole.

The assumed direction of the current flow in each branch is then drawn on the circuit. The current flow in resistors R_1, R_2, R_4 and R_5 is self-evident, since it is from the positive pole of the battery to the negative pole. What is not so obvious is the direction of current flow in resistor R_3; it may flow either from C to F or in the reverse direction. Quite arbitrarily we decide

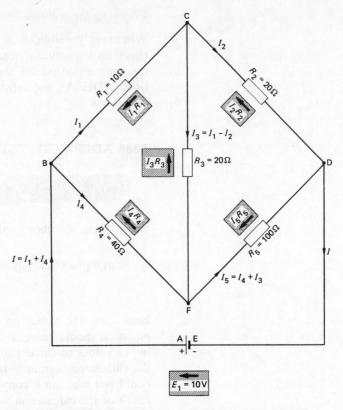

Fig. 4.4 Application 2 of the branch current method

that it flows from C to F; the accuracy of our choice will be decided later.

Next we must decide how many equations are needed to solve the circuit. Applying Kirchhoff's current law to each junction in turn we have

at junction B $\qquad I = I_1 + I_4$

at junction C $\qquad I_3 = I_1 - I_2$

at junction F $\qquad I_5 = I_4 + I_3 = I_4 + I_1 - I_2$

We need not consider junction D since we can calculate the value of I from I_1 and I_4 (see junction B above). From the above equations we see that, if we know the values of the three currents I_1, I_2 and I_4, then we can calculate all the other currents in the circuit. Hence we need three independent sets of equations to solve the circuit. There are many possible closed loops in the circuit including ABCDEA, BCFB, CDFC, ABCFDEA, ABFCDEA and ABFDEA. We will take the first three of these.

Loop ABCDEA Applying the rules outlined earlier, the loop equation is

$$-I_1R_1 - I_2R_2 + E_1 = 0$$

or

$$E_1 = I_1R_1 + I_2R_2$$

Substituting values gives

$$10 = 10I_1 + 20I_2 \tag{4.6}$$

Loop BCFB The loop equation is

$$-I_1R_1 - I_3R_3 + I_4R_4 = 0$$

but $I_3 = I_1 - I_2$, hence

$$
\begin{aligned}
0 &= -I_1R_1 - I_3R_3 + I_4R_4 \\
&= -I_1R_1 - (I_1 - I_2)R_3 + I_4R_4 \\
&= -I_1(R_1 + R_3) + I_2R_3 + I_4R_4
\end{aligned}
$$

Substituting values yields

$$0 = -30I_1 + 20I_2 + 40I_4 \tag{4.7}$$

Loop CDFC The loop equation is

$$-I_2R_2 + I_5R_5 + I_3R_3 = 0$$

but $I_3 = I_1 - I_2$ and $I_5 = I_4 + I_1 - I_2$, hence

$$
\begin{aligned}
0 &= -I_2R_2 + I_5R_5 + I_3R_3 \\
&= -I_2R_2 + (I_4 + I_1 - I_2)R_5 + (I_1 - I_2)R_3 \\
&= I_1(R_5 + R_3) - I_2(R_2 + R_3 + R_5) + I_4R_5
\end{aligned}
$$

Substituting circuit values gives

$$0 = 120I_1 - 140I_2 + 100I_4 \tag{4.8}$$

Solving the equations

A general strategy used to solve three simultaneous equations is to reduce the three equations to a pair of equations containing only two of the unknowns, which allows us to determine two currents. Afterwards the two values of current can be substituted into one of the equations to determine the third current. Our equations are

$$10 = 10I_1 + 20I_2$$
$$0 = -30I_1 + 20I_2 + 40I_4$$
$$0 = 120I_1 - 140I_2 + 100I_4$$

Since I_4 is absent from the first equation, we will eliminate it from the final pair of equations, leaving us with two equations containing only I_1 and I_2. To eliminate I_4 from equations (4.7) and (4.8), we multiply eqn. (4.8) by -0.4 and add it to eqn. (4.7).

$$0 = -30I_1 + 20I_2 + 40I_4 \qquad (4.7)$$
$$\underline{0 = -48I_1 + 56I_2 - 40I_4} \qquad \text{eqn. } (4.8) \times (-0.4)$$
$$0 = -78I_1 + 76I_2 \qquad \text{result of addition}$$

hence

$$I_1 = 76I_2/78 \qquad\qquad (4.9)$$

Substituting eqn. (4.9) into eqn. (4.6) gives

$$10 = \left(10 \times \frac{76I_2}{78}\right) + 20I_2 = I_2(9.744 + 20)$$

Therefore

$$I_2 = 10/29.744 = 0.3362 \text{ A}$$

To determine the value of I_1 we substitute the value of I_2 into eqn. (4.9) as follows

$$I_1 = 76I_2/78 = 76 \times 0.3362/78 = 0.3276 \text{ A}$$

Knowing the values of I_1 and I_2 allows us to calculate I_4 either from eqn. (4.7) or eqn. (4.8). Using eqn. (4.7) gives

$$0 = -30I_1 + 20I_2 + 40I_4$$
$$40I_4 = 30I_1 - 20I_2 = (30 \times 0.3276) - (20 \times 0.3362)$$
$$= 3.104$$

therefore

$$I_4 = 3.104/40 = 0.0776 \text{ A}$$

Hence

$$I = I_1 + I_4 = 0.3276 + 0.0776 = 0.4052 \text{ A}$$
$$I_1 = 0.3276 \text{ A}$$
$$I_2 = 0.3362 \text{ A}$$
$$I_3 = I_1 - I_2 = 0.3276 - 0.3362 = -0.0086 \text{ A}$$

$$I_4 = 0.0776 \text{ A}$$

$$I_5 = I_4 + I_3 = 0.0776 + (-0.0086) = 0.069 \text{ A}$$

Note that I_3 has a negative value. The implication of this is discussed in section 4.5.

The power consumed by the circuit is given by

$$P = EI = 10 \times 0.4052 = 4.052 \text{ W}$$

From the circuit diagram in figure 4.4, we see that

$$V_{CF} = I_3 R_3 = (-0.0086) \times 20 = -0.172 \text{ V}$$

That is, point C is negative relative to point F.

As a check on the accuracy of the calculations, take any of the closed loops not used in the above calculations, and verify that the sum of the e.m.f.s and p.d.s is zero (or practically so—depending on the rounding errors).

4.5 The Implications of a Negative Current

Let us determine the current flow in figure 4.5. The current arrows are drawn on the basis that both batteries discharge into R_3. It is left as an exercise to verify that the following equations are correct.

Loop ABCDA $4 = 20I_1 + 25I_2$

Loop ADEFA $10 = 30I_1 + 20I_2$

Solving these equations gives

$$I_1 = 0.486 \text{ A} \quad \text{and} \quad I_2 = -0.229 \text{ A}$$

The negative sign associated with I_2 implies that we have chosen the "wrong" direction for I_2 [this also applies to current I_3 in Application 2 of the branch current method (see figure 4.4)]. Note however that *this does not affect the accuracy of the calculation*, since battery E_2 is merely being charged by a current of 0.229 A rather than discharging into the circuit. A point of importance to note is that *although one of the currents has a negative value, we must not alter any of the circuit equations*. For example at junction A, $I_3 = I_1 + I_2$. All that we have to do to obtain the correct value of I_3 is to substitute the calculated values of I_1 and I_2 as follows.

$$I_3 = I_1 + I_2 = 0.486 + (-0.229) = 0.257 \text{ A}$$

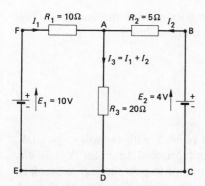

Fig. 4.5 Example illustrating a negative current

4.6 Calculation of the P.D. between Two Points in a Circuit

It is often necessary to calculate the potential difference existing between two points in a circuit (if only from the point of view of electrical safety!). This can be done using the "potential arrow" notation developed in this chapter. We shall illustrate this by means of the following examples.

EXAMPLE 4.1

In figure 4.6 calculate the potential of point Y with respect to point X (V_{YX}) given that $R_1 = 10\ \Omega$, $R_2 = 20\ \Omega$, $R_3 = 30\ \Omega$, $R_4 = 40\ \Omega$, $R_5 = 50\ \Omega$, $E_1 = 10\ V$, $E_2 = 20\ V$, $E_3 = 30\ V$.

Solution   It is first necessary to label the circuit diagram with e.m.f. arrows and also to select the direction of flow of current in each branch. This is illustrated in figure 4.6. The p.d. arrows associated with each resistor can then be drawn on the circuit diagram.

The following solutions are obtained for the currents. (Test your knowledge by verifying these solutions.)

$$I_1 = 0.4286\ A$$
$$I_2 = 0.1429\ A$$
$$I_3 = I_1 + I_2 = 0.5715\ A$$

To determine the potential of point Y with respect to point X, we commence at point X and proceed to point Y *via any complete path* (we must not attempt to pass through a break or open-circuit in the wiring). Whichever path we choose, the p.d. between Y and X will always have the same value (allowing of course for any rounding up errors in the calculation of I_1 and I_2). Suppose we choose path XABCY as follows.

Path XABCY   We start at point X and finish at Y so that potential of Y relative to X is

$$V_{YX} = V_{AX} + V_{BA} + V_{CB} + V_{YC}$$
$$= E_3 - I_2 R_4 + I_1 R_2 - E_2$$
$$= 30 - (0.1429 \times 40) + (0.4286 \times 20) - 20$$
$$= 12.853\ V$$

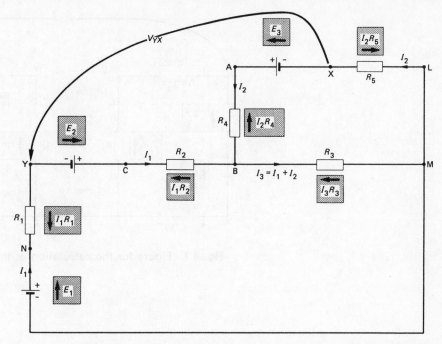

Fig. 4.6 Figure for the calculation of the p.d. between X and Y

That is, assuming point X to be at zero volts (consider it to be "earthed" or "grounded"), then the potential of Y is +12.853 V relative to the reference point X. We will check our solution by taking path XLMNY.

Path XLMNY Potential of Y relative to X is

$$V_{XY} = I_2 R_5 + E_1 - I_1 R_1$$
$$= (0.1429 \times 50) + 10 - (0.4286 \times 10)$$
$$= 12.859 \text{ V} \quad (Ans.)$$

Note that the two results agree within about 0.05 per cent of one another.

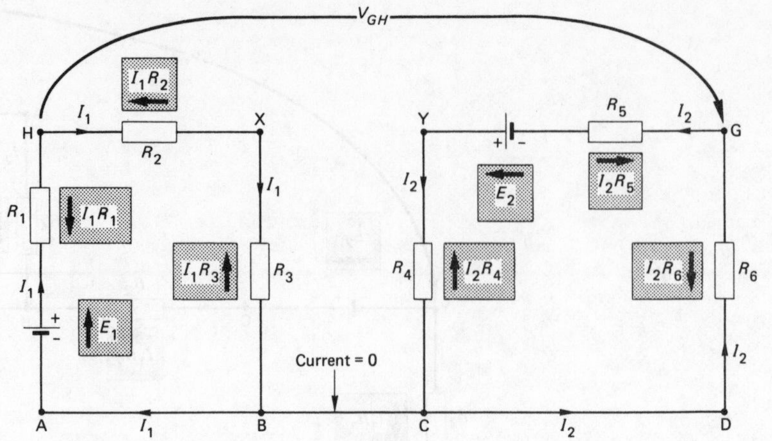

Fig. 4.7 Figure for the calculation of the p.d. between G and H

EXAMPLE 4.2

Calculate the potential of point G in figure 4.7 relative to point H. The values are $E_1 = 60$ V, $E_2 = 75$ V, $R_1 = 10\,\Omega$, $R_2 = 20\,\Omega$, $R_3 = 30\,\Omega$, $R_4 = 40\,\Omega$, $R_5 = 50\,\Omega$ and $R_6 = 60\,\Omega$.

Solution This is an interesting problem since it illustrates the calculation of the p.d. between two points in a circuit which has only one wire in common between the two parts of the circuit; that is to say, no current can circulate between the loops HABXH and GYCDG, the common link being BC. This situation occurs where two circuits are connected to a common chassis or frame, such as in a t.v. receiver. We may therefore calculate I_1 and I_2 separately as follows.

$$I_1 = \frac{E_1}{R_1 + R_2 + R_3} = \frac{60}{10 + 20 + 30} = 1\text{ A}$$

$$I_2 = \frac{E_2}{R_4 + R_5 + R_6} = \frac{75}{40 + 50 + 60} = 0.5\text{ A}$$

The direction of current flow is as shown in figure 4.7. Having drawn the current arrows on the circuit, the p.d. arrows are then drawn. To obtain the potential of G relative to H, we start at H and proceed to G via any complete path (which means that we *must* pass through link BC). Path HABCDG is selected arbitrarily.

Path HABCDG Potential of G relative to H is

$$V_{GH} = V_{AH} + V_{BA} + V_{CB} + V_{DC} + V_{GD}$$
$$= I_1 R_1 - E_1 + 0 + 0 + 0 - I_2 R_6$$
$$= (1 \times 10) - 60 - (0.5 \times 60) = -80 \text{ V} \quad (Ans.)$$

That is the potential of G is -80 V with respect to the datum point H.

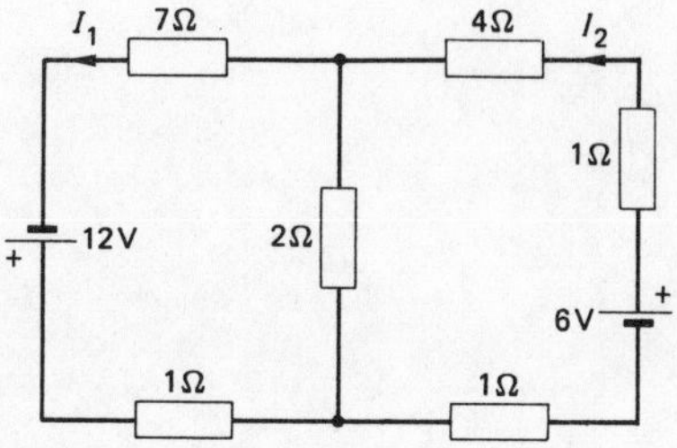

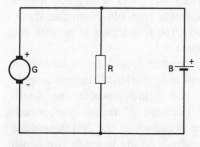

Fig. 4.8

Fig. 4.9

Exercises

4.1 State and explain Kirchhoff's first and second laws.

4.2 For the circuit in figure 4.8, determine *a*) the value of I_1 and I_2, *b*) the p.d. across the 2 Ω resistor (state which end of the resistor is at the most positive potential), *c*) the power consumed by the circuit.

[*a*) 1.42 A; 1.105 A; *b*) 0.63 V (B positive with respect to A); *c*) 23.66 W]

4.3 Two cells having e.m.f.s of 1.0 V and 3.0 V, respectively, each having an internal resistance of 2 Ω are connected in parallel with one another with like terminals being connected together. A 5 Ω resistor is connected between their terminals. Calculate the current in each battery and in the resistor.

[0.33 A; 0.66 A; 0.33 A]

4.4 In the circuit in figure 4.9, the resistance of R is 2 Ω. The generator G has an internal resistance of 0.5 Ω and generates a voltage of 17.0 V, and the e.m.f. and internal resistance of battery B are 12.6 V and 0.1 Ω, respectively. Determine the value of the current through R and also that through the battery (state if the battery is being charged or discharged).

[6.4 A; 2 A, charging]

4.5 A circuit of the kind in figure 4.4 has the following values: $R_1 = 100$ Ω, $R_2 = 100$ Ω, $R_3 = 50$ Ω, $R_4 = 200$ Ω, $R_5 = 201$ Ω. Determine the value of the current in R_3 if $E_1 = 2$ V.

[12.5 μA]

5 The Magnetic Field

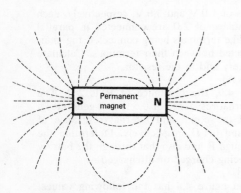

Fig. 5.1 Magnetic field pattern of a bar magnet

5.1 Introduction

Since we do not fully understand what a magnetic field is, we simply describe it in terms of its effect on materials such as iron filings. A magnetic field is invisible, but evidence of its existence can be observed when we cover a magnet with a sheet of glass or paper and sprinkle iron filings on the sheet. When the sheet is tapped lightly, the iron filings align with the magnetic field as shown in figure 5.1.

When a bar magnet is suspended freely on a thread, it always points with one end towards the North magnetic pole of the earth, and the other end points towards the South magnetic pole of the earth. The end of the magnet which points towards the North pole is known as the **North-seeking pole** or **N-pole**, and the end which points towards the south pole is known as the **South-seeking pole** or **S-pole**.

When two bar magnets are suspended close to one another, it is found that the N-pole of one magnet is attracted to the S-pole of the other magnet. That is, **unlike magnetic poles are attracted towards one another**. An investigation of the magnetic field pattern between two opposite poles yields the pattern in figure 5.2*a*.

It is also found that the N-pole of one magnet repels the N-pole of another magnet. Also the S-pole of the first magnet repels the S-pole of the second magnet. That is, **like magnetic poles repel one another**. The flux pattern between two like poles is shown in figure 5.2*b*.

5.2 Direction of a Magnetic Field

In practice a magnet always has one N-pole and one S-pole. However, let us assume that we can obtain a single "free"

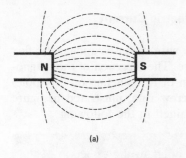

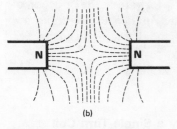

Fig. 5.2 Magnetic field pattern between (*a*) unlike poles, (*b*) like poles

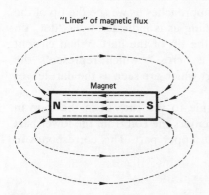

Fig. 5.3 Lines of magnetic force

N-pole. If we place this pole close to the N-pole of a fixed magnet, the force of repulsion between them causes the free N-pole to move away from the N-pole of the fixed magnet and towards its S-pole. The line that the free N-pole traces out as it moves from the N-pole of the fixed magnet to its S-pole is known as a **line of magnetic flux**. On this basis we say that a line of magnetic flux *leaves* a N-pole and *enters* a S-pole. When the free N-pole arrives at the S-pole of the fixed magnet, it returns to the N-pole "inside" the magnet as shown in figure 5.3.

The concept of the movement of a hypothetical free N-pole leads to the idea that something "flows" out of the N-pole and into a S-pole. This concept is sometimes convenient as an aid to the understanding of the operation of electrical machines but, alas, nothing actually flows in practice. A line of magnetic flux is simply a stationary line indicating the direction of the force which an isolated N-pole would experience if placed on the line.

Note that *lines of magnetic flux never intersect one another*, that is they never cross.

5.3 Magnetic Flux and Flux Density

The **magnetic flux** Φ (phi) is related to the number of lines of magnetic force either emanating from or entering into a magnetized surface. A magnet with a strong magnetic field produces more lines of flux than does a magnet with a weak field. The SI unit of flux is the weber (symbol Wb) after Wilhelm Weber, a German physicist.

A measure of the magnetic flux entering unit area (i.e. 1 m²) is the **magnetic flux density** B where

$$\text{Flux density } B = \frac{\Phi}{a} \text{ tesla(T)} \qquad (5.1)$$

where a is the area (in m²) through which flux Φ (Wb) passes.

EXAMPLE 5.1

Calculate the value of the magnetic flux density when a flux of 80 μWb passes through an area of 4 cm².

Solution $\Phi = 80 \ \mu\text{Wb} = 80 \times 10^{-6} \text{ Wb}$

$a = 4 \text{ cm}^2 = 4 \times (10^{-2})^2 \text{ m}^2 = 4 \times 10^{-4} \text{ m}^2$

From eqn. (5.1)

$B = \Phi/a = 80 \times 10^{-6}/4 \times 10^{-4} = 0.2 \text{ T}$ (*Ans.*)

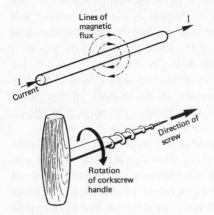

Fig. 5.4 The screw rule for the direction of the magnetic flux around a conductor

5.4 Magnetic Effect of an Electric Current

When a current flows through a wire it causes a magnetic flux to be established around the wire. The direction of the magnetic flux (defined by the direction of force acting on a N-pole) can be predicted by the **corkscrew rule**, illustrated in figure 5.4. The corkscrew rule is explained in the following.

> If we imagine a corkscrew to point in the direction of the current flow in the wire, and then if we turn the corkscrew handle in a direction to propel it forward in the direction of the current, the direction of the rotation of the corkscrew handle gives the direction of the lines of magnetic flux around the conductor.

5.5 Flux Pattern Produced by a Single-Turn Coil

Consider the single-turn coil in figure 5.5a carrying current in the direction shown. If we look on top of the coil and take a section through the coil at X–X, we obtain the view in figure 5.5b. The direction of the current is indicated by the following notation. If we regard the current as being the movement of a dart, then when the current approaches us we see the tip of the dart; hence current approaching us is indicated by a "dot" on the conductor representing the tip of the dart. When current leaves us it is shown by a "cross" which represents the "crossed feathers" of the dart which are seen as the dart leaves us.

Applying the corkscrew rule to the current in the loop in figure 5.5b, we see that flux enters the coil from the lower part of figure 5.5b and leaves the upper part. This corresponds in

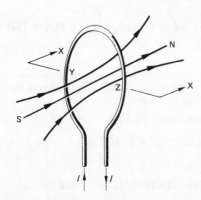

(a)

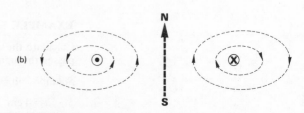

(b)

Fig. 5.5 Flux pattern produced by a single-turn coil

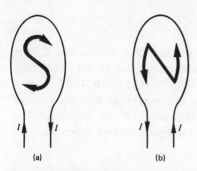

Fig. 5.6 Magnetic field produced by a conductor loop

figure 5.5*a* to flux entering from the left (causing a S-pole at that end) and leaving from the right (causing a N-pole at that end).

Looking at the end elevation of a single conductor loop, the magnetic polarity can be predicted from figure 5.6. When the current flows in the direction shown in figure 5.6*a*, a S-pole is produced at the end viewed by us. When the current flows in the direction in figure 5.6*b*, a N-pole is produced at the end viewed by us.

5.6 Flux Pattern Produced by a Solenoid

A **solenoid** is a multi-turn coil with an **air-core**, a section through a solenoid being shown in figure 5.7. The solenoid is wound or is "formed" on an insulating material known as the coil **former**.

With the direction of current shown, the current in the conductors at the top of the solenoid approaches us, and the current in the conductors at the bottom of the solenoid flows away from us. In addition to the individual flux paths around each conductor, as shown, there is a combined flux pattern which produces a N-pole at the right-hand end of the solenoid and a S-pole at the left-hand end.

As an exercise, verify that the magnetic polarity is reversed if either *a*) the direction of the current is reversed or *b*) the direction of the current is unchanged, but the coil is rewound in the opposite direction (i.e. the left-hand conductor passes round the back of the coil former, and the right-hand conductor passes over the front of the former).

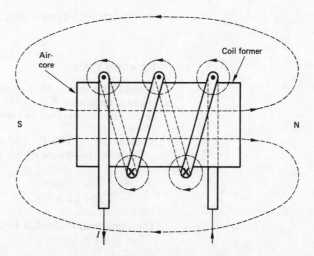

Fig. 5.7 Magnetic field around a solenoid

5.7 Magnetomotive Force

When the current through a conductor is increased, the magnetic field around it also increases. The current therefore not only causes the magnetic field to be established but, in a coil with an air core, causes the magnetic flux to vary in proportion to the current. The force which produces the magnetic field is known as the **magnetomotive force** (m.m.f.) and is given by

$$\text{m.m.f. } F = IN \text{ ampere turns or ampere (A)} \qquad (5.2)$$

where I is the current flowing in the conductors of the coil and N is the number of turns on the coil. Since the m.m.f. is equal to the product (current × number of turns) it is often given the unit of the ampere turn. However, since the number of turns is, in fact, merely a number (that is, it is a dimensionless quantity), then the m.m.f. has the dimensions of current, i.e. the ampere.

Since m.m.f. can be regarded as the driving force behind the magnetic flux, it is convenient to think of m.m.f. as the "magnetic p.d." in a magnetic circuit.

EXAMPLE 5.2

Calculate the m.m.f. produced by a coil of 1000 turns when it carries a current of 4 A.

Solution $I = 4$ A, $N = 1000$ turns.
  From eqn. (5.2)

$$F = IN = 4 \times 1000 = 4000 \text{ A} \quad (Ans.)$$

EXAMPLE 5.3

A coil of resistance 10 Ω is connected to a battery of e.m.f. 15 V and internal resistance 5 Ω. If the m.m.f. produced by the coil is 250 A, determine the number of turns on the coil.

Solution $E = 15$ V, $F = 250$ A.
  The total resistance of the circuit is

$$R_T = R_{coil} + R_{battery}$$
$$= 10 + 5 = 15 \ \Omega$$

The current in the coil is $I = E/R_T = 15/15 = 1$ A.
  But $F = IN$, hence

$$N = F/I = 250/1 = 250 \text{ turns} \quad (Ans.)$$

5.8 Magnetic Field Intensity

The **magnetic field intensity** is the m.m.f. per unit length of the magnetic circuit. This is analogous in the electric circuit to the p.d. per unit length along a current carrying conductor.

$$\text{Magnetic field intensity } H = \frac{IN}{l} = \frac{F}{l} \text{ ampere per metre} \quad (5.3)$$

The magnetic field intensity is also known as the **magnetizing force** or as the **magnetic field strength**.

EXAMPLE 5.4

A coil of length 20 cm is wound with 2000 turns of wire and carries a current of 10 A. Calculate the magnetic field intensity at the centre of the coil.

Solution $l = 20\,\text{cm} = 0.2\,\text{m}$, $N = 2000$ turns, $I = 10\,\text{A}$.

From eqn. (5.3)

$$H = IN/l = 10 \times 2000/0.2 = 100\,000\,\text{A/m}$$

5.9 The Absolute Permeability of a Magnetic Material

If an iron rod is placed close to one end of a permanent magnet, and a brass rod is placed close to the other end of the magnet (see figure 5.8), then when the magnetic field pattern is

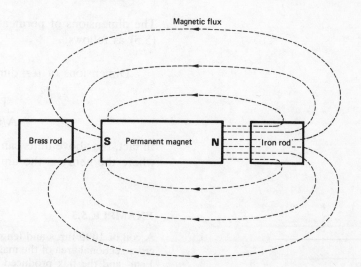

Fig. 5.8 The effect of the permeability of different materials

investigated we find that the magnetic field is concentrated in the iron rod, whilst the brass rod has little effect on the magnetic field.

The reason for this phenomenon is that the iron has a lower "magnetic resistance" than that of the surrounding air path. The magnetic flux concentrates in the low magnetic resistance of the iron. The magnetic resistance of brass has much the same value as that of the surrounding air, so that the brass has little effect on the magnetic flux pattern.

Much as every material has a particular value of electrical conductivity, then every material also has a specific value of what is known as **magnetic permeability** which enables us to calculate its "resistance" to magnetic flux. More will be said about this later.

The **absolute permeability** μ (mu) of a magnetic material can be defined in terms of the following relationship

Flux density = absolute permeability × magnetic field intensity

or

$$B = \mu H \qquad (5.4)$$

hence

$$\mu = \frac{B}{H} \qquad (5.5)$$

The dimensions of permeability can be determined from eqn. (5.5) as follows:

$$\text{Dimensions of } \mu = \text{dimensions of } \frac{B}{H}$$

$$= \frac{\text{T}}{\text{A/m}} \quad \text{or} \quad \text{tesla/(ampere per metre)}$$

In fact, the above units can be reduced to henrys/metre (H/m), where the henry is the unit of inductance (see chapter 6).

EXAMPLE 5.5

A coil of 1000 turns and length 0.2 m carries a current of 5 A. If the cross-sectional area of the magnetic circuit perpendicular to the flux is 1 cm² and the flux produced by the coil is 0.15 mWb, calculate the absolute permeability of the magnetic material.

Solution $N = 1000$ turns, $l = 0.2$ m, $I = 5$ A, $a = 1 \text{ cm}^2 = 10^{-4} \text{ m}^2$, $\Phi = 0.15$ mWb $= 0.15 \times 10^{-3}$ Wb.

From eqn. (5.1)

Flux density $B = \Phi/a = 0.15 \times 10^{-3}/10^{-4} = 1.5$ T

From eqn. (5.3)

Magnetic field intensity $H = IN/l$

$$= 5 \times 1000/0.2 = 25\,000 \text{ A/m}$$

and from eqn. (5.5)

Absolute permeability $\mu = B/H$

$$= 1.5/25\,000 = 60 \times 10^{-6} \text{ H/m} \quad (Ans.)$$

5.10 Permeability of Free Space and Relative Permeability

The **permeability of free space** or **magnetic space constant** is the permeability of a vacuum and is given the symbol μ_0 which has the value

$$\mu_0 = 4\pi \times 10^{-7} \text{ H/m or T/(A/m)}$$

For all practical purposes the *permeability of air has much the same value as that of free space.*

The absolute permeability μ of a material is given by

Absolute permeability $= \mu_0 \times$ relative permeability μ_r

or

$$\mu = \mu_0 \mu_r \tag{5.6}$$

hence

$$\mu_r = \frac{\mu}{\mu_0} \tag{5.7}$$

From eqn. (5.7) we see that μ_r is a dimensionless quantity since

$$\text{Dimensions of } \mu_r = \text{dimensions of } \frac{\mu}{\mu_0} = \frac{\text{H/m}}{\text{H/m}}$$

The value of μ_r for the material in the core of the coil in example 5.5 can be calculated by inserting the value for μ ($= 60 \times 10^{-6}$) into eqn. (5.7) as follows

$$\mu_r = \mu/\mu_0 = 60 \times 10^{-6}/4\pi \times 10^{-7} = 47.75$$

A value of μ_r which is greater than unity can be interpreted as follows. Suppose we have a coil with an air-core whose magnetic field intensity is 25 000 A/m (see example 5.5), then for this coil the effective value of μ is equal to μ_0. Hence for this coil

$$B = \mu_0 H = (4\pi \times 10^{-7}) \times 25\,000 = 0.0314 \text{ T}$$

If a magnetic material whose value of μ_r is 47.75 (or $\mu = 60 \times 10^{-6}$ H/m) is inserted into the core of the coil, then the flux density in the core rises to 1.5 T (see example 5.5). That is to say, when the value of μ_r is greater than unity, then the flux density (and also the value of the magnetic flux) increases above that for an air core by an amount equal to the relative permeability. Conversely, if the value of μ_r is less than unity (see section 5.11), the flux density is less than that for an air-core.

EXAMPLE 5.6

A battery of e.m.f. E and of negligible internal resistance is connected to a coil wound with 1000 turns of wire of resistance 20 Ω. The coil has an iron core of relative permeability 300, the length of the iron circuit being 0.25 m and its cross-sectional area 10 cm². For an m.m.f. of 100 ampere turns calculate *a*) the required battery voltage, *b*) the flux density in the core, and *c*) the magnetic flux in the core.

Solution $N = 1000$ turns, $R = 20\,\Omega$, $\mu_r = 300$, $l = 0.25$ m, $a = 10$ cm² $= 0.001$ m², $F = 100$ A.
a) From eqn. (5.2) $F = NI$, hence

$$I = F/N = 100/1000 = 0.1 \text{ A}$$

Also

$$E = IR = 0.1 \times 20 = 2 \text{ V} \quad (Ans.)$$

b) Magnetic field intensity, $H = F/l = 100/0.25 = 400$ A/m.
From eqn. (5.4)

$$B = \mu H = \mu_r \mu_0 H$$
$$= 300 \times (4\pi \times 10^{-7}) \times 400 = 0.151 \text{ T} \quad (Ans.)$$

c) From eqn. (5.1), $B = \Phi/a$, hence

$$\Phi = Ba = 0.151 \times 0.001 = 0.000\,151 \text{ Wb} \quad (Ans.)$$

5.11 Ferromagnetic, Paramagnetic and Diamagnetic Materials

Depending on the value of the relative permeability, materials can be classified into one of the above three groups.

A **ferromagnetic material** has a value of μ_r which is considerably greater than unity. Included in this group are iron, steel, and a number of their alloys such as those containing nickel and cobalt.

A **paramagnetic material** has a value of μ_r which is slightly greater than unity; the material becomes weakly magnetized in the direction of the magnetizing field. Included in this group are aluminium and chromium.

The relative permeability of a **diamagnetic material** is slightly less than unity; the material becomes weakly magnitized in the opposite direction to the magnetizing field. Included in this group are gold and silver.

5.12 The Magnetization Curve of a Ferromagnetic Material

The molecular structure of iron and other ferromagnetic materials can be regarded as a collection of minute magnets known as **domains** or **dipole magnets**, each having a N-pole and a S-pole. In a demagnetized material, the domains point in random directions, the "randomness" being such that the overall magnetic field is zero (see figure 5.9a).

When an iron bar is placed inside a coil which carries current, the domains begin to align with the magnetic field produced by the coil. The overall effect is to produce a magnetic field which is greater than that produced by the current in the coil itself (this accounts for the relative permeability of iron being greater than unity).

Increasing the current in the coil causes more domains to align with the magnetic field produced by the coil. However, a point is reached when further increase in current produces very little change in the magnetic field. This condition arises when most of the domains have already aligned with the magnetic field, so that only a few remain to be aligned.

Finally a point is reached at which all the domains have aligned with the magnetic field (see figure 5.9b). When this occurs, the iron is said to be magnetically **saturated**.

If we plot the flux density B in the iron to a base of the magnetic field intensity H (i.e. the ampere-turns per metre produced by the coil), we obtain a curve known as the **B-H curve** or **magnetization curve** of the iron which has the shape in figure 5.10.

At low values of current (between the origin O and the "knee" of the curve) we see that the flux density increases rapidly; this is due to the alignment of a large number of magnetic domains in the iron with the field of the coil. The knee of the curve marks the onset of saturation, after which progressively fewer domains remain to be aligned. Finally, in the region marked "magnetic saturation" in figure

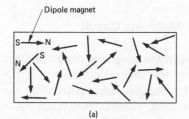

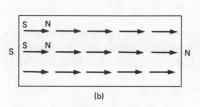

Fig. 5.9 (a) Demagnetized material, (b) magnetized material

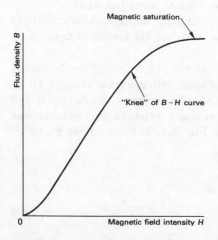

Fig. 5.10 B-H curve for a ferromagnetic material

5.10, all the domains have aligned with the magnetic field. Any further small increase in the magnetic flux with increase in magnetizing current is due to the increase in m.m.f. of the coil current alone, and is not due to the iron core in the coil.

From the shape of the B-H curve, it is possible to predict that the value of μ_r is low both at low values and high values of B. The relative permeabilities of ferromagnetic materials therefore have a peak value somewhere between the two extremes. The value of μ_r for iron can have almost any value between about 50 and a few thousand, depending on the operating flux density (see also example 5.10).

5.13 "Ohm's Law" for the Magnetic Circuit

There is a direct analogy between the magnetic circuit and the electrical circuit if we say that the magnetic "e.m.f." is the magnetomotive force F (m.m.f.), the magnetic "current" is the magnetic flux Φ, and the magnetic circuit "resistance" is a quantity known as the **reluctance** (symbol S) of the magnetic circuit, then

Magnetic "e.m.f." = magnetic "current" × magnetic "resistance"

or

$$F = \Phi S \quad \text{A (or ampere turn)} \tag{5.8}$$

where F is in amperes (or ampere turns), Φ is in webers, and S is in ampere per weber (or ampere turns per weber).

The analogy between the magnetic and the electrical circuit is sufficiently close to allow us to use the circuit in figure 5.11 to represent eqn. (5.8).

Many students have difficulty in remembering the bewildering range of equations associated with electrical circuits. However, since there is an association between the electrical and the magnetic circuit, there is also a link between the equations of the two types of circuit. For the electrical circuit we have

$$E = IR \tag{5.9}$$

and for the magnetic circuit

$$F = \Phi S \tag{5.10}$$

If the lower "bar" of the letter E is removed in eqn. (5.9), we are left with the letter F in the equivalent position in eqn.

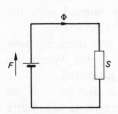

Fig. 5.11 Equivalent circuit corresponding to equation (5.8)

(5.10). Now, if we bend the removed "bar" from the letter E into a circle and place it on the upright of the letter I in eqn. (5.9) we get the letter Φ in eqn. (5.10). Also if we regard the removed lower bar as the number 1, and we think of the letter in the alphabet which is "one" greater than the letter R, we get the letter S in eqn. (5.10).

EXAMPLE 5.7

Calculate the reluctance of a magnetic circuit which is uniformly wound with a coil producing an m.m.f. of 500 A, the flux in the core being 250 μ Wb.

Solution $F = 500$ A, $\Phi = 250\ \mu\text{Wb} = 250 \times 10^{-6}$ Wb.

From eqn. (5.8)

$$S = F/\Phi = 500/250 \times 10^{-6} = 2 \times 10^6 \text{ A/Wb} \quad (Ans.)$$

5.14 Reluctance and Permeance of a Magnetic Circuit

Consider the simple magnetic circuit in figure 5.12. Here the m.m.f. produced by the coil is

$$F = NI \text{ A} \tag{5.11}$$

and the magnetic flux in the core is given by

$$\Phi = \text{flux density} \times \text{area} = Ba \text{ Wb}$$

But

$$B = \mu H \text{ T}$$

where μ is the absolute permeability of the iron circuit, therefore

$$\Phi = Ba = \mu Ha \text{ Wb}$$

However, $H = F/l$, where l is the mean length of the magnetic circuit, hence

$$\Phi = \mu \frac{F}{l} a \text{ Wb} \tag{5.12}$$

From eqns. (5.8) and (5.12), the **reluctance** of the magnetic circuit is

$$\text{Reluctance } S = \frac{F}{\Phi} = \frac{F}{\mu \dfrac{F}{l} a} = \frac{l}{\mu a} = \frac{l}{\mu_r \mu_0 a} \text{ A/Wb} \tag{5.13}$$

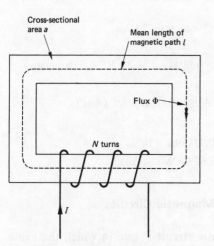

Cross-sectional area a

Mean length of magnetic path l

Flux Φ

N turns

I

Fig. 5.12 Calculation of the reluctance of a magnetic circuit

The **permeance** (symbol Λ) of the magnetic circuit is given by

$$\text{Permeance } \Lambda = \frac{1}{S} = \frac{\mu a}{l} \text{ Wb/A} \qquad (5.14)$$

Hence

$$F = \frac{\Phi}{\Lambda} \text{ A} \qquad (5.15)$$

EXAMPLE 5.8

Calculate the reluctance and the permeance of a ferromagnetic circuit of mean length 0.2 m, of area 10 cm^2, and having a relative permeability of 100. If the magnetic circuit is uniformly wound with 1000 turns of wire which carries a current of 0.1 A, determine the magnetic flux in the core.

Solution $l = 0.2$ m, $a = 10$ cm$^2 = 0.001$ m^2, $\mu_r = 100$, $N = 1000$, $I = 0.1$ A.

$$\mu = \mu_r\mu_0 = 100 \times 4\pi \times 10^{-7} = 4\pi \times 10^{-5} \text{ H/m}$$

From eqn. (5.13)

$$S = l/\mu a = 0.2/(4\pi \times 10^{-5} \times 0.001) = 159.2 \times 10^6 \text{ A/Wb} \quad (Ans.)$$

From eqn. (5.14)

$$\Lambda = 1/S = 1/159.2 \times 10^6 = 6.28 \times 10^{-9} \text{ Wb/A} \quad (Ans.)$$

and from eqn. (5.8)

$$\Phi = F/S = NI/S = 1000 \times 0.1/159.2 \times 10^6$$
$$= 0.628 \times 10^{-6} \text{ Wb or } 0.628 \,\mu\text{Wb} \quad (Ans.)$$

5.15 Series-connected Magnetic Circuits

A **series-connected magnetic circuit** is one in which the **same flux** is established in all parts of the circuit (this assumes no magnetic leakage).

A typical series magnetic circuit is shown in figure 5.13a, and consists of an iron part of length l_1 and an air-gap of length l_2. A coil is uniformly wound on the iron part, and produces an m.m.f. of $F = NI$. The equivalent circuit diagram which enables us to calculate the flux is shown in figure 5.13b.

The rules used to calculate the equivalent reluctance of the series magnetic circuit follow those for the resistance of a series-connected electrical circuit as follows.

$$\text{Equivalent reluctance } S_T = S_1 + S_2 \text{ A/Wb} \qquad (5.16)$$

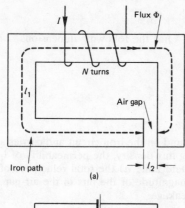

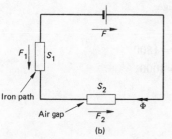

Fig. 5.13 (a) Series-connected magnetic circuit and (b) its equivalent circuit

where S_1 and S_2 are the respective reluctances of the iron path and the air gap. Hence

$$\text{Magnetic flux } \Phi = FS_T \text{ Wb} \qquad (5.17)$$

The m.m.f. F_1 required to produce flux Φ in the iron path is $F_1 = \Phi S_1$ and the m.m.f. required for the air gap is $F_2 = \Phi S_2$. The total m.m.f. requirement is

$$F = F_1 + F_2 = \Phi(S_1 + S_2) \qquad (5.18)$$

The above discussion assumes that all the flux remains in the magnetic circuit, i.e. no flux "leaks" away from the circuit. In practice there is some leakage flux, and the method of coping with this problem is dealt with in section 5.16.

EXAMPLE 5.9

An electromagnet has an iron path 0.9 m long and is wound with a coil of 750 turns. The electromagnet must produce a flux density of 0.65 T in its 2 mm air-gap. Determine the current in the coil if the relative permeability of the iron is 2000. Neglect the effects of magnetic leakage.

Solution The magnetic circuit is generally similar to that in figure 5.13a, and the quantities are defined in terms of figure 5.13a.

$I_1 = 0.9$ m, $N = 750$, $B = 0.65$ T, $l_2 = 2$ mm $= 2 \times 10^{-3}$ m, $\mu_r = 2000$.

Applying eqn. (5.4) to the iron circuit gives

$$H_{iron} = B/\mu = B/\mu_r\mu_0 = 0.65/(2000 \times 4\pi \times 10^{-7}) = 258.6 \text{ A/m}$$

The m.m.f. required for the IRON PATH is calculated from eqn. (5.3) as follows:

$$F_{iron} = H_{iron}l_1 = 258.6 \times 0.9 = 232.74 \text{ A}$$

For the air-gap

$$H_{air} = B/\mu_0 = 0.65/4\pi \times 10^{-7} = 517.3 \times 10^3 \text{ A/m}$$

and the m.m.f. required for the AIR-GAP is

$$F_{air} = H_{air}l_2 = 517.3 \times 10^3 \times 2 \times 10^{-3} = 1034.6 \text{ A}$$

Note that a far greater m.m.f. is required to produce the same flux density in the 0.002 m air-gap than is required to produce it in the 0.9 m iron path.

The total m.m.f. F needed to produce a flux density of 0.65 T is

$$F = F_{iron} + F_{air} = 232.74 + 1034.6 = 1267.34 \text{ A}$$

Now $F = NI$, hence

$$I = F/N = 1267.34/750 = 1.69 \text{ A} \quad (Ans.)$$

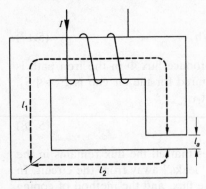

Fig. 5.14

EXAMPLE 5.10

The magnetic circuit in figure 5.14 has the following dimensions

$$l_1 = 16 \text{ cm, area } a_1 = 4 \text{ cm}^2$$
$$l_2 = 10 \text{ cm, area } a_2 = 2 \text{ cm}^2$$

and for the air-gap

$$l_a = 2 \text{ mm, area } a_a = 4 \text{ cm}^2$$

A coil of 1000 turns of wire is wound on the iron circuit and carries a current of 1.5 A. At the operating flux density, the permeability of l_1 is 1800 and that of l_2 is 1000. Determine a) the total reluctance of the magnetic circuit and b) the magnitude of the flux in the air-gap. Neglect the effects of magnetic leakage.

Solution

$$l_1 = 0.16 \text{ m, } a_1 = 4 \times 10^{-4} \text{ m}^2, \ \mu_{r1} = 1800$$
$$l_2 = 0.1 \text{ m, } a_2 = 2 \times 10^{-4} \text{ m}^2, \ \mu_{r2} = 1000$$
$$l_a = 0.002 \text{ m, } a_a = 4 \times 10^{-4} \text{ m}^2$$
$$N = 1000, \ I = 1.5 \text{ A}$$

a) For length l_1 of the iron circuit

$$S_1 = l_1/\mu_0\mu_{r1}a_1 = 0.16/(4\pi \times 10^{-7} \times 1800 \times 4 \times 10^{-4})$$
$$= 1.77 \times 10^5 \text{ A/Wb}$$

For length l_2 of the iron circuit

$$S_2 = l_2/\mu_0\mu_{r2}a_2 = 0.1/(4\pi \times 10^{-7} \times 1000 \times 2 \times 10^{-4})$$
$$= 3.98 \times 10^5 \text{ A/Wb}$$

For the air-gap

$$S_a = l_a/\mu_0 a_a = 0.002/(4\pi \times 10^{-7} \times 4 \times 10^{-4}) = 39.79 \times 10^5 \text{ A/Wb}$$

The total reluctance S of the magnetic circuit is

$$S = S_1 + S_2 + S_a = (1.77 + 3.98 + 39.79) \times 10^5$$
$$= 45.54 \times 10^5 \text{ A/Wb} \quad (Ans.)$$

b) The m.m.f. F produced by the coil is

$$F = NI = 1000 \times 1.5 = 1500 \text{ A}$$

hence

$$\Phi = F/S = 1500/45.54 \times 10^5 = 0.33 \times 10^{-3} \text{ Wb}$$

or

$$0.33 \text{ mWb} \quad (Ans.)$$

EXAMPLE 5.11

An iron rod 0.75 m long is bent into a ring having a 1 mm air-gap between the ends of the rod, the area of the rod being 5 cm². The rod is uniformly wound with 1000 turns of wire. Calculate the current in the coil if the magnetic flux in the air-gap is 0.3 mWb. Neglect the effects of magnetic leakage. Data for the iron is given below.

B(tesla)	0.4	0.65	0.8
H(A/m)	80	160	240

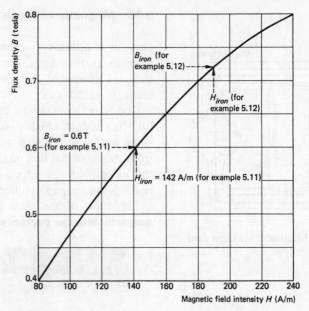

Fig. 5.15

Solution In this case the operating conditions are obtained from the *B-H* curve of the magnetic circuit which is plotted in figure 5.15 from the values given in the problem. Other data is as follows:

$l_{iron} = 0.75$ m, $l_{air} = 10^{-3}$ m, $a = 5 \times 10^{-4}$ m^2, $N = 1000$, $\Phi = 0.3 \times 10^{-3}$ Wb.

Flux density $B = \Phi/a = 0.3 \times 10^{-3}/5 \times 10^{-4} = 0.6$ T

From the *B-H* curve for the iron, this flux density corresponds to a magnetic field intensity in the iron of

$$H_{iron} = 142 \text{ A/m}$$

Hence the m.m.f. F_{iron} for the iron path is

$$F_{iron} = H_{iron}l_{iron} = 142 \times 0.75 = 106.5 \text{ A}$$

For the air-gap

$$S_{air} = l_{air}/\mu_0 a = 10^{-3}/(4\pi \times 10^{-7} \times 5 \times 10^{-4}) = 1.59 \times 10^6 \text{ A/Wb}$$

and the m.m.f. F_{air} for the air-gap is

$$F_{air} = \Phi S_{air} = 0.3 \times 10^{-3} \times 1.59 \times 10^6 = 477 \text{ A}$$

The total m.m.f. F required to produce flux Φ is

$$F = F_{iron} + F_{air} = 106.5 + 477 = 583.5 \text{ A}$$

Now $F = NI$, therefore

$$I = F/N = 583.5/1000 = 0.5835 \text{ A} \quad (Ans.)$$

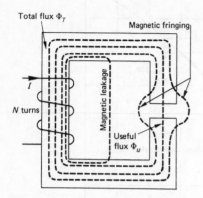

Fig. 5.16 Magnetic leakage and fringing

5.16 Magnetic Leakage and Fringing

Since it is difficult to effectively "insulate" a magnetic circuit from its surroundings, not all the magnetic flux produced by the coil arrives at the intended destination which, in many cases, is an air-gap.

Consider the magnetic circuit in figure 5.16. Here the "useful" flux is that which passes directly across the air-gap to do some useful work (such as, for example, attracting a piece of iron). Some of the flux produced by the coil **fringes** or bypasses the air-gap at the edges of the gap. Some flux never even reaches the air-gap, typified by the **leakage flux** in figure 5.16.

The ratio of the total flux to useful flux is given by the **magnetic leakage coefficient** as follows.

$$\text{Leakage coefficient} = \frac{\text{total flux}}{\text{useful flux}} = \frac{\Phi_T}{\Phi_U} \qquad (5.18)$$

The value of this coefficient is typically in the range 1.05 to 1.4, the higher value corresponding to a "leaky" magnetic circuit.

EXAMPLE 5.12

If the leakage coefficient in example 5.11 is 1.2, calculate the current in the coil to produce a flux in the air-gap of 0.3 mWb (the relevant details are given below for the convenience of the reader).

Solution $l_{iron} = 0.75$ m, $l_{air} = 10^{-3}$ m, $a = 5 \times 10^{-4}$ m^2, $N = 1000$, $\Phi_{air} = 0.3 \times 10^{-3}$ Wb, leakage coefficient = 1.2.

Flux density in the air-gap $B_{air} = \Phi_{air}/a$
$$= 0.3 \times 10^{-3}/5 \times 10^{-4} = 0.6 \text{ T}$$

Since the air-gap parameters are unchanged for this problem, then from the results of example 5.11

$$S_{air} = 1.59 \times 10^6 \text{ A/Wb}$$

and

$$F_{air} = \Phi_{air}S_{air} = 477 \text{ A}$$

However, since the leakage factor is 1.2, the magnetic flux in the iron part is

$$(0.3 \times 10^{-3}) \times 1.2 = 0.36 \times 10^{-3} \text{ Wb}$$

giving a flux density in the iron path of

$$0.36 \times 10^{-3}/5 \times 10^{-4} = 0.72 \text{ T}$$

From the B-H curve in figure 5.13, the magnetic field intensity corresponding to this flux density is $H_{iron} = 190$ A/m. Hence

$$F_{iron} = H_{iron}l_{iron} = 190 \times 0.75 = 142.5 \text{ A}$$

The total m.m.f. requirement to produce a flux of 0.3 Wb in the air gap is

$$F = F_{iron} + F_{air} = 142.5 + 477 = 619.5 \text{ A}$$

Hence

Current in the coil, $I = 619.5/1000 = 0.6195$ A (*Ans.*)

Comparing the current requirement in examples 5.11 and 5.12 (0.5835 A and 0.6195 A, respectively), we see that a larger current is needed in the second example since the coil must produce not only the same flux in the air-gap but must also provide the leakage flux.

5.17 Parallel-connected Magnetic Circuits

A parallel magnetic circuit can be dealt with in much the same way as a parallel electric circuit. The magnetic circuit in figure 5.17a can be reduced to the equivalent circuit in figure 5.17b, in which

$$S_1 = l_1/\mu_1 a_1 \text{ A/Wb}$$
$$S_2 = l_2/\mu_2 a_2 \text{ A/Wb}$$
$$S_3 = l_3/\mu_3 a_3 \text{ A/Wb}$$

Branches S_2 and S_3 are in parallel with one another, hence they have the same m.m.f. across each of them which is

$$S_2\Phi_2 = S_3\Phi_3 \text{ A}$$

Also, if we can neglect the effect of magnetic leakage, then the magnetic flux "approaching" junctions L and M, respectively, in figure 5.15b is equal to the flux "leaving" each junction. From the comments made earlier in the chapter, it will be appreciated that the flux does not actually "flow" in the circuit.

Hence

$$\Phi_1 = \Phi_2 + \Phi_3$$

The effective reluctance of the parallel branches S_1 and S_2 is

$$S_2S_3/(S_2 + S_3)$$

Since this combination is in series with S_1, the **total reluctance** S_T of the circuit is

$$S_T = S_1 + \frac{S_2S_3}{S_2 + S_3}$$

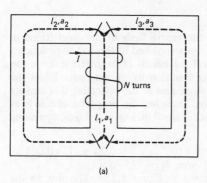

Fig. 5.17 (*a*) A magnetic circuit with three parallel-connected branches and (*b*) its equivalent circuit

The value of the flux Φ_1 can be calculated from the expression

$$\Phi_1 = F/S_T$$

The way in which the flux Φ_1 divides into Φ_2 and Φ_3 at junction L can be estimated using the method developed in section 3.7 for current division between parallel electrical circuits as follows.

$$\Phi_2 = \Phi_1 \times \frac{S_3}{S_2 + S_3}$$

$$\Phi_3 = \Phi_1 \times \frac{S_2}{S_2 + S_3}$$

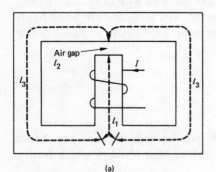

(a)

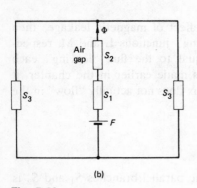

(b)

Fig. 5.18

EXAMPLE 5.13

A 750-turn coil is wound on the centre limb of the steel frame in figure 5.18a. Determine the current required in the coil to produce a flux of 1.6 mWb in the air-gap if the effects of magnetic leakage can be neglected. At the operating flux density in the outer limbs the magnetic field intensity is 525 A/m, and at the operating flux density in the inner limb it is 900 A/m. Data for the magnetic circuit is as follows: area = 16 cm², $l_1 = 0.24$ m, $l_2 = 0.001$ m, $l_3 = 0.6$ m, operating flux density = 1 T.

Solution $N = 750$ turns, $a = 16 \times 10^{-4}$ m², $l_1 = 0.24$ m, $l_2 = 0.001$ m, $l_3 = 0.6$ m, $B = 1.0$ T, $H_1 = 900$ A/m, $H_3 = 525$ A/m.

The equivalent circuit is shown in figure 5.18b. The flux in the centre limb divides between the two outer limbs, and since both have the same physical dimensions the flux density B_3 is one-half that in the centre limb, i.e. it is 0.5 T. The permeability of the inner and outer limbs is calculated as follows:

$$\mu_1 = B_1/H_1 = 1/900 = 1.11 \times 10^{-3} \text{ H/m}$$

$$\mu_3 = B_3/H_3 = 0.5/525 = 9.52 \times 10^{-4} \text{ H/m}$$

The reluctance of each part of the magnetic circuit can now be calculated.
For the centre limb,

$$\begin{aligned} S_1 &= l_1/\mu_1 a \\ &= 0.24/(1.11 \times 10^{-3} \times 16 \times 10^{-4}) \\ &= 135\,135 \text{ A/Wb} \end{aligned}$$

For each outer limb,

$$\begin{aligned} S_3 &= l_3/\mu_3 a = 0.6/(9.52 \times 10^{-4} \times 16 \times 10^{-4}) \\ &= 393\,908 \text{ A/Wb} \end{aligned}$$

For the air-gap,

$$\begin{aligned} S_2 &= l_2/\mu_0 a = 10^{-3}/(4\pi \times 10^{-7} \times 16 \times 10^{-4}) \\ &= 497\,359 \text{ A/Wb} \end{aligned}$$

Since the outer limbs are in parallel with one another, their effective reluctance is

$$S_3 \times S_3/(S_3 + S_3) = S_3/2 = 196\,954 \text{ A/Wb}$$

The effective reluctance of the magnetic circuit is

$$S_T = S_1 + S_2 + \tfrac{1}{2}S_3 = 135\,135 + 497\,359 + 196\,954$$

$$= 829\,448 \text{ A/Wb}$$

Now

m.m.f. $F = \Phi S = BaS$

$$= 1 \times (16 \times 10^{-4}) \times 829\,448 = 1327 \text{ A}$$

Hence

$$I = F/N = 1327/750 = 1.77 \text{ A} \quad (Ans.)$$

5.18 B-H Loop for a Ferromagnetic Material

Once a specimen of ferromagnetic material such as iron or steel has been magnetized, it is found that when the magnetizing force is removed it retains some of its magnetic field. The remaining flux density is known as the **remanent flux density** B_r (see figure 5.19).

In order to reduce the flux density in the specimen to zero, it is necessary to reverse the magnetic field until its intensity is H_c (see figure 5.19), where H_c is known as the **coercive force**.

Materials used in permanent magnets must not only retain a high flux density after they have been magnetized (B_r is typically 1 T), but must also be difficult to demagnetize (H_c is typically 50 000 A/m); these materials are known as **magnetically hard** materials. On the other hand, materials used in electromagnets must rapidly lose their magnetism when the current is switched off, so that they have a low remanence and a low coercive force; these materials are described as **magnetically soft** materials.

If the reverse magnetic field is increased beyond H_c, the specimen will eventually become magnetically saturated again but in the reverse direction (see point X in figure 5.19). If the magnetizing current is again reduced to zero, the material retains the remanent flux but in the reverse direction (see point Y in figure 5.19).

If the magnetizing force is increased again in the "forward" direction, the material finally becomes saturated again (see point Z in figure 5.19). Repeated reversals of the magnetizing force cause the state of magnetization of the core to traverse the **B-H loop** in figure 5.19 in an anticlockwise direction.

The loop in figure 5.19 is also known as a **hysteresis loop**.

(Hysteresis means "coming late" or "lagging behind", and in a magnetic sense means that the magnetic field lags behind the force producing it.) For instance, when H is reduced to zero, the flux density does not fall to zero (it falls to B_r), and when H is increased to H_c in the reverse direction, B finally falls to zero.

5.19 Hysteresis Loss

If a ferromagnetic material is placed in a coil in which the current is continually reversed, the state of magnetization of the material will continually be reversed. Each time the magnetic field is reversed, the magnetic domains in the material are also forced to reverse. In order to do this, the electrical circuit must transfer energy to the magnetic circuit. The energy absorbed by the material appears in the form of heat, and the power which has to be supplied by the electrical circuit is known as the **hysteresis power loss** P_h.

Clearly, increasing the rate of the flux reversals (that is increasing the frequency f of the reversals) increases the rate at which power is consumed. That is, the hysteresis loss increases with the frequency of reversals of the current in the coil, hence

$$P_h \propto f$$

Also if the maximum flux density B_m in the specimen is increased, the hysteresis loss is also increased. It is found that

$$P_h \propto B_m^n$$

where n is a number known as the **Steinmetz index**, and has a value in the range 1.6 to 2.2. Moreover, if the volume v of the specimen is increased, there are more magnetic domains to reverse, causing the hysteresis loss to be further increased. Hence

$$P_h = kvfB_m^n \text{ W} \tag{5.19}$$

where k is the *hysteresis coefficient* of the specimen.

5.20 Magnetic Screening

It is sometimes necessary to protect delicate instruments from the effects of magnetic fields. A popular method of achieving this end is to provide a magnetic "short-circuit" around the instrument so that the instrument operates in a space in which the magnetic field is zero (or nearly so).

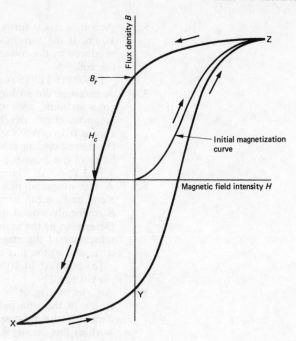

Fig. 5.19 *B-H* loop for a ferromagnetic material

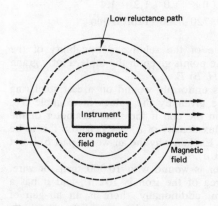

Fig. 5.20 Magnetic screen

This situation is illustrated in figure 5.20, in which the instrument is placed inside a magnetic screen made from a material which has a very low reluctance. The magnetic screen thereby provides a magnetic path which bypasses the instrument so that the magnetic field inside the screen is very low (ideally zero).

Exercises

In the following take $\mu_0 = 4\pi \times 10^{-7}$ H/m.

5.1 An electromagnet is wound on a cylindrical former, the diameter of the former being 3 cm. If the magnetic flux produced by the electromagnet is 0.6 mWb, determine the flux density in the core.

[0.849 T]

5.2 An electromagnet produces a flux density of 0.75 T in its core. If the section through the magnetic core is a circle of diameter 3.5 cm, what is the magnitude of the flux in the core?

[0.72 mWb]

5.3 A coil of 1000 turns is wound on a ring of mean diameter 10 cm. If the current in the coil is 5 A, determine the m.m.f. produced by the coil and also the magnetic field intensity inside the coil.

[5000 A; 15 915 A/m]

5.4 A magnetic circuit has a mean length of 40 cm and a uniform cross-sectional area of 5 cm². When a coil wound on the magnetic circuit develops a m.m.f. of 200 A, the flux in the core is 0.15 mWb. Determine the flux density in the core and the corresponding values of permeability and relative permeability of the magnetic circuit.

[0.3 T; 6×10^{-4} H/m; 477]

5.5 A non-magnetic ring has a uniform cross-sectional area of 8 cm² and a mean circumference of 55 cm. A coil of 1000 turns is uniformly wound on the ring and carries a current of 5 A. Determine *a*) the m.m.f., *b*) the magnetic field intensity, *c*) the reluctance of the magnetic circuit, *d*) the magnetic flux in the core, and *e*) the flux density in the magnetic circuit.

[*a*) 5000 A; *b*) 9091 A/m; *c*) 49×10^6 A/Wb; *d*) 0.1 mWb; *e*) 0.125 T]

5.6 An electromagnet is wound with 1000 turns of wire. The length of the iron path is 100 cm, and that of the air-gap is 2 mm. If the relative permeability of the iron path at the working flux density is 2500, calculate the current in the coil to produce a flux density of 0.5 T in the air-gap. Neglect the effect of magnetic leakage.

[0.955 A]

5.7 If the magnetic leakage coefficient in example 5.6 is 1.2, calculate the current in the coil to produce the same flux density in the air-gap.

[0.987 A]

5.8 The following results were obtained from tests on a specimen of cast steel:

B (tesla)	0.4	0.6	0.8	1.0	1.2	1.4
H (A/m)	450	600	720	900	1230	2000

Determine the value of the relative permeability of the material for each of the points given in the table. Plot a graph of μ_r to a base of *a*) *H*, *b*) *B*.

5.9 A coil of 500 turns is uniformly wound on a cast steel ring having the *B*-*H* curve given by the values in example 5.8. Estimate the current in the coil if the mean diameter of the ring is 0.15 m, and a flux density of *a*) 0.4 T, *b*) 0.8 T is to be established in the ring. Explain why the answer in part *b*) is not twice the value in part *a*).

5.10 An iron-cored inductor is wound with 10 000 turns of wire. The cross-sectional area of the iron is 10 cm², and it has a mean length of 50 cm; additionally, there is an air-gap of 2 mm. Calculate the current required to establish a magnetic flux of 1.2 mWb in the magnetic circuit if the magnetization curve of the iron is as follows:

B (tesla)	0.6	1.05	1.375	1.5	1.55	1.6
H (amperes per metre)	100	200	400	800	1000	1400

[0.205 A]

5.11 A coil of 800 turns is uniformly wound on an iron ring of mean circumference 45 cm and uniform cross-sectional area 5 cm², and has a resistance of 25 Ω. The relative permeability of the iron at the working flux density is 800. If the coil is connected to a 20 V d.c. supply, calculate *a*) the m.m.f., *b*) the magnetic field intensity, *c*) the magnetic flux in the iron, and *d*) the reluctance of the iron ring.

[*a*) 640 A; *b*) 1422 A/m; *c*) 0.715 mWb; *d*) 0.895×10^6 A/Wb]

5.12 An iron rod of length 0.5 m and cross-sectional area 5 cm², is bent into a ring with an air-gap of 2 mm between the ends of the rod. The iron ring is wound with 500 turns of wire. Calculate the current required in the coil to give a flux density of 0.25 T in the air-gap if the relative permeability of the iron at the operating flux density is 800, and the leakage coefficient is 1.2.

[1.094 A]

5.13 A transformer has an iron core of volume 8000 cm³, and the windings are energized at a frequency of 50 Hz. If the maximum magnetic flux density in the core is 1.2 T, calculate the power loss due to hysteresis effects if the Steinmetz index is 1.8 and the hysteresis coefficient is 255.

[141.6 W]

6 Electromagnetism

6.1 Induced E.M.F. due to Motion

If a conductor is placed in a magnetic field as shown in figure 6.1, and a voltmeter is connected between the ends of the conductor, then when the conductor is moved in the magnetic field an e.m.f. is induced in the conductor.

In the case considered in figure 6.1, during the period when the conductor is moved downwards, the induced e.m.f. causes end A to be positive with respect to end B. When the conductor is moved upwards, end A is negative with respect to end B. (The method of determining the direction of the induced e.m.f. is explained in section 6.2.) That is to say,

an e.m.f. is induced in the conductor whenever it cuts lines of magnetic flux.

However, if the conductor is moved from left to right, or from right to left, the induced e.m.f. is zero. In this case the conductor moves in the "direction" of the lines of flux and does not "cut" across the flux. Therefore to induce an e.m.f. in the conductor, the conductor must cut through "lines" of flux.

Also, when the conductor is moved either upwards or downwards between the poles, we find that if the velocity of the conductor is increased then the magnitude of the induced e.m.f. also increases in proportion to the velocity.

The above discussion is summarized in **Faraday's law of electromagnetic induction** (also known as Neumann's law) as follows.

> **The magnitude of the induced e.m.f. is proportional to the rate of change of the magnetic flux linking with the circuit (or the conductor).**

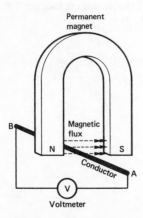

Fig. 6.1 Induced e.m.f. due to the motion of a conductor relative to magnetic flux

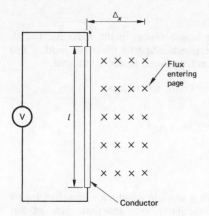

Fig. 6.2 E.m.f. induced in a conductor

In the SI system of units,

the induced e.m.f. is one volt when the flux linking with the circuit changes at the rate of one weber per second.

Suppose that the conductor in figure 6.2 cuts across a magnetic field so that it moves a distance Δx metre perpendicular to the magnetic field in a time Δt seconds. If the **active length** of the conductor in the magnetic field is l then the total magnetic flux cut by the conductor is

$$\Phi = \text{flux density} \times \text{area}$$
$$= B \times l \times \Delta x$$

The e.m.f. induced in the conductor can be predicted by Faraday's law as follows

$$E = k \times \text{rate of change of flux}$$

where k is a constant of proportionality, which in the SI system has the value of unity. Hence

$$E = \text{rate of change of flux} = Bl\frac{\Delta x}{\Delta t}$$

But $\dfrac{\Delta x}{\Delta t}$ = velocity of the conductor   therefore

$$\text{Average induced e.m.f.} = B \times l \times \text{average velocity of conductor} \qquad (6.1)$$

Rewriting the above using the calculus notation gives

$$e = Bl\frac{dx}{dt} = Blv \text{ V} \qquad (6.2)$$

where e is the instantaneous value of the induced e.m.f., and dx/dt and v are expressions for the instantaneous velocity of the conductor *perpendicular* to the magnetic field.

If the conductor is moved at some angle θ to the line of action of the magnetic field (see figure 6.3), then the velocity of the conductor perpendicular to the magnetic field is $v \sin \theta$. To account for this situation, equation (6.2) is modified as follows.

$$e = Blv \sin \theta \qquad (6.3)$$

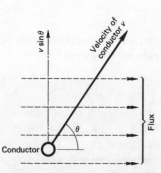

Fig. 6.3 Effect of moving a conductor at an angle to the magnetic field

EXAMPLE 6.1

A straight conductor of active length 60 cm in the magnetic field is moved at a speed of 10 m/s perpendicular to a magnetic field of flux density 0.2 T. Calculate the e.m.f. induced in the conductor.

Solution $B = 0.2$ T, $l = 60$ cm $= 0.6$ m, $v = 10$ m/s.
From eqn. (6.2)

$$e = Blv = 0.2 \times 0.6 \times 10 = 1.2 \text{ V} \quad (Ans.)$$

EXAMPLE 6.2

An e.m.f. of 10 V is induced in a straight conductor of active length 1.25 m when it moves perpendicularly to a magnetic field of flux density 0.8 T. Determine the velocity of the conductor.

Solution $e = 10$ V, $B = 0.8$ T, $l = 1.25$ m.
From eqn. (6.2), $e = Blv$, hence

$$v = e/Bl = 10/(0.8 \times 1.25) = 10 \text{ m/s} \quad (Ans.)$$

EXAMPLE 6.3

A straight conductor is moved at an angle to a magnetic field of flux density 0.9 T. The conductor is 0.4 m in length, and when its velocity is 2 m/s the induced e.m.f. is 0.5 V. Calculate the angle of movement of the conductor relative to the magnetic field.

Solution $e = 0.5$ V, $B = 0.9$ T, $l = 0.4$ m, $v = 2$ m/s.
From eqn. (6.3), $e = Blv \sin \theta$, hence

$$\sin \theta = e/Blv = 0.5/(0.9 \times 0.4 \times 2) = 0.6944$$

therefore

$$\theta = \sin^{-1} 0.6944 = 43.98° \quad (Ans.)$$

6.2 Direction of Induced E.M.F.—Fleming's Right-hand Rule

The direction of the e.m.f. induced in a conductor can be deduced by **Fleming's right-hand rule** as follows:

> If the thumb, the first finger and the second finger of the right hand are held so that they are mutually perpendicular to one another as shown in figure 6.4, and if the thuMb points in the direction of the Movement of the conductor *relative to the flux*, and the First finger points in the direction of the magnetic Flux, then the sEcond finger points in the direction of the induced E.m.f.

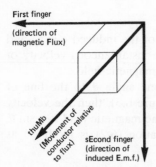

First finger
(direction of magnetic Flux)

thuMb
(Movement of conductor relative to flux)

sEcond finger
(direction of induced E.m.f.)

Fig. 6.4 Fleming's right-hand rule

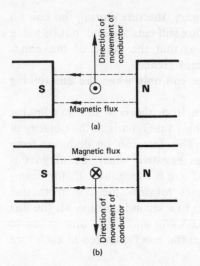

Fig. 6.5 Application of Fleming's right-hand rule

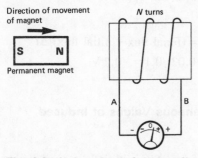

Fig. 6.6 Induced e.m.f. in a coil when a magnet is moved towards the coil

Applying the above rule to figure 6.5a, we see that the e.m.f. acts in a direction to cause current to flow towards us (that is out of the page). In the case of figure 6.5b, the induced e.m.f. causes the current to enter the page. Use Fleming's right-hand rule to verify the statements in section 6.1 (see figure 6.1) referring to the direction of the induced e.m.f.

6.3 E.M.F. Induced in a Coil

If we move a permanent magnet towards the coil in figure 6.6, the flux linking with the coil is increased. If a voltmeter is connected between the ends of the coil, we find that, during the time when the magnet is approaching the coil (that is when the flux linking with the coil is changing), an e.m.f. is induced in the coil. In the case considered, we will find that end B is positive with respect to end A (the reason for this is given in section 6.6).

The magnitude of the e.m.f. induced in the coil can be predicted by means of Faraday's law as follows. If the flux changes by an amount $\Delta\Phi$ in time Δt seconds, then the rate of change of flux is $\Delta\Phi/\Delta t$ Wb/s. The average e.m.f. induced in *each turn* of the coil is, by Faraday's law,

$$\text{Average induced e.m.f.} = \text{average rate of change of flux}$$
$$= \frac{\Delta\Phi}{\Delta t}\text{ volts}$$

If the coil has N turns, then the **average** value of the e.m.f. induced in the coil is

$$\text{Average induced e.m.f.} = N\frac{\Delta\Phi}{\Delta t}\text{ V}$$

Using the calculus notation, the **instantaneous** value of the induced e.m.f. e is

$$e = N\frac{d\Phi}{dt}\text{ V} \tag{6.4}$$

where $d\Phi/dt$ is the rate of change of flux during the very short interval of time dt.

When the magnet is stationary, the flux cutting the coil no longer changes in value (the flux still cuts the coil, but its value is constant). The net result is that the value of the e.m.f. induced in the coil falls to zero! Hence,

An e.m.f. is induced in the coil only when the flux linking with it changes.

If the magnet is withdrawn from the coil, the flux linking with the coil reduces. When this situation arises, the polarity of the induced e.m.f. reverses. This fact can be deduced from eqn. (6.4) since $\Delta\Phi$ becomes negative when the magnet is withdrawn, hence the induced e.m.f. is negative. If, for example, when moving the magnet *towards* the coil from one position (which we will call L) to a second position M, the flux increases from 0.01 Wb to 0.03 Wb, and if the time taken to make this change is 0.1 s, then the e.m.f. induced in each turn of the coil is

$$\text{Induced e.m.f.} = \Delta\Phi/\Delta t = (\text{Final flux} - \text{initial flux})/\Delta t$$
$$= (0.03 - 0.01)/0.1 = 0.2 \text{ V}$$

If the magnet is then moved in the opposite direction *at the same speed*, then

$$\text{Induced e.m.f.} = \Delta\Phi/\Delta t = (\text{Final flux} - \text{initial flux})/\Delta t$$
$$= (0.01 - 0.03)/0.1 = -0.2 \text{ V}$$

6.4 Average and Instantaneous Values of Induced E.M.F.

Suppose that the magnet in figure 6.6 is initially moved slowly and, then, for the remainder of the movement it is moved quickly. A graph showing how the flux cutting the coil may change is illustrated in figure 6.7. When the magnet is stationary and is in its initial position, the flux cutting the coil is Φ_1; when the magnet is in its final position the flux cutting the coil is Φ_2; the total change in the flux is $\Delta\Phi = \Phi_2 - \Phi_1$. This flux change occurs during a time interval $\Delta t = t_2 - t_1$; the *average* rate of change of the flux is $\Delta\Phi/\Delta t$. Arising from this, the **average induced e.m.f.** in the coil during the period of time Δt is

Average induced e.m.f. $= N \times$ **average** rate of change of flux

It is the usual practice to assign CAPITAL letters to average values, so that over the period Δt

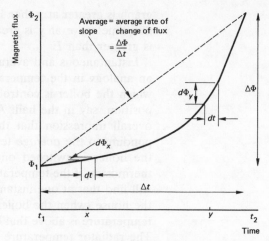

Fig. 6.7 Illustrating the meaning of average value and instantaneous value

$$\text{Average induced e.m.f. } E = N\frac{\Delta\Phi}{\Delta t} \tag{6.5}$$

However, if we consider the value of the e.m.f. induced in the coil at the instant of time x (see figure 6.7), then over the very short period of time dt the flux changes by $d\Phi_x$. Provided that dt is vanishingly small, then we can say that the **instantaneous value of e.m.f.** induced in the coil at time x is

$$\text{Instantaneous induced e.m.f. at } x = N\frac{d\Phi_x}{dt}$$

It is also the practice that we assign lower case letters to instantaneous values, hence

$$e_x = N\frac{d\Phi_x}{dt}$$

Since the slope of the flux/time curve at x is less than the average slope of the curve, then the instantaneous induced voltage at x (i.e. e_x) is less than the average voltage E induced during Δt.

Some time later, at time y in figure 6.7, the velocity of approach of the magnet is increased; this results in the flux change $d\Phi_y$ in the time interval dt being greater than $d\Phi_x$. The instantaneous induced e.m.f. at time y is

$$e_y = N\frac{d\Phi_y}{dt}$$

where e_y is greater than e_x since the slope of the flux/time graph is greater at y than it is at x. Also, since the slope of the flux/time curve at y is greater than the average slope, then e_y is greater than E.

Instantaneous and average values in electrical circuits have an analogy in the temperature of a centrally heated house in which the boiler is controlled by a thermostat situated in one position, say in the hall. Anyone entering the house gains an overall impression that the temperature is constant (corresponding to the *average* temperature of the house). However, the boiler is switched on and off under the control of the thermostat; if the temperature of the radiators is measured, we will find that at one instant their temperature is below that of the house (when the boiler is off) and at another instant their temperature is above that of the house (when the boiler is on). The radiator temperature represents the instantaneous values in the analogy.

EXAMPLE 6.4

A coil of 1000 turns is wound on a former having an air core. If the flux linking the coil changes from a) 100 mWb to 150 mWb and b) 90 mWb to 20 mWb in a 5 ms time interval, calculate in each case the value of the induced e.m.f. in the coil.

Solution $N = 1000$ turns.
  For part *a*) $\Phi_1 = 0.1$ Wb, $\Phi_2 = 0.15$ Wb.
  For part *b*) $\Phi_1 = 0.09$ Wb, $\Phi_2 = 0.02$ Wb; $\Delta t = 5 \times 10^{-3}$ s.

a) $\Delta\Phi = \Phi_2 - \Phi_1 = 0.15 - 0.1 = 0.05$ Wb.
From eqn. (6.5)

  Average induced e.m.f. $E = \Delta\Phi/\Delta t = 0.05/5 \times 10^{-3} = 10$ V   (*Ans.*)

b) $\Delta\Phi = \Phi_2 - \Phi_1 = 0.02 - 0.09 = -0.07$ Wb

hence

  $E = \Delta\Phi/\Delta t = -0.07/5 \times 10^{-3} = -14$ V   (*Ans.*)

6.5 Electromagnetic Induction and an Introduction to Mutual Induction

A rather similar effect to that which occurs when a permanent magnet is moved towards a coil can be achieved by the circuit in figure 6.8.

Suppose that the slider of resistor R is at the centre of the resistor when switch S is closed. Prior to the closure of the switch the flux produced by coil X is zero, so that the e.m.f. induced in coil Y is zero. After the switch is closed, the current builds up in coil X to a value which is limited by the resistance

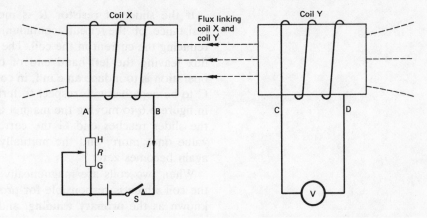

Fig. 6.8 An e.m.f. is induced in coil Y when the current in coil X changes

of the circuit; during this interval of time the flux produced by coil X also builds up. Arising from the change in flux linking with coil Y, an e.m.f. is induced in it. This e.m.f. is known as a **mutually induced e.m.f.**, and arises from the magnetic flux which mutually links both coils. The coils are said to have the property of **mutual inductance** M; more will be said about this later. This part of the operation is analogous to the state of affairs in figure 6.6 when the magnet is moved towards the coil.

Once the flux produced by coil X has built up to its full value (this occurs when the current has reached its full value), the mutually induced e.m.f. in coil Y falls to zero (remember, $e = N \, d\Phi/dt$, and when the current in coil X is constant then the flux is constant and $d\Phi = 0$, hence $e = 0$). That is to say,

An e.m.f. is mutually induced in one coil only when the current is changing in the other coil.

When the current in coil X is constant, the operation is analogous to the state of affairs in figure 6.6 when the magnet remains stationary.

If the slider of resistor R in figure 6.8 is moved from the centre position towards end H, the total resistance of the circuit is reduced and the current increases. In turn this causes the flux which enters coil Y to increase, and an e.m.f. is induced in coil Y once more. The polarity of the induced e.m.f. in this case is such as to make terminal C positive with respect to terminal D (see also section 6.6). When the slider reaches end H, the current reaches a steady value again, so that the flux linking coil Y reaches a new steady value. When this occurs, the e.m.f. induced in coil Y again falls to zero (since $d\Phi$ is zero again).

If the slider of resistor R is moved towards end G, the resistance of the circuit containing coil X is increased, so reducing the current in the coil. The net effect is to reduce the flux leaving the left-hand end of coil Y. The result of this operation is to induce an e.m.f. in coil Y which causes terminal C to be negative with respect to terminal D (this is analogous in figure 6.6 to moving the magnet away from the coil). When the slider reaches end G the current reaches a new steady value once more, and the mutually induced e.m.f. in coil Y again becomes zero.

When two coils are magnetically coupled, as in figure 6.8, the coil which is responsible for producing the flux (coil X) is known as the **primary winding**, and the circuit which carries current I is known as the **primary circuit**. The winding which receives energy by electromagnetic induction (coil Y) is known as the **secondary winding**.

6.6 Lenz's Law

The polarity or "direction" of the induced e.m.f. in a conductor or a coil can be predicted by **Lenz's law** which is stated below.

> **The e.m.f. induced in a conductor or a coil acts to circulate a current in a direction which opposes the change of magnetic flux which gave rise to the induced e.m.f.**

Lenz's law follows many natural laws insomuch that it says that any change is opposed.

We shall now interpret Lenz's law in specific cases. Consider first of all the arrangement in figure 6.9a. Suppose that we move the magnet towards the left-hand end of the coil; that is to say the flux *entering* the left-hand end of the coil is increased. According to Lenz's law, the polarity of the e.m.f. induced in the coil must act to cause a current to flow in the coil such that the flux produced by the coil opposes the change in the flux entering the left-hand end of the coil. That is to say, the current flowing in the coil must produce a N-pole at its left-hand end (see figure 6.9b); the flux produced by this pole opposes the increase in the flux entering that end of the coil. Applying the rule relating current flow in a coil to the magnetic polarity produced by the coil, we see that current must leave terminal B of the coil and enter terminal A. So far as the external circuit is concerned, the induced e.m.f. is such that end B is positive with respect to end A.

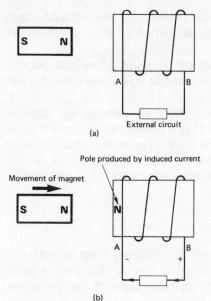

(a)

Pole produced by induced current

Movement of magnet

External circuit

(b)

Fig. 6.9 Determining the direction of the induced e.m.f.

If the N-pole of the magnet is moved further away from the coil, Lenz's law tells us that the induced current must flow in a direction which opposes the change. In this case the change is a *reduction* in the flux *entering* the left-hand end of the coil. The induced current must therefore flow in a direction which *increases* the flux *entering* the left-hand end of the coil. That is, the current must produce a S-pole at the left-hand end of the coil. To do this, current must flow in the external circuit from A to B, i.e. B is negative with respect to terminal A.

As an exercise, show that if the magnet is reversed (i.e. its S-pole is nearest to the left-hand end of the coil), then when the S-pole approaches the coil, terminal A is positive with respect to terminal B. When the magnet is moved away from the coil, terminal A is negative with respect to terminal B.

6.7 Self-inductance

When a conductor carries current, it is surrounded by its own magnetic field. If the current in the conductor increases, its own magnetic field increases. However, as shown by Lenz's law, this increase in flux causes an e.m.f. to be induced in the conductor to act in a way which opposes the change in flux (and therefore the change in current). This e.m.f. is known as a **self-induced e.m.f.**, and is related to a property of the circuit known as its **self-inductance** (symbol L) having the unit of the henry (unit symbol H) and is defined as follows.

> A **circuit** has a self-inductance of **one henry** if an e.m.f. of one volt is induced in the circuit when the current in the circuit changes at the rate of one ampere per second.

That is

> Self-induced e.m.f. $= L \times$ rate of change of current

> Average value of self-induced e.m.f. $E = L \times \dfrac{\Delta I}{\Delta t} \text{V}$

This is expressed in terms of instantaneous values as follows

> Instantaneous value of self-induced e.m.f. $e = L \times \dfrac{di}{dt} \text{V}$

(6.6)

where e is the instantaneous value of the self-induced e.m.f. during the infinitesimally small period of time dt when the current changes by di.

The inductance of a circuit can vary from a few microhenrys for a coil with an air core to many henrys in the case of a coil with an iron core.

An interesting point arises when we consider the implications of eqn. (6.6). Suppose that we could cut the current off in an inductive circuit in zero time; this implies that $di/dt = \infty$ since the current is reduced to zero in a time of $dt = 0$! Equation (6.6) implies that the value of the induced e.m.f. is

$$e = L\frac{di}{dt} = L \times \infty = \infty \text{ V}$$

That is, an infinitely large voltage is induced in the inductance!

Two immediate problems arise. One is that such a large voltage can result in electrical breakdown of the insulation between the turns of the coil.

The second problem is that a very high voltage appears between the contacts of the switch. Quite often it is the second of the two factors which brings further problems in its wake. For example, if a semiconductor device (such as a transistor) is used as the switch, the high voltage may cause the semiconductor device to break down. Another example of danger from this source is where the inductive circuit is used in an explosive atmosphere, such as in a coal mine (where a methane concentration may occur) or in a petroleum refinery; the high voltage between the contacts can produce an arc at the contacts, which may be sufficiently hot to ignite the gas in the surrounding atmosphere.

It is perhaps fortunate that the majority of circuits used in electrical engineering do not have a high value of inductance but, nevertheless, the danger of high values of induced voltage from this source should not be overlooked.

It was also shown in section 6.3 (eqn. (6.4)) that the e.m.f. induced in a circuit is given by

$$e = N\frac{d\Phi}{dt} \text{ V}$$

where N is the number of turns on the coil and $d\Phi/dt$ is the rate of change of magnetic flux. If the coil has an inductance of L, then the same value of induced e.m.f. can be expressed in the form

$$e = L\frac{di}{dt} \text{ V}$$

hence

$$L\frac{di}{dt} = N\frac{d\Phi}{dt}$$

or

$$L = N\frac{d\Phi}{di} \text{ H} \qquad (6.7)$$

where N is the number of turns on the coil and $d\Phi/di$ is the flux produced per ampere by the coil.

If the coil has a core in which the flux is proportional to the current in the coil, i.e. an air-core, then eqn. (6.7) can be re-written in the form

$$L = N\frac{\Phi}{I} \text{ H} \qquad (6.8)$$

In cases where the flux-current (or B–H) relationship is nonlinear (as in the case of a ferromagnetic material), then eqn. (6.7) is used.

EXAMPLE 6.5

Calculate the e.m.f. induced in a circuit of inductance 0.05 H when the current changes from 20 mA to 70 mA in 5 μs.

Solution $L = 0.05$ H, $di = (70 - 20)$ mA $= 0.05$ A,
$dt = 5$ μs $= 5 \times 10^{-6}$ s
From eqn. (6.6)

$$e = L\,di/dt = 0.05 \times 0.05/5 \times 10^{-6} = 500 \text{ V} \quad (Ans.)$$

EXAMPLE 6.6

Calculate the inductance of a coil if 80 V is induced in it when the current changes at the rate of 10 A/s.

Solution $e = 80$ V, $di/dt = 10$ A/s.
From eqn. (6.6).

$$L = e/(di/dt) = 80/10 = 8 \text{ H} \quad (Ans.)$$

EXAMPLE 6.7

A current of 2 A flows in a 500 turn coil which has an air core. If the inductance of the coil is 0.1 H, calculate the flux in the coil.

Solution $I = 2$ A, $N = 200$ turns, $L = 0.1$ H.
From eqn. (6.8)

$$\Phi = LI/N = 0.1 \times 2/500 = 0.4 \times 10^{-3} \text{ Wb or } 0.4 \text{ mWb} \quad (Ans.)$$

6.8 Dependence of the Self-inductance on Number of Turns

From equation (6.8), the inductance of a coil is

$L = N\Phi/I$

However, in a magnetic circuit

$$\Phi = \frac{\text{m.m.f.}}{\text{reluctance}} = \frac{F}{S} = \frac{NI}{S}$$

Substituting the above equation into that for L yields

$$L = \frac{N(NI/S)}{I} = \frac{N^2}{S} \text{ H} \qquad (6.9)$$

that is

$$L \text{ is proportional to } N^2$$

Hence if the number of turns on a coil is doubled, then the inductance of the coil is quadrupled.

Also, since the reluctance of a magnetic circuit is given by $S = l/\mu a$, where l is the length of the magnetic circuit, μ is the permeability of the magnetic circuit, and a is the cross-sectional area of the magnetic circuit, then

$$L = \frac{N^2}{S} = \frac{\mu a N^2}{l} \text{ H} \qquad (6.10)$$

EXAMPLE 6.8

Calculate the inductance of a coil with an air-core having 500 turns of wire wound on it. The length of the core is 0.2 m and the cross-sectional area of the core is 0.0004 m^2.

Solution $N = 500$ turns, $l = 0.2$ m, $a = 0.0004 \text{ m}^2$,
$\mu_0 = 4\pi \times 10^{-7}$ H/m
From eqn. (6.10)

$L = \mu a N^2/l = 4\pi \times 10^{-7} \times 0.0004 \times 500^2/0.2$
$= 0.628 \times 10^{-3} \text{ H or } 0.628 \text{ mH}$ (*Ans.*)

EXAMPLE 6.9

Calculate the inductance of the coil in example 6.8 if the number of turns is *a*) doubled, *b*) halved.

Solution If L_1 is the inductance when $N_1 = 100$ and L_2 is the inductance for N_2 turns, then

$$L_1 \propto N_1^2 \quad \text{and} \quad L_2 \propto N_2^2$$

or

$$\frac{L_2}{L_1} = \left(\frac{N_2}{N_1}\right)^2$$

hence

$$L_2 = L_1 \times \left(\frac{N_2}{N_1}\right)^2$$

a) $L_1 = 0.628 \, \text{mH}$, $N_1 = 100$, $N_2 = 200$
therefore

$$L_2 = L_1(N_2/N_1)^2 = 0.628(200/100)^2 \, \text{mH} = 2.512 \, \text{mH} \quad (Ans.)$$

b) $L_1 = 0.628 \, \text{mH}$, $N_1 = 100$, $N_2 = 50$
therefore

$$L_2 = L_1(N_2/N_1)^2 = 0.628(50/100)^2 \, \text{mH} = 0.157 \, \text{mH} \quad (Ans.)$$

6.9 More about Mutual Inductance

It was shown in section 6.5 that, when two coils are mutually coupled by a magnetic flux, a current change in one coil results in an e.m.f. being induced in the second coil. The e.m.f. induced in the second coil is known as a **mutually induced e.m.f.**, and is related to a property of the circuit known as the **mutual inductance** (symbol M) having the unit of the henry, and is defined as follows.

> **Two coupled circuits** have a mutual inductance of **one henry** if an e.m.f. of one volt is induced in one of them when a current in the other changes at the rate of one ampere per second.

The above definition can be expressed as follows

> Mutually induced e.m.f.
>
> = mutual inductance
>
>   × rate of change of the current which produced the flux

Consider the magnetically coupled coils in figure 6.10a, in which the coil of N_1 turns is energized by the supply voltage. If e_2 is the instantaneous value of the induced voltage in N_2, and the rate of change of the current in N_1 is dI_1/dt, then

$$e_2 = M\frac{dI_1}{dt}\,\text{V} \tag{6.11}$$

The total flux Φ_1 produced by the coil N_1 can be regarded as consisting of two parts. Namely, *a*) flux Φ_{11} (pronounced phi one, one) which is the part of the flux which links with N_1 but not with N_2 and *b*) Φ_{12} (pronounced phi one, two) which is the part of Φ_1 which links with both N_1 and N_2. That is

$$\Phi_1 = \Phi_{11} + \Phi_{12}$$

Flux Φ_{12} is the **mutual flux** which induces the voltage in coil N_2. Now, from Faraday's law of electromagnetic induction,

Induced e.m.f. in N_2

= mutual inductance × rate of change of flux in N_2

Hence

$$e_2 = N_2\frac{d\Phi_{12}}{dt} \tag{6.12}$$

Since equations (6.11) and (6.12) both represent identical voltages then

$$M\frac{dI_1}{dt} = N_2\frac{d\Phi_{12}}{dt}$$

or

$$M = N_2\frac{d\Phi_{12}}{dI_1}\,\text{H} \tag{6.13}$$

If the magnetic core has a constant reluctance, i.e. an air-core, then

$$M = N_2\frac{\Phi_{12}}{I_1}\,\text{H} \tag{6.14}$$

Alternatively, if we disconnect the supply from coil N_1 and connect it to N_2 (see figure 6.10*b*), then when current I_2 flows in N_2 the mutual flux is Φ_{21} (pronounced phi two, one). Using an analysis similar to that above yields

$$M = N_1\frac{d\Phi_{21}}{dI_2} \tag{6.15}$$

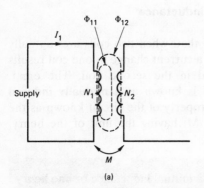

(a)

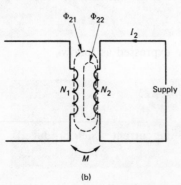

(b)

Fig. 6.10 A pair of magnetically coupled coils with (*a*) N_1 excited by the supply and (*b*) N_2 excited.

Also, if the flux is proportional to I_2 (i.e. the core has a constant reluctance), then

$$M = N_1 \frac{\Phi_{21}}{I_2} \qquad (6.16)$$

EXAMPLE 6.10

Two identical windings each having 1200 turns are wound on an air core, and it is found that 60 per cent of the flux produced by one coil links with the other coil. A current of 6 A in one of the coils is found to produce a total flux of 0.8 mWb. Calculate the inductance of each coil and also the value of the mutual inductance between the coils.

Solution $N_1 = N_2 = 1200$, $I_1 = 6$ A, $\Phi_{total} = 0.8$ mWb $= 0.8 \times 10^{-3}$ Wb, $\Phi_{12} = 0.6 \times 0.8 \times 10^{-3} = 0.48 \times 10^{-3}$ Wb.
From eqn. (6.8)

$$L_1 = N_1 \Phi_{total}/I_1 = 1200 \times 0.8 \times 10^{-3}/6 = 0.16 \text{ H}$$

Since the windings are identical, then $L_1 = L_2 = 0.16$ H   (*Ans.*)
From eqn. (6.14)

$$M = N_2 \Phi_{12}/I_1 = 1200 \times 0.48 \times 10^{-3}/6 = 0.096 \text{ H}   (Ans.)$$

6.10 Magnetic Coupling Coefficient

The term **magnetic coupling coefficient** k is used to describe the degree of magnetic coupling between magnetically coupled circuits. Referring to figure 6.10a, the flux Φ_1 produced by current I_1 is

$$\Phi_1 = \begin{bmatrix} \text{flux which links} \\ \text{only with } N_1 \end{bmatrix} + \begin{bmatrix} \text{flux which links} \\ N_1 \text{ and } N_2 \end{bmatrix}$$
$$= \Phi_{11} + \Phi_{12}$$

The coupling coefficient is given by

$$k = \frac{\text{flux linking } N_1 \text{ and } N_2}{\text{total flux produced}} = \frac{\Phi_{12}}{\Phi_1}$$

therefore

$$\Phi_{12} = k \Phi_1$$

where k has a value in the range between zero (no magnetic coupling) and unity (when all the primary winding flux links with the secondary winding). In cases where k has a small value, the coils are said to be **loosely coupled** (this occurs in many circuits in radio, t.v. and communications equipment); where k has a high value the coils are said to be **tightly coupled** (this occurs in power transformers).

It can also be shown for figure 6.10*b* that

$$\Phi_{21} = k\Phi_2$$

Now, from eqns. (6.14) and (6.16) we get

$$M = N_2 \frac{\Phi_{12}}{I_1} \quad \text{and} \quad M = N_1 \frac{\Phi_{21}}{I_2}$$

Multiplying both of the above equations together gives

$$M^2 = N_2 \frac{\Phi_{12}}{I_1} \times N_1 \frac{\Phi_{21}}{I_2}$$

$$= N_2 \frac{k\Phi_1}{I_1} \times N_1 \frac{k\Phi_2}{I_2}$$

$$= k^2 \left(N_1 \frac{\Phi_1}{I_1}\right)\left(N_2 \frac{\Phi_2}{I_2}\right)$$

but from eqn. (6.8)

$$L_1 = N_1\Phi_1/I_1 \quad \text{and} \quad L_2 = N_2\Phi_2/I_2$$

hence

$$M^2 = k^2 L_1 L_2$$

or

$$k = \frac{M}{\sqrt{(L_1 L_2)}} \tag{6.17}$$

EXAMPLE 6.11

Two coils A and B have a mutual inductance of 100 mH. If the self-inductance of coil A is 0.85 H and that of coil B is 1.2 H, calculate the value of the magnetic coupling coefficient.

Solution $M = 100 \text{ mH} = 0.1 \text{ H}$, $L_A = 0.85 \text{ H}$, $L_B = 1.2 \text{ H}$.
From eqn. (6.17)

$$k = M/\sqrt{(L_A L_B)} = 0.1/\sqrt{(0.85 \times 1.2)} = 0.099 \quad (Ans.)$$

6.11 Force between Two Magnetic Fields—Motor Action

When two like magnetic poles are brought close to one another (see figure 6.11), each experiences a repulsive force away from the other. In fact, the force acts to produce motion from the area of strong field to an area of weak field.

A similar situation exists when a current-carrying conductor is situated in a magnetic field (see figure 6.12). Suppose that

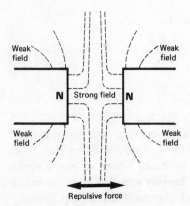

Fig. 6.11 Repulsive force between two magnetic poles

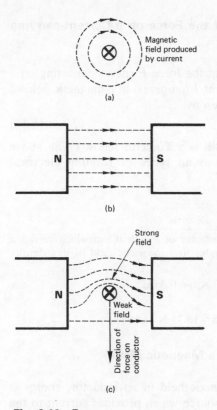

Fig. 6.12 Force on a current-carrying conductor

the current-carrying conductor in figure 6.12*a* is placed in the magnetic field of the permanent magnet in figure 6.12*b*. The combined effect of the two magnetic fields is shown in figure 6.12*c*. Here we see that the magnetic field immediately above the conductor is strengthened, whilst the field below it is weakened. Consequently, the conductor experiences a force in a downward direction, that is the force acts to move the conductor from the stronger field to the weaker field.

The above discussion assumes that the permanent magnet is "fixed" and that the conductor is free to move. However, there is an equal and opposite (i.e. upward) force on the permanent magnet. If the conductor was clamped and the permanent magnet was free to move, then the magnet would move upwards—in fact it would levitate!

6.12 Fleming's Left-hand Rule

The direction of the force acting on a current-carrying conductor can be predicted by **Fleming's left-hand rule** as follows.

> If the thumb, first finger and second finger of the left hand are held so that they are mutually perpendicular to one another as shown in figure 6.13, and if the **F**irst finger points in the direction of the magnetic **F**lux, and the se**C**ond finger points in the direction of the **C**urrent in the conductor, then the thu**M**b points in the direction of the **M**ovement of the conductor relative to the flux (i.e. it points in the direction of the force acting on the conductor).

As an exercise, use the above rule to verify the direction of the force acting on the current-carrying conductor in figure 6.12*b*. As a further exercise, it is useful to verify, both by Fleming's left-hand rule and by drawing magnetic flux patterns, that the direction of the force on the current carrying conductor in figure 6.12*b* is reversed if *a*) the direction of the current is reversed, the magnetic polarity being unchanged, or *b*) if the current is unchanged but the magnetic polarity is reversed.

To discriminate between applications of Fleming's left-hand rule and right-hand rule it is useful to remember that in Britain, *Motors* drive on the *left-hand* side of the road (*left-hand* rule for *Motors*).

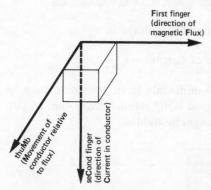

Fig. 6.13 Fleming's left-hand rule

6.13 The Magnitude of the Force on a Current-carrying Conductor

Experiment has shown that the force F (newtons) acting on a conductor carrying a current I (amperes) in a magnetic field of flux density B tesla is given by

$$F = BIl \text{ N} \tag{6.18}$$

(A useful mnemonic is **Bill** is a **F**orceful fellow.) The above equation is fundamental to all types of rotating electrical machine.

EXAMPLE 6.12

Calculate the force on a conductor of length 0.5 m which carries a current of 150 A at right-angles to a magnetic field of flux density 0.25 T.

Solution $B = 0.25$ T, $I = 150$ A, $l = 0.5$ m.
  From eqn. (6.18)

$$F = BIl = 0.25 \times 150 \times 0.5 = 18.75 \text{ N} \quad (Ans.)$$

6.14 Energy Stored in a Magnetic Field

When building up a magnetic field in an inductor, energy is supplied from the power source which provides current to the coil of the inductor. This energy is stored in the magnetic field, and is returned to the electrical circuit when the field finally collapses.

We will determine the expression for the energy stored in the magnetic field during the time interval Δt when the current in the inductor increases uniformly from zero to I amperes. The **average energy** W consumed by the inductive circuit is

$$W = \begin{bmatrix} \text{average value of} \\ \text{induced voltage} \end{bmatrix} \times \text{average current} \times \text{time} \tag{6.19}$$

The average value of the induced voltage is

$$E = L \times \text{rate of change of current} = L\frac{I}{\Delta t}$$

Since the current increases uniformly from zero to I, then its average value over this period is $I/2$. Hence from eqn. (6.19), the **energy stored in the magnetic field** is

$$W = L\frac{I}{\Delta t} \times \frac{I}{2} \times \Delta t = \tfrac{1}{2}LI^2 \text{ J} \tag{6.20}$$

EXAMPLE 6.13

Calculate the energy stored in an inductance of 8 H when the current flowing through it is 2 A.

Solution $L = 8 \, \text{H}$, $I = 2 \, \text{A}$.
From eqn. (6.20)

$$W = \tfrac{1}{2}LI^2 = \tfrac{1}{2} \times 8 \times 2^2 = 16 \, \text{J} \quad (Ans.)$$

6.15 The Equivalent Electrical Circuit of an Inductor

Since wire has electrical resistance, a practical coil also has resistance; if only for this reason, a practical coil can never be thought of as a pure inductor. Moreover, if the coil has an iron core, a certain amount of energy loss occurs in the iron circuit. The energy loss from this cause (I^2R loss in the iron core) can be regarded as occurring in a resistance R (see figure 6.14) which is connected in series with an ideal inductor of inductance L.

In addition to its inductance, the coil also has a property known as **capacitance** (see C in figure 6.14). Capacitance is studied in detail in chapter 7, but we will very briefly state here the effect of and the reason for the capacitance of the coil. Capacitance is the property by which a pair of parallel conductors which are separated by an insulator can store electrical energy.

In a coil, each pair of adjacent turns constitutes a pair of parallel conductors separated by insulation and hence form a capacitor of small value. The total capacitance is *distributed* throughout the coil, i.e. between pairs of turns, but the effective capacitance or **lumped capacitance** can be shown as C.

The effect of the capacitance of the coil does not normally trouble the user at d.c. or at main frequency (50 Hz or 60 Hz), but it becomes very important in coils operated at radio frequency and t.v. frequency.

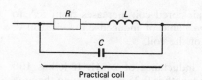

Fig. 6.14 Equivalent circuit of a practical coil

Exercises

6.1 A straight conductor of length 50 cm is moved in a direction perpendicular to a magnetic field of flux density 0.5 T at a speed of 500 m/s. Calculate the e.m.f. induced in the conductor.
[125 V]

6.2 A straight conductor has an e.m.f. of 20 V induced in it when it is moved perpendicular to a magnetic field of flux density 0.8 T at a velocity of 10 m/s. Determine the length of the conductor.
[2.5 m]

6.3 A straight conductor of length 25 cm is moved at a constant velocity of 5 m/s at an angle of 55° to the line of action of a magnetic field. If the magnetic flux density is 0.4 T, calculate the value of the e.m.f. induced in the conductor.
[0.41 V]

6.4 An aircraft of wingspan 50 m flies horizontally at a speed of 1000 km/h. If the vertical component of the flux density of the earth's magnetic field is 4×10^{-5} T, calculate the value of the induced voltage between the wing tips.
[0.555 V]

6.5 A current of 5 A produces a magnetic flux of 10 μWb in an air-cored coil. If the coil has 1500 turns of wire, what is the inductance of the coil?
[3 mH]

6.6 When the current in an air-cored coil changes value, the magnetic flux in the core is found to change by 5 mWb in 0.1 s. Calculate the number of turns on the coil if the average value of the induced e.m.f. is 50 V.
[1000]

6.7 If the coil of an electric bell has an effective inductance of 2 H, calculate the e.m.f. induced in the coil when a current of 0.25 A is reduced to zero in 2 ms.
[250 V]

6.8 When the current in an air-cored coil increases from 5 A to 20 A in 0.2 s, the average value of induced e.m.f. is 100 V. Calculate the inductance of the coil.
[1 H]

6.9 An air-cored coil has an inductance of 2 mH. If it has 100 turns of wire on it, and its length is 0.25 m, determine the area of the core.
[3.98 cm^2]

6.10 If the number of turns on the coil in example 6.9 is increased by 40 per cent, calculate the new value of inductance of the coil.
[3.92 mH]

6.11 When a current of 10 A flowing through coil X is reversed, the magnetic flux linking with an adjacent coil Y amounts to 20 mWb-turns. Determine the mutual inductance between the coils.
[2 mH]

6.12 If the self-inductance of coil A is 0.2 H and that of coil B is 0.6 H, determine the coefficient of magnetic coupling given that the mutual inductance between the coils is 100 mH.
[0.289]

6.13 When 5 A flows in a coil of 1000 turns of wire, the flux produced is 10 mWb. Calculate the average value of the e.m.f. induced in the coil when the current is reduced to zero in 10 ms.

A coil of 800 turns which is adjacent to the above coil is linked by 40 per cent of the flux produced by the first coil. Determine a) the mutual inductance between the coils, b) the average value of e.m.f. induced in the second coil when the flux in the first coil reduces at an average rate of 10 mWb in 10 ms.
[1000 V; a) 0.64 H; b) 320 V]

6.14 A coil of 1000 turns is uniformly wound on a non-magnetic ring of mean diameter 15 cm and cross-sectional area 5 cm². A second coil of 500 turns is wound over the top of the first coil. If the coefficient of magnetic coupling between the two coils is 0.7, calculate the mutual inductance between the two coils.

[0.466 mH]

6.15 A straight conductor 50 cm long carries a current of 30 A perpendicular to a magnetic field of flux density 0.5 T. Calculate the force acting on the conductor.

[7.5 N]

6.16 The coil of a galvonometer has 25 turns of wire and carries a current of 20 mA. The active length of each coil side in the magnetic field is 2 cm, and the coil sides are perpendicular to a magnetic field of flux density 0.15 T. Calculate the total force acting on the coil.

[3 mN]

6.17 A coil of inductance 2.0 H and resistance 1 Ω is connected to a 10 V battery having negligible internal resistance. Determine the energy stored in the magnetic field when the current has reached its steady value.

[100 J]

7 Electrostatics

ELECTROMAGNETISM 109

7.1 Positive and Negative Charges

It was discovered in ancient Greece that when two substances, such as amber and fur, were rubbed together that both were left with the ability to attract light objects. The reason for this phenomenon is that the rubbing action causes electrons to transfer from one substance to the other; the substance gaining electrons acquiring a negative charge, and the substance losing electrons acquiring a positive charge.

Moreover it is found that

when two objects having like electrical charges are freely suspended close to one another, they repel one another.

When **unlike charges** are similarly suspended they **attract one another**. Also it is found that *whatever the polarity of the charge on a body, it has the ability to attract an uncharged object.*

7.2 Electric Flux

When two conductive plates are isolated from one another and are connected to the opposite poles of an electrical supply, as shown in figure 7.1, an **electrostatic field** is found to exist between them (this is analogous to the magnetic field produced by an electromagnet). The presence of the electrostatic field can be detected if the plates are supported in an insulating material, and mica dust is sprinkled over the insulator whilst a voltage of several kilovolts is applied between the plates. The mica dust arranges itself in the type of pattern shown in figure 7.1.

The lines indicated by the mica dust are known as **lines of electric flux**. As with magnetic systems, the lines of flux are imaginary lines and are stationary in space. A line of electric

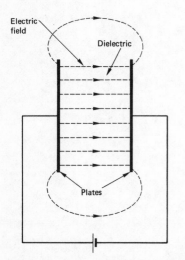

Fig. 7.1 The electric field between a pair of parallel plates

flux is the path which would be traced out by a "free" positive electric charge if it were released. Since like electrical charges repel one another and unlike charges attract, a "free" positive charge moves away from the positive plate and towards the negative plate. Thus the **direction of the electric field** at any point is given by the direction of the force acting on a positive charge placed at that point.

In the SI system of units, one unit of electrostatic flux emanates from a unit charge of one coulomb, so that Q lines of flux emanate from a charge of Q coulombs. Hence

$$\text{Electrostatic flux} = Q \text{ coulombs (C)} \qquad (7.1)$$

The two-electrode structure in figure 7.1 is known as a **parallel-plate capacitor**, and has the property of storing energy in its electric field (the energy is stored in the region between and around the plates—the majority of the energy being stored between the plates, where the field is strongest). The insulating material between the plates (which could be one of a large number of materials including air, paper, mica, plastic, etc.) is known as a **dielectric**.

As with magnetic fields, some of the flux fringes or leaks from the capacitor and is represented by the lines leaving the back of the plates.

The ability of a capacitor to store energy is illustrated by the hydraulic analogy in figure 7.2. The piston in the figure is analogous to the power supply in an electrical circuit, and the hydraulic reservoir is analogous to a capacitor. Moving the piston to the left supplies energy to the hydraulic system, which causes fluid to be stored in the reservoir; this is equivalent to storing energy in the capacitor. The process of storing the energy is known as **charging** the capacitor.

If the piston is released, the energy stored in the reservoir causes the hydraulic fluid to return to the cylinder. As energy is extracted from the reservoir, the piston returns to its original position; the process of extracting energy from the capacitor is known as **discharging** the capacitor.

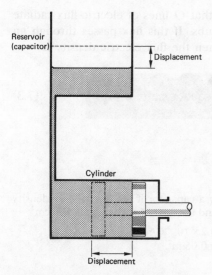

Reservoir (capacitor)

Displacement

Cylinder

Displacement

Fig. 7.2 Mechanical analogy of energy storage in a capacitor

7.3 Electric Field Intensity

If the voltage applied between the plates of the capacitor is V volts and the distance between the plates is d metres, then the

electric field intensity or **potential gradient** E between the plates is

$$E = \frac{V}{d} \quad \text{V/m} \tag{7.2}$$

EXAMPLE 7.1

Calculate the voltage applied to a parallel-plate capacitor if the plates are 2 mm apart and the electric field intensity in the dielectric 0.1 MV/m.

Solution $E = 0.1\,\text{MV/m} = 0.1 \times 10^6\,\text{V/m}, \; d = 2\,\text{mm} = 2 \times 10^{-3}\,\text{m}.$
From eqn. (7.2)

$$V = Ed = (0.1 \times 10^6) \times (2 \times 10^{-3}) = 200\,\text{V} \quad (Ans.)$$

7.4 Electric Flux Density

It was shown in eqn. (7.1) that Q lines of electric flux radiate from a charge of Q coulombs. If this flux passes through an area of a square metres, then the flux electric density is

$$D = \frac{Q}{a} \quad \text{coulomb per square metre (C/m}^2) \tag{7.3}$$

EXAMPLE 7.2

Calculate the charge stored by a capacitor if the electric flux density in the dielectric is 0.2 mC/m^2 and the area of each plate is 500 cm^2.

Solution $D = 0.2\,\text{mC/m}^2 = 0.2 \times 10^{-3}\,\text{C/m}^2,$
$a = 500\,\text{cm}^2 = 500 \times (10^{-2})^2 = 0.05\,\text{m}^2.$
From eqn. (7.3)

$$Q = Da = (0.2 \times 10^{-3}) \times 0.05 = 10 \times 10^{-6}\,\text{C} \;\text{or}\; 10\,\mu\text{C} \quad (Ans.)$$

7.5 The Relationship between Electric Flux Density and Electric Field Intensity—Permittivity

The relationship is given by

$$\text{Flux density } D = \text{a factor} \times \text{field intensity } E$$

The factor in the above equation is the **absolute permittivity** (symbol ϵ), and has dimensions of farads per metre (F/m). Thus

$$D = \epsilon E \text{ C/m}^2 \tag{7.4}$$

Compare this with the equivalent equation ($B = \mu H$) for the magnetic circuit.

The permittivity of free space (i.e. that of a vacuum) is given the special symbol ϵ_0, where

$$\epsilon_0 = 8.85 \times 10^{-12} \text{ F/m}$$

For all practical purposes, *the absolute permittivity of air has the same value as that of free space.*

The absolute permittivity ϵ of any material is given by the equation

$$\epsilon = \epsilon_r \epsilon_0$$

where ϵ_r is the relative permittivity of the material. For materials used in electric circuits the value of ϵ_r is greater than unity; this implies that for a given voltage applied between the plates of a capacitor, the electric flux in the dielectric is greater than in the case when the dielectric is a vacuum (or air). A list of values of relative permittivity is given in Table 7.1 Note that the relative permittivity of air can, for all practical purposes, be taken as unity.

Table 7.1 Relative permittivities

Material	Relative permittivity
Vacuum	1.0
Air	1.0006
Paper (dry)	2–2.5
Rubber	2–3.5
Plastic	2–4
Oil	2–5
Mica	3–8
Soil	3–10
Glass	5–10
Ceramics	80–1200

7.6 The Capacitance of a Capacitor

The **capacitance** (symbol C) of a capacitor is a measure of the ability of a capacitor to store electric charge. The unit of capacitance is the **farad** (unit symbol F). The farad is a very large value of capacitance, and typical sub-units are

$$1 \text{ microfarad} = 1 \text{ } \mu\text{F} = 10^{-6} \text{ F}$$
$$1 \text{ nanofarad } = 1 \text{ nF} = 10^{-9} \text{ F}$$
$$1 \text{ picofarad } = 1 \text{ pF} = 10^{-12} \text{ F}$$

It has been found experimentally that the relationship between the charge stored (in coulombs), the capacitance (in farads), and the voltage (in volts) across a capacitor is given by

$$Q = CV \text{ coulombs (C)} \tag{7.5}$$

Note that the symbol for capacitance (C) and the unit symbol for charge (C) use the same alphabetical character; this is something which engineers and scientists must learn to live with.

The unit of capacitance can be defined from eqn. (7.5) as **A capacitor having a capacitance of one farad stores a charge of one coulomb when a p.d. of one volt appears between its terminals.**

EXAMPLE 7.3

A 10 μF capacitor connected to a d.c. supply stores a charge of 5 mC. Calculate the value of the supply voltage.

Solution $\quad Q = 5 \text{ mC} = 5 \times 10^{-3} \text{ C}; \quad C = 10 \text{ } \mu\text{F} = 10 \times 10^{-6} \text{ F}.$
From eqn. (7.5)

$$V = Q/C = 5 \times 10^{-3}/10 \times 10^{-6} = 500 \text{ V} \quad (Ans.)$$

7.7 Capacitor Charging Current

Suppose that the capacitor C in figure 7.3 is initially discharged (that is it initially has zero voltage across it), and we begin to move the wiper of the potentiometer towards the upper end. As the voltage across the capacitor gradually increases, so the amount of charge stored also increases (note from eqn. (7.5) that the charge is proportional to the capacitor voltage). As the slider moves upwards, so the upper plate of the capacitor becomes positively charged with respect to the lower plate (which can be assumed to be at zero potential).

If the *average* charging current I amperes which flows during the time interval Δt when the capacitor voltage in-

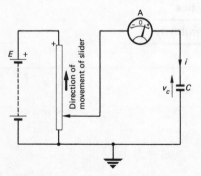

Fig. 7.3 Capacitor charging current

creases by ΔV_C volts, then from eqn. (7.5) the change in stored charge ΔQ is given by

$$\Delta Q = C \, \Delta V_C \text{ coulombs}$$

also

$$\Delta Q = I \, \Delta t \text{ coulombs}$$

Since the value ΔQ is the same for both equations, then

$$I \, \Delta t = C \, \Delta V_C$$

or

$$I = C \frac{\Delta V_C}{\Delta t} \text{ A} \qquad (7.6)$$

that is

> Average charging current
>
> $$= \text{capacitance} \times \begin{bmatrix} \text{average rate of change} \\ \text{of capacitor voltage} \end{bmatrix}$$

If we modify eqn. (7.6) to account for the instantaneous value of charging current i, which flows during the very short interval of time dt during which the capacitor voltage changes by the small amount dv_C volts, then we may write in the calculus notation

$$i = C \frac{dv_C}{dt} \text{ A} \qquad (7.7)$$

Finally, when the slider in figure 7.3 has reached the top of the potentiometer, the capacitor voltage can no longer increase any further and $dv_C/dt = 0$. When this occurs, the upper plate of the capacitor is charged to $+E$ volts with respect to the lower plate. Also, note from eqn. (7.7) that, when $dv_C/dt = 0$, the charging current also becomes zero.

EXAMPLE 7.4

A capacitor is charged by means of the circuit in figure 7.3, and it is found that when the voltage across the capacitor rises from 100 V to 300 V in 4 seconds, the average charging current is 5 mA. Calculate the capacitance of the capacitor.

Solution Since the change of voltage is large and the time period relatively long, the form of expression in eqn. (7.6) is used.

Hence $\Delta V_C = $ final value $-$ initial value $= 300 - 100 = 200$ V, $\Delta t = 4$ s, $I = 5$ mA $= 5 \times 10^{-3}$ A.

From eqn. (7.6)

$$C = I \, \Delta t / \Delta V_C = (5 \times 10^{-3}) \times 4/200$$
$$= 100 \times 10^{-6} \, \text{F or } 100 \, \mu\text{F} \quad (Ans.)$$

7.8 Capacitor Discharge

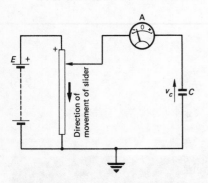

Fig. 7.4 Capacitor discharge

Let us assume that capacitor C in figure 7.4 is fully charged to voltage E by the method outlined in section 7.7. When the slider of the potentiometer is moved downwards, the upper plate of the capacitor is momentarily at a higher potential than that of the slider of the potentiometer. Under this condition the capacitor discharges energy into the system. That is to say, **current flows out of the upper plate of the capacitor**, as shown by the meter in figure 7.4.

The equation for the discharge current remains as for capacitor charging [see eqns. (7.6) and (7.7)] with the exception that $\Delta V_C / \Delta t$ and dv_C/dt are negative so that the "charging" current is "negative", i.e. the current flow is reversed.

EXAMPLE 7.4

The voltage across a capacitor of $100 \, \mu\text{F}$ capacitance is reduced from 350 V to 200 V in 1.5 s. Calculate the average value of the discharge current.

Solution ΔV_C = final value − initial value = $200 - 350 = -150$ V, i.e. a reduction of 150 V; $C = 100 \, \mu\text{F} = 100 \times 10^{-6}$ F, $\Delta t = 1.5$ s.
  From eqn. (7.6)

$$I = C \, \Delta V_C / \Delta t = (100 \times 10^{-6}) \times (-150)/1.5$$
$$= -0.01 \, \text{A} \quad (Ans.)$$

7.9 Energy Stored in a Capacitor

When charging current flows into a capacitor, energy is stored in its electric field. This energy is restored to the electric circuit when the capacitor is discharged.

Let us determine an expression for the energy stored in a capacitor in the time interval Δt when the voltage across the capacitor uniformly increases from zero to V volts. The **average energy** W consumed by the capacitor is

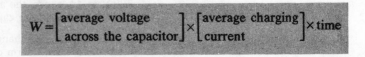

$$W = \begin{bmatrix} \text{average voltage} \\ \text{across the capacitor} \end{bmatrix} \times \begin{bmatrix} \text{average charging} \\ \text{current} \end{bmatrix} \times \text{time}$$

(7.8)

Since the capacitor voltage increases uniformly from zero to V volts, the average voltage across the capacitor during the time interval Δt is $V/2$ volts. The average current flowing in the capacitor is given by eqn. (7.6) as follows:

$$\text{Average current} = C \times \text{change in voltage/time}$$

$$= C \times V/\Delta t$$

Substituting the above into eqn. (7.8) gives

$$\text{Average energy } W = \frac{V}{2} \times C \frac{V}{\Delta t} \times \Delta t$$

hence

$$W = \tfrac{1}{2}CV^2 \text{ J} \tag{7.9}$$

Other versions of eqn. (7.9) can be obtained as follows. Since $Q = CV$, then

$$W = \tfrac{1}{2}CV \times V = \frac{QV}{2} \text{ J} \tag{7.10}$$

Also, since $V = Q/C$, then

$$W = \tfrac{1}{2}C\left(\frac{Q}{C}\right)^2 = \frac{Q^2}{2C} \text{ J} \tag{7.11}$$

EXAMPLE 7.5

Determine the energy stored in a $10 \ \mu\text{F}$ capacitor when the voltage between its terminals is $50 \ \text{V}$.

Solution $C = 10 \ \mu\text{F} = 10 \times 10^{-6} \text{ F}$, $V = 50 \text{ V}$.
  From eqn. (7.9)

$$W = \tfrac{1}{2}CV^2 = \tfrac{1}{2} \times (10 \times 10^{-6}) \times 50^2 = 0.0125 \text{ J} \quad (Ans.)$$

EXAMPLE 7.6

Calculate the capacitance of a capacitor if it stores a charge of $2 \ \mu\text{C}$ when the energy supplied to it is $10 \ \mu\text{J}$.

Solution $W = 10 \ \mu\text{J} = 10 \times 10^{-6} \text{ J}$, $Q = 2 \ \mu\text{C} = 2 \times 10^{-6} \text{ C}$.
  From eqn. (7.11)

$$C = Q^2/2W = (2 \times 10^{-6})^2/(2 \times 10 \times 10^{-6})$$

$$= 0.2 \times 10^{-6} \text{ F or } 0.2 \ \mu\text{F} \quad (Ans.)$$

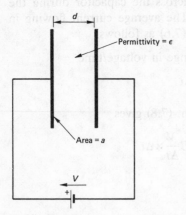

Fig. 7.5 Capacitance of a parallel-plate capacitor

7.10 Capacitance of a Parallel-plate Capacitor

A parallel-plate capacitor is shown in figure 7.5. Let us assume that all the electric flux passes through the dielectric between the two plates, i.e. none of the flux fringes around the outside of the capacitor. If the area of the dielectric (i.e. the plate area) is a m², then the electric flux density D in the dielectric is

$$D = \frac{Q}{a} \text{ C/m}^2$$

where Q is the charge stored by the capacitor. The electric field intensity E in the dielectric is

$$E = \frac{V}{d} \text{ V/m}$$

where V is the voltage between the plates of the capacitor and d is the thickness of the dielectric in metres. Now, from eqn. (7.4),

$$D = \epsilon E \text{ C/m}^2$$

hence

$$\frac{Q}{a} = \epsilon \frac{V}{d} \text{ C/m}^2$$

but $Q = CV$, hence

$$\frac{CV}{a} = \epsilon \frac{V}{d} \text{ C/m}^2$$

From the above expression, the capacitance of the parallel-plate capacitor is

$$C = \frac{\epsilon a}{d} = \frac{\epsilon_0 \epsilon_r a}{d} \text{ F} \tag{7.12}$$

The above equation tells us the following:

1 Increasing the permittivity ϵ gives a proportional increase in capacitance. That is, a capacitor with, say, mica or paper as a dielectric has a greater capacitance than a similar capacitor with air as the dielectric.
2 Increasing the area of the plates gives a proportional increase in capacitance.
3 Increasing the distance between the plates reduces the capacitance (the capacitance is inversely proportional to the distance between the plates).

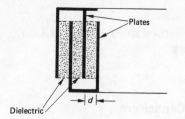

Fig. 7.6 Capacitance of a multi-plate capacitor

Certain types of capacitor are constructed with a **multiple-plate** structure, as shown in figure 7.6. Bearing in mind that the charge is stored in the dielectric material, the capacitance of a multiple-plate capacitor is greater than that of a simple parallel-plate capacitor having the same plate area and spacing. A capacitor having n plates has $(n-1)$ dielectrics (this assumes that there is no fringing, that is to say no energy is stored between the outer plates). The capacitance of the parallel-plate capacitor is therefore given by the expression

$$C = \frac{(n-1)\epsilon a}{d} = \frac{(n-1)\epsilon_r \epsilon_0 a}{d} \text{ F} \qquad (7.13)$$

EXAMPLE 7.7

A capacitor consists of two plates each of area 0.01 m^2 spaced 0.15 mm apart. Calculate the capacitance of the capacitor in picofarads if the dielectric a) is air and b) has a relative permittivity of 8.

Solution a) $\epsilon = \epsilon_0 = 8.85 \times 10^{-12}\text{ F/m}$, $a = 0.01\text{ m}^2$, $d = 0.15\text{ mm} = 0.15 \times 10^{-3}\text{ m}$.

From eqn. (7.12)

$$C = \epsilon_0 a/d = 8.85 \times 10^{-12} \times 0.01/0.15 \times 10^{-3}$$
$$= 590 \times 10^{-12}\text{ F or } 590\text{ pF} \quad (Ans.)$$

b) $\epsilon = 8\epsilon_0 = 70.8 \times 10^{-12}\text{ F/m}$.

From eqn. (7.12)

$$C = \epsilon a/d = 70.8 \times 10^{-12} \times 0.01/0.15 \times 10^{-3}$$
$$= 4720 \times 10^{-12}\text{ F or } 4721\text{ pF} \quad (Ans.)$$

EXAMPLE 7.8

A multi-plate capacitor has nine plates, each pair of adjacent plates being separated by a dielectric of thickness 0.2 mm and relative permittivity 2.5: a) if the capacitance of the capacitor is 20 nF, calculate the area of each plate; b) If the d.c. applied voltage is 200 V, determine i) the charge stored and ii) the energy stored.

Solution $n = 9$, $d = 0.2\text{ mm} = 0.2 \times 10^{-3}\text{ m}$, $\epsilon_r = 2.5$.
a) $C = 20\text{ nF} = 20 \times 10^{-9}\text{ F}$.

From eqn. (7.13)

Area $a = Cd/(n-1)\epsilon_0 \epsilon_r$

$$= 20 \times 10^{-9} \times 0.2 \times 10^{-3}/([9-1] \times 8.85 \times 10^{-12} \times 2.5)$$
$$= 0.0226\text{ m}^2 \quad (Ans.)$$

b) $C = 20 \times 10^{-9}\text{ F}$, $V = 200\text{ V}$.
i) From eqn. (7.5)

$$Q = CV = 20 \times 10^{-9} \times 200 = 4 \times 10^{-6}\text{ C} = 4\ \mu\text{C} \quad (Ans.)$$

ii) From eqn. (7.9)

$$W = \tfrac{1}{2}CV^2 = \tfrac{1}{2} \times 20 \times 10^{-9} \times 200^2 = 0.4 \times 10^{-3}\,\text{J} = 0.4\,\text{mJ} \quad (Ans.)$$

7.11 Parallel Connection of Capacitors

When capacitors are connected in parallel with one another, the overall effect is the same as adding the area of all the plates together. From the conclusions drawn from eqn. (7.12), we would expect that the parallel connection of capacitors leads to an increase in the total capacitance. Justification of this conclusion is given below.

If the plate area of capacitor C_1 is a_1, that of capacitor C_2 is a_2, that of C_3 is a_3, etc., then the total plate area a_P of a number of parallel-connected capacitors is

$$a_P = a_1 + a_2 + a_3 + \cdots \text{etc.}$$

and since the capacitance of a capacitor is proportional to the plate area, then the capacitance C_P of the **equivalent capacitor to the parallel combination** is given by

$$C_P = C_1 + C_2 + C_3 + \cdots \tag{7.14}$$

That is

The equivalent capacitance of parallel-connected capacitors is given by the sum of the individual capacitances.

Moreover, the *equivalent capacitance of the parallel combination is GREATER than the largest individual capacitance in the circuit.*

Equation (7.14) can also be derived as follows. Consider the two-capacitor parallel circuit in figure 7.7a. The charge stored by capacitor C_1 is C_1V coulombs, and that stored by C_2 is C_2V coulombs. The total charge stored is therefore

$$C_1V + C_2V = (C_1 + C_2)V$$

If a capacitor C_P whose capacitance is equivalent to the parallel combination of C_1 and C_2 is connected to the same supply voltage (see figure 7.7b), then the charge stored by C_P is C_PV. For the circuits in a) and b) to be equivalent to one another, then

Charge stored by fig. 7.7a = charge stored by fig. 7.7b

that is

$$C_PV = (C_1 + C_2)V$$

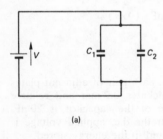

(a)

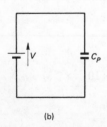

(b)

Fig. 7.7 Equivalent capacitance of parallel-connected capacitors

hence

$$C_P = C_1 + C_2$$

Extending the above argument to include the case where a large number of capacitors are connected in parallel gives

$$C_P = C_1 + C_2 + C_3 + \cdots$$

EXAMPLE 7.9

Three capacitors C_1, C_2 and C_3 are connected in parallel with one another to give an equivalent capacitance of $1\,\mu\text{F}$. If the d.c. supply to the parallel combination is $10\,\text{V}$, the capacitance of C_1 is $0.4\,\mu\text{F}$, and the charge stored by C_2 is $5\,\mu\text{C}$, determine a) the capacitance of C_2 and of C_3, b) the energy stored by each capacitor, and c) the total charge stored.

Solution $C_P = 1\,\mu\text{F} = 10^{-6}\,\text{F}$, $V = 10\,\text{V}$, $C_1 = 0.4\,\mu\text{F} = 0.4 \times 10^{-6}\,\text{F}$, $Q_2 = 5\,\mu\text{C} = 5 \times 10^{-6}\,\text{C}$.
a) From eqn. (7.5)

$$C_2 = Q_2/V = 5 \times 10^{-6}/10 = 0.5 \times 10^{-6}\,\text{F} = 0.5\,\mu\text{F} \quad (Ans.)$$

and from eqn. (7.14)

$$C_P = C_1 + C_2 + C_3$$

hence

$$C_3 = C_P - C_1 - C_2 = (1 - 0.4 - 0.5) \times 10^{-6}\,\text{F}$$
$$= 0.1 \times 10^{-6}\,\text{F or } 0.1\,\mu\text{F} \quad (Ans.)$$

b) From eqn. (7.9), the energy stored is

$$W_1 = \tfrac{1}{2}C_1 V^2 = \tfrac{1}{2} \times (0.4 \times 10^{-6}) \times 10^2 = 20 \times 10^{-6}\,\text{J or } 20\,\mu\text{J} \quad (Ans.)$$
$$W_2 = \tfrac{1}{2}C_2 V^2 = \tfrac{1}{2} \times (0.5 \times 10^{-6}) \times 10^2 = 25 \times 10^{-6}\,\text{J or } 25\,\mu\text{J} \quad (Ans.)$$
$$W_3 = \tfrac{1}{2}C_3 V^2 = \tfrac{1}{2} \times (0.1 \times 10^{-6}) \times 10^2 = 5 \times 10^{-6}\,\text{J or } 5\,\mu\text{J} \quad (Ans.)$$

c) From eqn. (7.5)

$$Q_P = C_P V = (1 \times 10^{-6}) \times 10 = 10 \times 10^{-6}\,\text{C or } 10\,\mu\text{C} \quad (Ans.)$$

Note: the value of Q_P could, alternatively, be calculated from the sum of the individual charges on the capacitors.

7.12   Series Connection of Capacitors

When capacitors are connected in series with one another, it is equivalent to increasing the thickness of the dielectric. According to the comments made at the end of section 7.10, this has the effect of reducing the effective capacitance of the series circuit below that of the smallest individual capacitor. The equivalent capacitance of a series circuit is determined below.

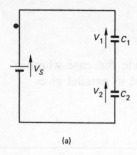

(a)

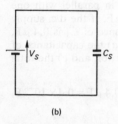

(b)

Fig. 7.8 Equivalent capacitance of series-connected capacitors

Consider the circuit in figure 7.8a. When the supply voltage V_S is connected to the circuit, the *same value of charging current flows through each capacitor for the same length of time*. Now, since the stored charge is given by (current × time), then each of the capacitors in figure 7.8a stores the same amount of charge Q. That is

Charge stored by C_1 = charge stored by C_2

hence

$$Q = C_1 V_1 = C_2 V_2$$

where V_1 and V_2 are the potentials across C_1 and C_2, respectively.

Moreover, if the series combination is replaced by an equivalent capacitor C_S (see figure 7.8b) which also stores charge Q when connected to V_S, then

Charge Q stored by $C_S = C_S V_S$

Applying Kirchhoff's second law to figure 7.8a gives

$$V_S = V_1 + V_2$$

Now

$$V_S = Q/C_S \qquad V_1 = Q/C_1 \quad \text{and} \quad V_2 = Q/C_2$$

hence

$$\frac{Q}{C_S} = \frac{Q}{C_1} + \frac{Q}{C_2}$$

therefore

$$\frac{1}{C_S} = \frac{1}{C_1} + \frac{1}{C_2} \tag{7.15}$$

If a large number of capacitors are connected in series then the equation for the reciprocal of the **equivalent capacitance** is

$$\frac{1}{C_S} = \frac{1}{C_1} + \frac{1}{C_2} + \frac{1}{C_3} + \cdots \tag{7.16}$$

That is

The reciprocal of the equivalent capacitance of series-connected capacitors is the sum of the reciprocals of the individual capacitances.

Moreover, the *equivalent capacitance of the series circuit is LESS than the smallest individual capacitance in the circuit.*

In the special case where two capacitors are connected in series (eqn. (7.15)), the equation for the equivalent capacitance reduces to

$$C_S = \frac{C_1 C_2}{C_1 + C_2}$$

EXAMPLE 7.10

Three capacitors C_1, C_2 and C_3 are connected in series with one another. The capacitance of C_1 is $1\,\mu\text{F}$, the voltage across C_2 is 8 V, and C_3 stores a charge of $2\,\mu\text{C}$. If the supply voltage is 20 V d.c., calculate the equivalent capacitance of the combination.

Solution $V_S = 20\,\text{V}$, $C_1 = 1\,\mu\text{F} = 10^{-6}\,\text{F}$, $V_2 = 8\,\text{V}$, $Q_3 = 2\,\mu\text{C} = 2 \times 10^{-6}\,\text{C}$.

Since each capacitor in series carries the same charge, then

$$Q_1 = Q_2 = Q_3 = Q = 2 \times 10^{-6}\,\text{C}$$

For C_2 $\quad Q = C_2 V_2$

hence

$$C_2 = Q/V_2 = 2 \times 10^{-6}/8 = 0.25 \times 10^{-6}\,\text{F or } 0.25\,\mu\text{F}$$

Now $\quad Q = C_1 V_1$

hence

$$V_1 = Q/C_1 = 2 \times 10^{-6}/10^{-6} = 2\,\text{V}$$

therefore

$$V_3 = V_S - V_1 - V_2 = 20 - 8 - 2 = 10\,\text{V}$$

From the above it follows that

$$C_3 = Q/V_3 = 2 \times 10^{-6}/10 = 0.2 \times 10^{-6}\,\text{F or } 0.2\,\mu\text{F}$$

From eqn. (7.16)

$$\frac{1}{C_S} = \frac{1}{C_1} + \frac{1}{C_2} + \frac{1}{C_3} = \frac{1}{10^{-6}} + \frac{1}{0.25 \times 10^{-6}} + \frac{1}{0.2 \times 10^{-6}}$$
$$= 10 \times 10^6\,\text{F}^{-1}$$

or

$$C_S = 0.1 \times 10^{-6}\,\text{F or } 0.1\,\mu\text{F} \quad (Ans.)$$

It is of interest to determine the voltage distribution between the series-connected capacitors, which is as follows.

Capacitance	Voltage
C_1 (1 μF)	2 V
C_2 (0.25 μF)	8 V
C_3 (0.2 μF)	10 V

That is,

When capacitors are connected in series with one another, the largest capacitance supports the smallest value of voltage, and the smallest value of capacitance supports the largest value of voltage.

7.13 Series-Parallel Connection of Capacitors

The equivalent capacitance of a complex network of capacitors can be determined by reducing the circuit to basic blocks of series and parallel combinations.

Consider the capacitor combination in figure 7.9. First, the series-connected combination C_2 and C_3 are combined to form the equivalent capacitor C_{S1} (see figure 7.9b). Next, the parallel combination C_{S1} and C_4 are combined to form the equivalent capacitor C_P (see figure 7.9c). Finally, capacitors C_1 and C_P are treated as a series combination to give the equivalent capacitance of the complete circuit.

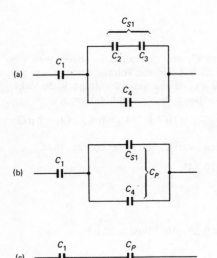

Fig. 7.9 A series-parallel capacitor circuit

EXAMPLE 7.11

Calculate the equivalent capacitance of a circuit of the type in figure 7.9 given that $C_1 = 1\ \mu\text{F}$, $C_2 = 2\ \mu\text{F}$, $C_3 = 3\ \mu\text{F}$, and $C_4 = 4\ \mu\text{F}$.

Solution   Referring to figure 7.9

$$C_{S1} = C_2C_3/(C_2+C_3) = (2\times10^{-6})\times(3\times10^{-6})/(2+3)\times10^{-6}$$
$$= 1.2\times10^{-6}\ \text{F}$$
$$C_P = C_{S1}+C_4 = (1.2+4)\times10^{-6} = 5.2\times10^{-6}\ \text{F}$$

The equivalent capacitance C_E of the complete circuit is

$$C_E = C_1C_P/(C_1+C_P)$$
$$= (1\times10^{-6})\times(5.2\times10^{-6})/(1+5.2)\times10^{-6}$$
$$= 0.839\times10^{-6}\ \text{F or } 0.839\ \mu\text{F}\quad (Ans.)$$

7.14 Construction of Capacitors

The name given to a capacitor largely depends not only on its mode of construction but also on the type of dielectric used. Capacitors are also classified either as **fixed capacitors**, whose capacitance is constant (or nearly so), or as **variable capacitors**, whose capacitance can be altered, usually by manual control.

Air dielectric capacitors

These are capacitors (usually parallel-plate types) used mainly as laboratory standards, the plates being separated by an air dielectric. Variable air capacitors have a set of moveable vanes, usually made from rigid aluminium or brass sheet, which can be moved relative to a set of fixed vanes; this allows the effective area of the air dielectric to be altered. A sectional view of a variable capacitor is shown in figure 7.10; the diagram shows the capacitor with the vanes *a*) fully in (maximum capacitance) and *b*) partially out.

Paper dielectric capacitor

A popular form of construction is shown in figure 7.11. In this case, continuous sheets of metal foil (the plates) are separated by layers of Kraft paper dielectric (which is a highly purified paper). Connections to the metal foil may be made either by means of metal discs which are pressed on to the ends of the capacitor (illustrated), or by means of tinned copper tags which are inserted during the winding of the capacitor. Finally, the paper is impregnated with one of a number of materials including mineral oil, petroleum jelly or polystyrene, after which the capacitor is sealed in a container.

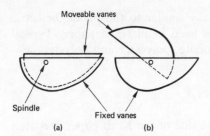

Fig. 7.10 (*a*) and (*b*) end view of a variable capacitor and (*c*) circuit symbol

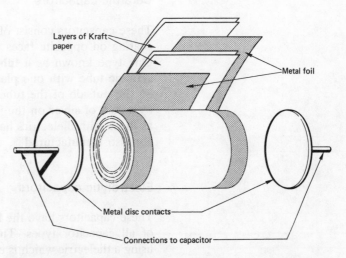

Fig. 7.11 One form of construction of a tubular paper capacitor

Plastic film capacitors

These capacitors are generally similar to the paper dielectric type, but plastic material is used in place of paper. Typical dielectrics include polycarbonate, polyester and polystyrene.

Metallized paper capacitors

In this type of capacitor, one side of the Kraft paper is coated with a thin layer of metal, the metal forming one plate. Two such papers are rolled together to form a parallel-plate capacitor.

An advantage of this form of construction over other types is that, should a localized short-circuit develop between the "plates", the metallizing in the region of the fault quickly evaporates to clear the fault. This property is particularly valuable where the capacitor is used in high voltage circuits such as automobile ignition circuits.

Mica dielectric capacitors

Mica can be split into thin sheets and can be used to construct multiple-plate capacitors of the type shown in figure 7.6. A variation of this type is the **silvered mica capacitor**, in which one of the plates is formed by a coat of silver on one side of the mica sheet.

Ceramic capacitors

These capacitors consist of a ceramic dielectric having a silver coating on opposite faces of the dielectric to form the plates. One type known as a **tubular ceramic capacitor** comprises a ceramic tube with one plate being formed by a coat of silver on the outside of the tube, and the other plate being formed by a coat of silver on the inside of the tube. Other types such as those with dielectrics having the shape of a disc or of a cup are also manufactured.

Electrolytic capacitors

These capacitors have the highest capacitance per unit volume of all capacitor types. The high capacitance is obtained by using a dielectric which is only a few millionths of a centimetre thick. The dielectric is an oxide layer formed on one of the plates, which is usually either aluminium or tantalum.

7.15 The Equivalent Circuit of a Capacitor

It is an unfortunate fact of life that every electrical component has a number of imperfections, and the humble capacitor can, indeed, become a most complex device under certain circumstances. In many cases, such as in d.c. circuits or in mains-frequency a.c. circuits (50 Hz or 60 Hz), the effects of the imperfections are so small as to be negligible. However, at high frequency (such as at radio and t.v. frequency) it may be another matter, and the imperfections become important.

One form of equivalent circuit is shown in figure 7.12. In addition to the capacitance C of the capacitor, it has a dielectric loss resistance R_d (which usually has a value of the order of a fraction of an ohm), and a leakage resistance R_l. The **dielectric loss resistor** is associated with the energy loss in the dielectric (this is analogous to the iron loss in an iron-cored coil).

Since the dielectric material is not perfect, some of the charge stored by the capacitor leaks away when the supply is disconnected. This leakage effect is allowed for in circuit calculations by shunting the capacitor by the **leakage resistance**. The value of R_l is very high in many capacitors (it may be 100 MΩ or greater in plastic dielectric capacitors), but can be fairly low in electrolytic capacitors (less than, say, 0.5 MΩ).

In addition to the above, all capacitors have some inductance (that is, they produce some magnetic flux when current flows through them). Electrolytic capacitors are particularly poor in this respect, and have a comparatively large inductance. On the other hand, mica and ceramic capacitors have very little inductance.

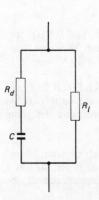

Fig. 7.12 Equivalent circuit of a practical capacitor

Exercises

In the following, take $\mu_0 = 8.85 \times 10^{-12}$ F/m.

7.1 A potential difference of 200 V is applied between two plates 2 μm apart. Calculate the electric field intensity between the plates.
[100 MV/m]

7.2 Calculate the charge stored by a parallel-plate capacitor if the electric flux density in the dielectric is 0.2 mC/m² and the area of each plate of the capacitor is 500 cm².
[10 μC]

7.3 A potential difference of 200 V is applied between the plates of a parallel-plate capacitor of capacitance 50 nF. If the area of each plate is 400 cm² and the relative permittivity of the dielectric is 2.25, calculate a) the electric flux density and b) the electric field intensity in the dielectric.
[a) 0.3125 mC/m²;   b) 15.69 MV/m]

7.4 A $10 \, \mu F$ capacitor is charged at a constant current. If the voltage across the capacitor rises from zero to 200 V in 50 ms, calculate the value of the charging current.
[40 mA]

7.5 A capacitor is discharged through a resistor. If the average discharge current is 5 mA during a 2 s period of time, calculate the capacitance of the capacitor if the voltage falls from 100 V to 50 V during this period of time.
[200 μF]

7.6 When a capacitor is fully charged to 200 V, it stores a charge of $5 \, \mu C$. Determine a) the capacitance of the capacitor and b) the energy stored.
[a) 25 nF; b) 0.5 mJ]

7.7 Two capacitors have capacitances of $0.1 \, \mu F$ and $0.5 \, \mu F$, respectively. Calculate the energy stored when they are connected a) in parallel and b) in series across a 10 V supply.
[a) 30 μJ; b) 4.17 μJ]

7.8 Two capacitors A and B of capacitance $0.04 \, \mu F$ and $0.06 \, \mu F$, respectively, are connected in series across a d.c. supply. If the energy stored by capacitor A is $0.72 \, \mu J$, determine the value of the supply voltage.
[10 V]

7.9 A capacitor consists of two metal plates each of area 50 cm^2 and separated by 0.1 mm. If the dielectric a) is air, b) has a relative permittivity of 3.6, calculate the capacitance of the capacitor.
[a) 442.5 pF; b) 1.593 nF]

7.10 A multiple-plate parallel-plate capacitor has 9 plates. Each pair of plates is separated by a dielectric of relative permittivity 2.5 and of thickness 0.5 mm; the area of each plate is 250 cm^2. Calculate a) the capacitance of the capacitor and b) the energy stored in it when it is fully charged to 200 V.
[a) 8.85 nF; b) 0.177 mJ]

7.11 Two capacitors having capacitance $0.2 \, \mu F$ and 400 nF, respectively, are connected a) in parallel, b) in series. Determine the equivalent capacitance in each case.
[a) 0.6 μF; b) 0.133 μF]

7.12 The effective capacitance of two series-connected capacitors is $0.4 \, \mu F$. If the capacitance of one capacitor is $1.0 \, \mu F$, determine the capacitance of the second capacitor.
[0.667 μF]

7.13 Capacitors A, B and C having capacitances of $10 \, \mu F$, $5 \, \mu F$ and $20 \, \mu F$, respectively, are connected in series with one another. Determine the equivalent capacitance of the circuit.

If 35 V d.c. is applied to the series circuit, determine a) the voltage across each capacitor, b) the charge stored by each capacitor, and c) the energy stored by each capacitor.
[2.857 μF; a) 10 V, 20 V, 5 V; b) 100 μC; c) 0.5 mJ, 1.0 mJ, 0.25 mJ]

7.14 Calculate the equivalent capacitance of the circuits in figure 7.13.
[a) 0.829 μF; b) 0.239 μF]

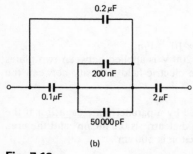

(a)

(b)

Fig. 7.13

7.15 Two capacitors A and B are connected *a*) in parallel, *b*) in series to a constant voltage supply. The capacitance of capacitor A is $1 \mu F$, and when A and B are connected in series their combined capacitance is $0.8 \mu F$. Calculate the capacitance of capacitor B. What percentage of the total energy is stored by the smaller capacitor for each method of connection?

$[4 \mu F; \quad a) \; 20\%; \quad b) \; 80\%]$

7.16 A multiple-plate capacitor has 9 plates, each having an area of $0.05 \, m^2$. If each pair of plates is separated by paper of thickness $0.5 \, mm$ and relative permittivity 2.0, calculate *a*) the capacitance of the capacitor in μF and *b*) the energy stored when its terminal voltage is 100 V.

$[a) \; 7.08 \, nF; \quad b) \; 35.4 \, \mu J]$

7.17 A capacitor stores $0.5 \, \mu C$ of electricity when the applied voltage is 10 V. If the total length of the dielectric is 1.0 m, and its relative permittivity is 2.5 and its thickness is 0.02 mm, calculate the width of the dielectric.

$[45.2 \, mm]$

8 Direct Current Switching Circuits

8.1 Response of Circuit Elements to a Sudden Change in Voltage

If the voltage applied to a pure RESISTOR is suddenly changed from zero to a finite value, the only factor limiting the flow of current is the resistance itself. If the voltage changes at time $t = 0$ (see figure 8.1a), the current instantly becomes $I = E/R$ and is maintained at this value so long as the supply voltage remains at E volts.

In the case of an INDUCTIVE LOAD, when the supply is first switched on, the current begins to rise; note that, when a current changes in an inductance, a back e.m.f. is induced in the inductor (as predicted by Lenz's law), this e.m.f. opposing the rise in current. That is to say, the rise in current is delayed in the manner shown in figure 8.1b. The curve in figure 8.1b follows one form of **exponential equation**. The rate of rise of current is related to the ratio

$$\frac{\text{inductance}}{\text{resistance}} \text{ or } \frac{L}{R} \text{ of the circuit}$$

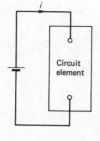

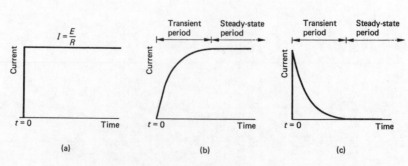

(a) (b) (c)

Fig. 8.1 Current from a d.c. supply in (a) a pure resistor, (b) an inductive circuit, (c) a capacitive circuit

This ratio is known as the **time constant** T of the circuit. For an **inductive circuit**

$$T = \frac{L}{R} \text{ seconds} \qquad (8.1)$$

where L is the inductance of the circuit in henrys and R is the circuit resistance in ohms.

When a d.c. supply is suddenly connected to a discharged CAPACITOR at $t = 0$, the capacitor current instantaneously rises to a peak value, after which it decays to zero (see figure 8.1c). At the instant of switch-on the voltage across the capacitor is zero, so that the only factor limiting the initial rush of current is the resistance of the circuit; if the circuit has a small resistance, the initial charging current has a very high value. As the capacitor acquires electrical charge, the voltage across the capacitor increases and the charging current diminishes. Finally, when the capacitor is fully charged, the voltage across the capacitor is equal to the supply voltage and the current has decayed to zero.

The waveshape in figure 8.1c follows another form of exponential law. The decay of the charging current can be described in terms of the time constant T of the **capacitive circuit** where

$$T = RC \text{ seconds} \qquad (8.2)$$

where R is the resistance of the circuit in ohms and C is the capacitance of the circuit in farads.

The waveforms in figures 8.1b and c are divided into two time periods, namely the transient period and the steady-state period. The **transient period** is the period of time during which the current changes with time (the supply voltage being assumed to be constant during this period). When the current reaches its final steady value, the circuit enters its **steady-state period**.

8.2 Plotting the Growth of Current in an *L-R* Circuit

Consider the L-R circuit in figure 8.2 in which the contact of switch S is closed at time $t = 0$. Prior to the switch closure, the instantaneous current i in the circuit is zero. After the closure, the current rises at a rate determined by the voltage E and the circuit time constant $T = L/R$. During the time that the current

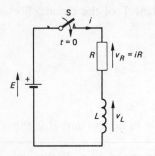

Fig. 8.2 Growth of current in an L-R circuit

in the circuit is changing (the transient period), an e.m.f. is induced in L (remember $v_L = L\, di/dt$) which opposes the rise in current. This e.m.f. is described as a **back e.m.f.** since it opposes the change in current.

Ultimately the current reaches its final value or steady-state value (see figure 8.1b). When this occurs, the rate of change of the current in the circuit is zero (i.e. $di/dt = 0$), so that the self-induced (back) e.m.f. is zero. The final value of the circuit current is then given by

$$I = \frac{E}{R}\ \text{A} \tag{8.3}$$

A feature of an exponentially increasing curve of the type in figure 8.1b is that in a time which is equal to $0.7\,T$ (i.e. 70 per cent of the time constant), the value increases or "grows" by 50 per cent of the difference between its value at the commencement of the time interval and the final value.

The above relationship is shown in detail in figure 8.3, in which the time scale is divided into time intervals of $0.7T$. At the commencement of the time interval OA, the value of the current is zero; at the end of the $0.7T$ time interval the current will have "grown" to a value of

$$0.5 \times (\text{final current} - \text{initial current}) = 0.5 \times (I - 0)$$
$$= 0.5I$$

where I is the final value of the current ($= E/R$).

At the commencement of the time interval AB the initial current is $0.5I$, so that at the end of this time interval the current will have increased by

$$0.5 \times (I - 0.5I) = 0.25I$$

above its initial value of $0.5I$. That is at time B the current is

$$(0.5I + 0.25I) = 0.75I = 0.75E/R$$

At the commencement of the time interval BC the initial current is $0.75I$. At the end of this time interval the current has grown by

$$0.5 \times (I - 0.75I) = 0.125I$$

that is its value at time C is

$$(0.75I + 0.125I) = 0.875I = 0.875E/R$$

This method can be used to verify the remainder of the curve in figure 8.3.

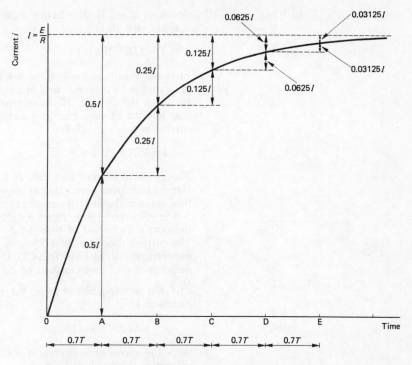

Fig. 8.3 Sketching a "growth" type of exponential curve

Table 8.1

Time	Current
0	0
0.7T	0.5I
1.4T	0.75I
2.1T	0.875I
2.8T	0.938I
3.5T	0.969I
4.2T	0.985I
4.9T	0.993I
5.6T	0.997I
6.3T	0.999I

A moment's thought will show that (theoretically at any rate) the current will continue rising and will never reach its final value. The reason for this is that the rise in current for each $0.7T$ time interval is only one-half of the remaining current step, so that there is always a small increment of current remaining. The results of the above exercise are given to three decimal places in Table 8.1.

In the time interval from zero to T (one time constant from switch-on) the current can be shown to rise to 63.2 per cent of its final value, i.e. to $0.632I$.

EXAMPLE 8.1

A coil having an inductance of 2 H and resistance 2 Ω is connected to a 20 V d.c. supply. Plot a graph showing the growth of current in the coil after switch-on and hence determine *a*) the current in the circuit 1 s after switch-on and *b*) the time taken to reach a current of 8 A.

Solution $L = 2\,\mathrm{H}$, $R = 2\,\Omega$, $V = 20\,\mathrm{V}$.
From eqn. (8.1)

$$T = L/R = 2/2 = 1\,\mathrm{s}$$

From the results in Table 8.1 it will be noted that there is little point in dealing with a time period much greater than about $6T = 6 \times 1\,\mathrm{s} = 6\,\mathrm{s}$, since the current will have practically reached its final value in that interval of time (see also section 8.6). Also, the final value of current is (see eqn. (8.3))

$$I = E/R = 20/2 = 10\,\mathrm{A}$$

The graph of current to a base of time is plotted in figure 8.4. The current rises from zero value at the origin to reach 50 per cent of the final value in the first 70 per cent of a time constant. That is, it rises to 5 A in 0.7 s (point A in figure 8.4). It then rises from 5 A to 7.5 A in the next 0.7 s period of time, to give a current at point B of 7.5 A. The current then rises to 8.75 A by point C, etc. The time intervals between points OA, AB, BC, CD, DE, etc. are each equal to seventy per cent of one time constant of the circuit, i.e. 0.7 s.

a) From an inspection of figure 8.4, the current in the circuit 1 s after switch-on is

$$I = 6.32\,\mathrm{A} \quad (Ans.)$$

Since the above time interval is equal to one time constant, we may generalize the result as follows:

Current after a time equal to the first time constant

= 63.2 per cent of the final value

b) Refering once again to figure 8.4, the time taken for the current to reach 8 A is 1.61 s. (*Ans.*)

8.3 Calculating the Growth of Current in an *L-R* Circuit

It can be shown that the instantaneous value of the current i in the circuit at time t after switch S in figure 8.2 has been closed is given by

$$i = I(1 - e^{-t/T}) \tag{8.4}$$

where I is the final value of the current ($I = E/R$), $e = 2.71828$ and is the base of natural logarithms, t is the time in seconds after switch-on, and T is the time constant ($T = L/R$) of the circuit. We will illustrate the use of the above equation by calculating the solutions to parts *a*) and *b*) of example 8.1.

Data for part a):

$$I = 10\,\mathrm{A}, \qquad T = 1\,\mathrm{s}, \qquad t = 1\,\mathrm{s}$$

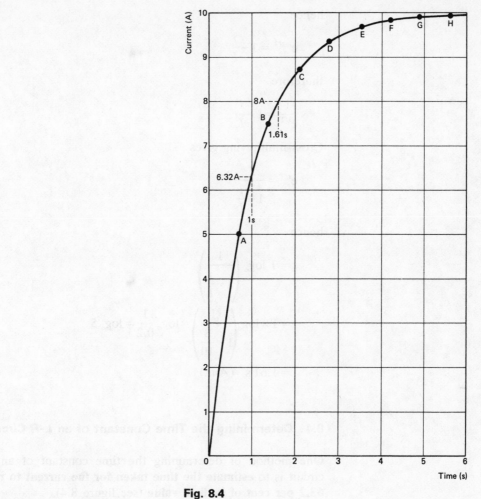

Fig. 8.4

From eqn. (8.4)

$$i = I(1 - e^{-t/T}) = 10(1 - e^{-1/1})$$
$$= 10(1 - 0.368) = 6.32 \text{ A} \quad (Ans.)$$

Data for part b):

$$I = 10 \text{ A}, \qquad T = 1 \text{ s}, \qquad i = 8 \text{ A}$$

From eqn. (8.4)

$$i = I(1 - e^{-t/T})$$

or

$$\frac{i}{I} = 1 - e^{-t/T}$$

hence

$$e^{-t/T} = 1 - \frac{i}{I}$$

therefore

$$\frac{1}{e^{t/T}} = 1 - \frac{i}{I}$$

Cross-multiplying gives

$$e^{t/T} = \frac{1}{1 - \frac{i}{I}}$$

hence

$$t = T \log_e \left(\frac{1}{1 - \frac{i}{I}} \right)$$

$$= 1 \times \log_e \left(\frac{1}{1 - \frac{8}{10}} \right) = \log_e \frac{1}{0.2} = \log_e 5$$

$$= 1.61 \, \text{s} \quad (Ans.)$$

8.4 Determining the Time Constant of an *L-R* Circuit

One method of determining the time constant of an *L-R* circuit is to **estimate the time taken for the current to rise to 63.2 per cent of its final value** (see figure 8.4).

An alternative method is as follows. Draw a tangent to the initial slope of the graph (see figure 8.5); the point at which this line intersects with the final value of the current gives the time constant of the circuit. This method is generally not as reliable as that outlined in the first paragraph of this section.

8.5 Estimating the Rise-time of the Current in an *L-R* Circuit

The **rise-time** t_r of a waveform is generally defined as **the time taken for the waveform to rise from 10 per cent to 90 per cent of the final value** (see figure 8.5). The value of the rise-time can either be estimated from the current/time graph, or it can be calculated from eqn. (8.4).

Using eqn. (8.4), we find that the time taken for the current to reach 10 per cent of I is $0.1T$ (where T is the time constant

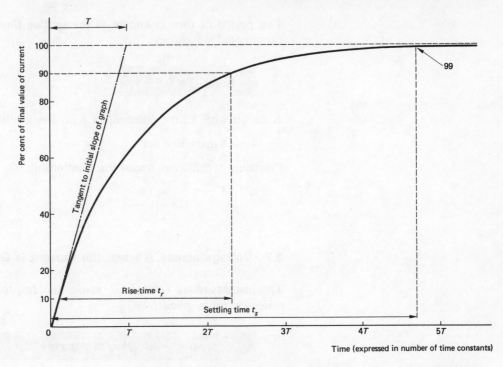

Fig. 8.5 The rise-time and settling-time of an exponential curve

of the circuit), and the time taken to reach 90 per cent of the final current is $2.3T$, hence rise time for figure 8.5 is

$$t_r = 2.3T - 0.1T = 2.2T \qquad (8.5)$$

Hence the rise-time of the current in a circuit whose time constant is 0.5 s is

$$2.2 \times 0.5 = 1.1 \text{ s}$$

8.6 The Settling Time of the Current in an *L-R* Circuit

The transient period of the waveform in figure 8.5 is defined as the period of time during which the current is changing. We say that the transient period of an exponential waveform has "settled" when it reaches one per cent of its final value. In the case of the current after switch-on, the transient is said to have settled when it reaches 99 per cent of the final value, i.e. $0.99I$. This period of time can either be estimated from a graph of the type in figure 8.5 or it can be calculated from eqn. (8.4).

This period of time is known as the **settling time**, and for an exponential waveform

$$\boxed{\text{Settling time } t_s = 4.6T} \tag{8.6}$$

A circuit with a time constant of 8 ms has a settling time of

$$4.6 \times 8 \text{ ms} = 36.8 \text{ ms}$$

Practising technicians round the relationship to

$$t_s = 5T$$

8.7 Voltage across *R* when the Current is Growing

The **instantaneous voltage** v_R across the resistor in an L-R series circuit is given by

$$\boxed{v_R = \text{instantaneous value of current} \times R = iR}$$

Clearly, since the resistor has a fixed value, the waveshape of the voltage/time graph will be the same as that of the current/time graph. If the initial value of the current is zero, then the initial value of the voltage across R is also zero. Since the final value of the current in the circuit is $I = E/R$ (see also figure 8.3), then the final value of the voltage across R is

$$IR = \frac{E}{R} \times R = E$$

The graph of the voltage across the resistor is shown in figure 8.6*a*; v_R reaches 62.3 per cent of its final value T seconds after the supply is connected to the circuit. The curve is plotted in much the same way as that of the current waveform; that is, v_R reaches 50 per cent of its final value after $0.7T$ s, and 75 per cent of its final value after $1.4T$ s, etc. The rise time of the v_R graph is $2.2T$ s, and its settling time is $4.6T$ s (or approximately $5T$ s).

Using the mathematical expression for the current in the circuit (eqn. (8.4)), the expression for v_R is

$$v_R = iR = I(1 - e^{-t/T}) \times R = \frac{E}{R}(1 - e^{-t/T}) \times R$$

$$\boxed{v_R = E(1 - e^{-t/T}) \text{ V}} \tag{8.7}$$

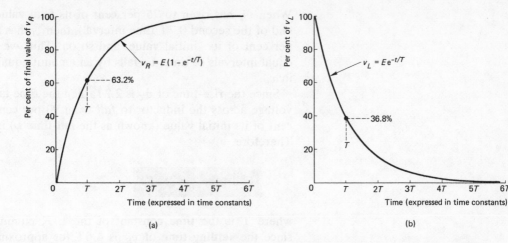

Fig. 8.6 (a) Voltage v_R across resistor R and (b) voltage v_L across inductor L

8.8 Voltage across L when the Current is Growing

Applying Kirchhoff's second law to the circuit in figure 8.2 gives

$$E = v_R + v_L \tag{8.8}$$

that is

$$v_L = E - v_R$$

If this subtraction is performed graphically, we get the curve in figure 8.6b. Initially (when $t = 0$) the value of $v_R = iR = 0$, hence the voltage across the inductor at $t = 0$ is

$$v_{L(t=0)} = E - 0 = E$$

After a time interval equal to T (when $v_R = 0.632E$) the value of v_L is

$$v_L = E - 0.632E = 0.368E$$

that is, the voltage across the inductor has fallen to 36.8 per cent of its initial value (see figure 8.6b).

The curve for v_L can be drawn using the information already known about the curve for v_R as follows. Since the supply voltage E is constant, then by the time that v_R has *risen* to 50 per cent of its final value, then v_L has *fallen* to 50 per cent of its initial value (this occurs in the first $0.7T$ time interval).

When v_R has risen to 75 per cent of its final value (after the end of the second $0.7T$ time interval), then v_L has fallen to 25 per cent of its initial value, and so on. Thus we see that in equal intervals of time, v_L falls by an amount equal to the rise in v_R.

Since the rise-time of v_R is $2.2T$, then the time taken for the voltage across the inductor to *fall* from 90 per cent to 10 per cent of its initial value (known as the **fall-time** t_f) is also $2.2T$. Therefore

$$\text{Fall-time } t_f = 2.2T \text{ s} \tag{8.9}$$

where T is the time constant of the L-R circuit. Similarly, since the **settling time** of v_R is $4.6T$ (or approximately $5T$), then the settling time for v_L is

$$\text{Settling time } t_s = 4.6T \text{ s} \tag{8.10}$$

In the above case the settling time is the time taken for the waveform to have fallen by 99 per cent of its initial value.

Since the final value of v_R is equal to E, then the final value of v_L can be computed as follows:

$$\text{Final value of } v_L = E - \text{final value of } v_R = E - E = 0$$

The mathematical expression for the voltage across the inductor can be obtained from eqns. (8.7) and (8.8) as follows:

$$v_L = E - v_R = E - E(1 - e^{-t/T})$$

that is

$$v_L = E e^{-t/T} \tag{8.11}$$

Table 8.2

Time	Voltage (V_m = initial value)
0	V_m
0.7T	$0.5V_m$
1.4T	$0.25V_m$
2.1T	$0.125V_m$
2.8T	$0.0625V_m$
3.5T	$0.0313V_m$
4.2T	$0.0156V_m$
4.9T	$0.0078V_m$
5.6T	$0.0039V_m$
6.3T	$0.002V_m$

8.9 Sketching an Exponentially Decaying Curve

The curve for the voltage v_L across the inductor in figure 8.6b is an exponentially decaying curve. The method of determining the instantaneous values for such a curve was outlined in section 8.8, and for completeness the results are given in Table 8.2. The values in the table are limited to four decimal places. Other relationships relating to the curve are as follows. The waveform falls to 36.8 per cent of the initial value in a time equal to the time constant (see figure 8.6b), the fall-time is $2.2T$, and the settling time is $4.6T$ (or approximately $5T$).

8.10 Decay of Current in an *L-R* Circuit

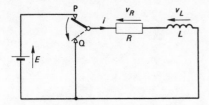

Fig. 8.7 Current switch-off in an inductive circuit

Suppose that the contact of the switch in figure 8.7 is in position P long enough for the current to build up to its final value (which is E/R) when it is suddenly switched to position Q. According to Lenz's law, an e.m.f. is induced in the coil which acts in a direction to maintain the current flow through the coil in its original direction (that is from left to right in figure 8.7). The current through the coil does not, therefore, instantaneously reduce to zero the moment that the switch is changed from P to Q (even though E is disconnected from the coil). In fact, current continues to flow in the direction shown in figure 8.7 until all the energy stored in the magnetic field has been dissipated. However, the reader will realize that the current through the coil decays gradually.

The **decay of current** in an inductive circuit can be shown to follow an exponential law of the type

$$i = I e^{-t/T} \text{ A} \tag{8.12}$$

where i is the instantaneous value of current at time t after the switch has changed from P to Q in figure 8.7, and I is the value of the current in the coil at the instant before the switch is changed from P to Q $(I = E/R)$. Since the current decays exponentially, then the decay of current is expressed in terms of the time constant T $(= L/R)$ of the inductive circuit.

EXAMPLE 8.2

If, in figure 8.7, $E = 10$ V, $R = 1$ Ω, $L = 2$ H, sketch the curve showing the current decay after the switch contact is changed from P to Q. Assume that the current has reached a steady value of 10 A $(= E/R)$ before the switch contact is changed over. Determine *a*) the time taken for the current to fall to 4 A and *b*) the current 5 s after the contacts are changed over.

Solution The time constant of the inductive circuit is

$T = L/R = 2/1 = 2$ s

Since the current curve follows a decaying exponential curve, it can be sketched using the method outlined in section 8.9. Since the initial current is 10 A, then the current falls to 5 A after the first $0.7T = 0.7 \times 2 = 1.4$ s (point A in figure 8.8).

It falls to 2.5 A after the next 1.4 s, i.e. 2.8 s after the switch contacts are changed to Q (point B in figure 8.8).

The current falls to 1.25 A after a total time of $(3 \times 1.4) = 4.2$ s (point C), and to 0.625 A after a time of $(4 \times 1.4) = 5.6$ s (point D), etc.

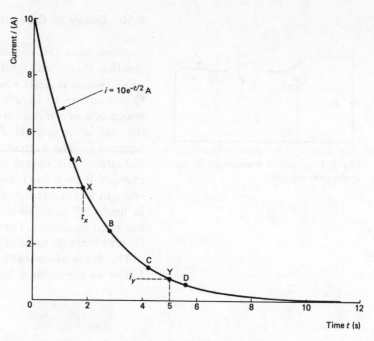

Fig. 8.8 Decay of current in an inductive circuit

The solution to parts *a*) and *b*) can be obtained either by reading the appropriate values from figure 8.8, or by using eqn. (8.12). Both methods are used here.

a) GRAPHICAL SOLUTION (see point X in figure 8.8) The time taken for the current to fall to 4 A is approximately 1.8 s   (*Ans.*)

MATHEMATICAL SOLUTION   From eqn. (8.12), the current is 4 A after a time equal to t_x, hence

$$4 = 10e^{-t_x/2}$$

or

$$0.4 = e^{-t_x/2} = 1/e^{t_x/2}$$

therefore

$$e^{t_x/2} = 1/0.4 = 2.5$$

Taking logarithms to base e gives

$$t_x = 2 \log_e 2.5 = 2 \times 0.9163 = 1.8326 \text{ s}   (\textit{Ans.})$$

b) GRAPHICAL SOLUTION (see point Y in figure 8.8) The current at time $t_y = 5$ s is approximately 0.8 A   (*Ans.*)

MATHEMATICAL SOLUTION   From eqn. (8.12)

$$i_y = 10e^{-5/2} = 10 \times 0.0821 = 0.821 \text{ A}   (\textit{Ans.})$$

8.11   Voltage across *R* and across *L* when the Current Decays

Since the voltage v_R across R is equal to iR (see figure 8.7), then the graph of v_R plotted to a base of time during the current decay period has the same general shape as that of the current graph. A graph showing how v_R in example 8.2 decays after the switch contact is changed from P to Q is shown in figure 8.9a. The equation for the voltage v_R across the resistor is

$$v_R = iR = \frac{E}{R}e^{-t/T} \times R$$

hence

$$v_R = Ee^{-t/T} \tag{8.13}$$

Thus the voltage across R just prior to the switch blade being changed from P to Q is 10 V. After a time equal to $0.7T$ ($= 1.4\,\text{s}$ in example 8.2), v_R decays to 5 V (see A′ in figure 8.9a); after 2.8 s the value of v_R is 2.5 V (see B′ in figure 8.9a); after 4.2 s the value of v_R is 1.25 V (see C′), etc.

The curve for the voltage v_L across the inductor can be determined from the fact that, after the switch contact in figure

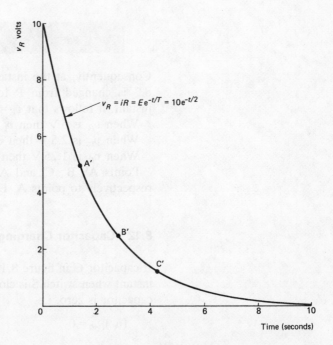

$$v_R = iR = Ee^{-t/T} = 10e^{-t/2}$$

Fig. 8.9a Waveform of the voltage across resistor *R* when the current decays

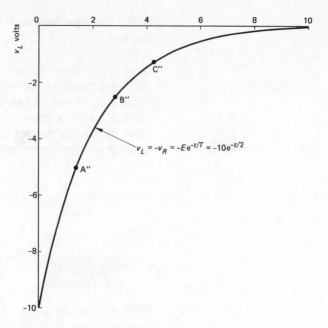

Fig. 8.9b Waveform of the voltage across inductor L when the current decays

8.6 is changed from P to Q, then the e.m.f. E is disconnected from the circuit, hence

$$v_L + v_R = 0$$

or

$$v_L = -v_R = -Ee^{-t/T} \tag{8.14}$$

Consequently, at the instant when the switch blade in figure 8.7 is changed from P to Q then, since $v_R = 10$ V at this instant, it follows that $v_L = -v_R = -10$ V.

When v_R is 5 V then $v_L = -5$ V (point A″ in figure 8.9b).

When v_R is 2.5 V then $v_L = -2.5$ V (point B″).

When v_R is 1.25 V then $v_L = -1.25$ V (point C″), etc.

Points A′, B′, C′ and A″, B″, C″ in figure 8.9 correspond respectively to points A, B, C in figure 8.8.

8.12 Capacitor Charging Current

If capacitor C in figure 8.10 is initially discharged, then at the instant when switch S is closed (at $t = 0$) the voltage across the capacitor is zero, i.e.

$$(v_C)_{t=0} = 0$$

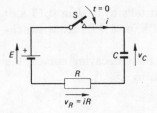

Fig. 8.10 Capacitor charging current

Applying Kirchhoff's second law to the circuit at $t = 0$ gives

$$E = \text{voltage across } R + \text{voltage across } C$$
$$= (v_R)_{t=0} + (v_C)_{t=0} = (v_R)_{t=0} + 0$$
$$= (iR)_{t=0}$$

That is to say, at the instant that $t = 0$ then

$$iR = E$$

Hence the initial rush of charging current is given by

$$(i)_{t=0} = \frac{E}{R} \text{ A} \tag{8.15}$$

If the supply voltage remains connected to the supply, the capacitor is eventually charged to E volts. Thus after an infinite period of time $(t = \infty)$ the circuit equation becomes

$$E = \text{voltage across } R + \text{voltage across } C$$
$$= (v_R)_{t=\infty} + (v_C)_{t=\infty}$$
$$= (v_R)_{t=\infty} + E$$

Hence the voltage across R after an infinite period of time is

$$(v_R)_{t=\infty} = E - E = 0$$

We can deduce from the above that

$$(iR)_{t=\infty} = 0$$

or

$$(i)_{t=\infty} = 0$$

That is to say, the capacitor charging current finally decays to zero when the capacitor is fully charged. It can be shown that the charging current curve follows a decaying exponential law having the general shape illustrated in figure 8.8. The equation of the **charging current curve** is

$$i = I e^{-t/T} \tag{8.16}$$

where i is the charging current t seconds after switch S in figure 8.10 has been closed, I is the initial value of the charging current $(I = E/R$ in figure 8.10 if C is initially discharged), $e = 2.718\,28$, and T is the time constant in seconds of the R-C circuit, where

$$T = RC \text{ s} \tag{8.17}$$

R is in ohms and C in farads.

The method of drawing the charging-current/time curve is as

outlined earlier. That is the current falls to $0.5I$ in $0.7T$ s, it falls to $0.25I$ in the following $0.7T$ s (or $1.4T$ s from switch-on), etc.

As in previous cases of exponentially decaying curves, the fall-time and settling time are given by

$$\text{Fall-time } t_f = 2.2T \text{ s} \qquad (8.18)$$

$$\text{Settling time } t_s = 4.6T \text{ s} \qquad (8.19)$$

EXAMPLE 8.3

A series circuit containing a capacitor C and a 1 kΩ resistance is suddenly connected to a 100 V d.c. supply. Calculate the initial value of the charging current. Calculate also the capacitance of the capacitor if it takes the charging current 0.223 ms to fall to 0.08 A.

Solution $R = 1 \text{ k}\Omega$, $E = 100 \text{ V}$, $i = 0.08 \text{ A}$ when $t = 0.223 \times 10^{-3}$ s. From eqn. (8.15)

Initial charging current = $E/R = 100/1000 = 0.1$ A   (*Ans.*)

From eqn. (8.16)

$$i = Ie^{-t/T}$$

or

$$0.08 = 0.1e^{-0.223 \times 10^{-3}/T}$$

hence

$$0.8 = e^{-0.223 \times 10^{-3}/T} = 1/(e^{0.223 \times 10^{-3}/T})$$

therefore

$$e^{0.223 \times 10^{-3}/T} = 1/0.8 = 1.25$$

Taking logarithms to base e gives

$$0.223 \times 10^{-3}/T = \log_e 1.25 = 0.223$$

giving

$$T = 0.223 \times 10^{-3}/0.223 = 10^{-3} \text{ s}$$

but $T = RC = 1000C$, hence

$$C = T/1000 = 10^{-3}/1000 = 10^{-6} \text{ F or } 1 \, \mu\text{F} \quad (\textit{Ans.})$$

8.13 Voltage across R and across C during the Capacitor Charging Period

When a capacitor which is initially discharged is connected to e.m.f. E via resistor R (see figure 8.10), the charging current waveform is as shown in figure 8.11a; the charging current falls to 36.8 per cent of its initial value in the first T seconds.

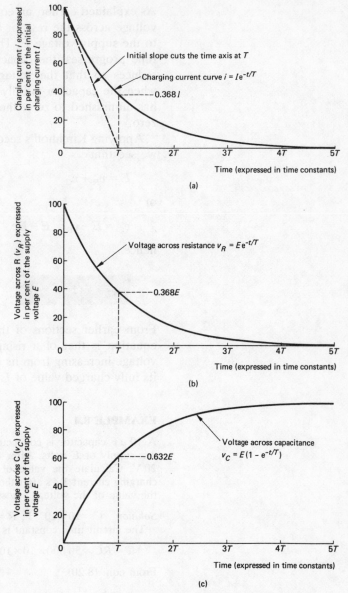

Fig. 8.11 (a) Charging current waveform together with waveforms for (b) v_R and (c) v_C

The equation for the voltage across the resistor is given by

$$v_R = iR = \frac{E}{R}e^{-t/T} \times R$$

hence

$$v_R = Ee^{-t/T} \tag{8.20}$$

As explained earlier, an equation of this kind implies that the voltage across the resistor at the instant of switch-on is equal to the supply voltage E. This is illustrated in figure 8.11b. As time progresses, the capacitor charging current progressively reduces so that the voltage across R also reduces. Finally, when the capacitor is fully charged and the capacitor current has diminished to zero, the voltage v_R has also diminished to zero.

Applying Kirchhoff's second law to the circuit in figure 8.10, we see that

$$E = v_R + v_C$$

or

$$v_C = E - v_R = E - Ee^{-t/T}$$

hence

$$v_C = E(1 - e^{-t/T}) \tag{8.21}$$

From earlier sections of the book, it is clear that the above equation is that of a rising exponential curve, the capacitor voltage increasing from its initially discharged value of zero to its fully charged value of E (see figure 8.11c).

EXAMPLE 8.4

A 10 μF capacitor is connected in series with a 50 kΩ resistor to a d.c. supply of E volts. After 0.7 s, the voltage across the resistor is 20 V. Calculate the value of E. Determine also the value of the charging current 1.4 s after the supply is connected and also calculate the value of the voltage across the capacitor at this time.

Solution $C = 10 \times 10^{-6}$ F, $R = 50\,000\ \Omega$, $v_R = 20$ V when $t = 0.7$ s.
   The circuit time constant is

$$T = RC = 50\,000 \times 10 \times 10^{-6} = 0.5 \text{ s}$$

From eqn. (8.20)

$$v_R = Ee^{-t/T}$$

hence

$$E = v_R/(e^{-t/T}) = v_R\, e^{t/T} = 20 \times e^{0.7/0.5} = 20 \times 4.05$$
$$= 81 \text{ V}\quad(Ans.)$$

The initial value of the charging current is

$$I = E/R = 81/50\,000 = 1.62 \times 10^{-3} \text{ A}$$

and from eqn. (8.16)

$$i = Ie^{-t/T} = 1.62 \times 10^{-3} \times e^{-1.4/0.5}$$
$$= 98.5 \times 10^{-6} \text{ A or } 98.5\ \mu\text{A}\quad(Ans.)$$

Also, from eqn. (8.21), the voltage across the capacitor after 1.4 s is

$$v_C = E(1 - e^{-t/T}) = 81(1 - e^{-1.4/0.5}) = 81(1 - 60.8 \times 10^{-3})$$
$$= 76.08 \text{ V} \quad (Ans.)$$

8.14 Capacitor Discharge

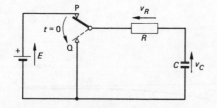

Fig. 8.12 Capacitor discharge

We will now study the discharge of the capacitor in figure 8.12. Suppose for the moment that the switch contact has been in position P long enough for the capacitor to be fully charged. At this point in time, the charging current is zero and the voltage v_R across the resistor is also zero so that $v_C = E$. If the switch contact is changed from P to Q at time $t = 0$, the capacitor begins to discharge via resistor R. Since the only opposition to current flow is resistor R, then the initial value of the discharge current is E/R. Note that the direction of the current flow through R during the discharge period is in the opposite direction to that during the charging period.

The discharge current has the effect of reducing the charge stored by the capacitor, which also reduces v_C; the net result is that the value of the discharge current progressively reduces with time; in fact it can be shown that the discharge current decays exponentially with a time constant of $T = RC$ s. The equation for the **instantaneous value of the discharge current** at time t is

$$i = I e^{-t/T} \tag{8.22}$$

where I is the initial value of the discharge current having the value $-E/R$ A (E in volts, R in ohms) [the negative sign showing that the capacitor is discharging]. The voltage v_R across the resistor, and v_C across the capacitor, are respectively

$$v_R = -E e^{-t/T} \tag{8.23}$$
$$v_C = E e^{-t/T} \tag{8.24}$$

EXAMPLE 8.5

Draw the graph of the discharge current, the voltage across the resistor and the voltage across the capacitor for the circuit in figure 8.12 when the capacitor of 0.1 μF, which is initially charged to 10 V, is discharged through a 1 kΩ resistor.

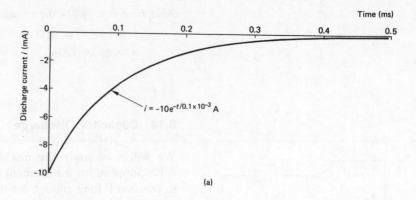

$i = -10e^{-t/0.1 \times 10^{-3}}$ A

(a)

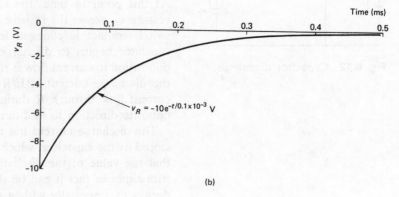

$v_R = -10e^{-t/0.1 \times 10^{-3}}$ V

(b)

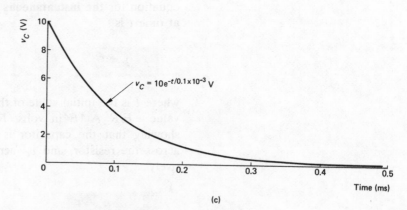

$v_C = 10e^{-t/0.1 \times 10^{-3}}$ V

(c)

Fig. 8.13

Solution $R = 1000\ \Omega$, $C = 0.1\ \mu\text{F} = 0.1 \times 10^{-6}\ \text{F}$, $E = 10\ \text{V}$.
The circuit time constant is

$$T = RC = 1000 \times 0.1 \times 10^{-6} = 0.1 \times 10^{-3}\ \text{s or } 0.1\ \text{ms}$$

The initial value of the discharge current is

$$-E/R = -10/1000 = -10 \times 10^{-3}\ \text{A or } -10\ \text{mA}$$

The graph of the discharge current is shown in figure 8.13a in which the current decays exponentially from -10 mA to zero (or nearly zero) in about $5T = 0.5$ ms.

The graph is drawn using the methods outlined earlier; the current decays to -5 mA in $0.7T$ (0.7 ms), then to -2.5 mA in the next 0.7 ms (i.e. after a total time of 1.4 ms), and reaches one per cent of the initial value, i.e. 0.1 mA, in $4.6T = 0.46$ ms (which is the settling time t_s of the circuit).

The voltage v_R across the resistor follows much the same pattern, with the voltage decaying exponentially from -10 V to -0.1 V in 0.46 ms (see figure 8.13b).

The waveshape of the voltage v_C is the mirror image of v_R (since during the discharge period $v_C = -v_R$), its value decaying exponentially from 10 V to 0.1 V in 0.46 ms.

Exercises

8.1   A coil has a resistance of 100 Ω and inductance 1.0 H. When the coil is connected to a 100 V supply; determine a) the steady-state value of the current in the coil; b) the initial rate of change of current in the coil, c) the time constant of the circuit, d) the energy stored in the magnetic field, e) the time taken for the current to reach 0.8 A, f) the value of the current 5 ms after the coil is connected to the supply.

[a) 1 A; b) 100 A/s; c) 10 ms; d) 0.5 J; e) 0.016 s; f) 0.393 A]

8.2   Draw a graph showing how the current through the coil in problem 8.1 varies with time from the instant that the supply is switched on.

8.3   A 200 V d.c. supply is suddenly connected to a coil which has a time constant of 5 ms. If the current in the coil reaches 0.2 A in 7 ms, determine a) the steady-state current in the coil, b) the resistance of the coil, and c) the inductance of the coil.

[a) 0.265 A; b) 754.7 Ω; c) 3.77 H]

8.4   A coil of inductance 1.0 H and resistance 80 Ω is connected to a d.c. supply for a sufficient time to allow the current to reach its steady-state value. When the coil is disconnected from the supply, it is arranged that a resistance of R Ω is connected to the terminals of the coil. If the current falls to 40 per cent of its initial value in 10 ms, calculate the value of R.

[11.74 Ω]

8.5   A coil of inductance 4 H and resistance 80 Ω is connected in parallel with a 200 Ω resistor of negligible inductance across a 200 V supply. Determine a) the current in the inductor and b) the current drawn from the supply 0.07 s after connecting the supply. Calculate c) the current drawn from the supply when the current in the coil has reached its steady-state value.

If the supply is suddenly disconnected from the coil, determine for the instant of time immediately after disconnecting the supply d) the current through the coil, e) the voltage across the coil. Also estimate f) the time taken for the current to decay to 10 per cent of its value at the instant of disconnecting the supply.

[a) 1.88 A; b) 2.88 A; c) 3.5 A; d) 2.5 A; e) 500 V, f) 0.115 s]

8.6   A 10 μF capacitor is connected in series with a 100 kΩ resistor to a 100 V d.c. supply. Calculate the time constant of the circuit, and draw to scale a graph showing how the charging current and the voltage across the capacitor vary with time. Assume the capacitor to be initially discharged.

[1.0 s]

8.7   A capacitor of 0.1 μF capacitance is connected in series with a 10 kΩ resistor. Determine the time constant of the circuit. If the combination is suddenly connected to a 100 V d.c. supply, determine a) the initial rate of rise of the p.d. across the capacitor, b) the initial value of the charging current, and c) the final value of energy stored by the capacitor.

[0.001 s; a) 100 kV/s; b) 0.01 A; c) 0.5 mJ]

8.8   A 10 μF capacitor is connected in series with a 10 MΩ resistor. An electrostatic voltmeter is connected across the resistor. If the capacitor is initially discharged, and the series combination is suddenly connected to a 100 V d.c. supply, determine the voltage indicated on the voltmeter 69.3 seconds after the supply is switched on.

[50 V]

8.9   A 10 μF capacitor has an insulation resistance of 20 MΩ. If the capacitor is charged to 200 V d.c., determine the time required after disconnection from the supply for the p.d. to fall to 80 V.

[9128 s]

8.10   A circuit comprising a 10 μF capacitor, a resistor R and an electrostatic voltmeter is connected in parallel to a 200 V d.c. supply. When the supply is disconnected, the voltmeter reading falls to 100 V in 56 s. When the resistor is disconnected and the test is repeated, the time taken for the same reduction in voltage is 400 s. Determine the resistance of the voltmeter and that of resistor R.

[57.7 MΩ; 9.4 MΩ]

9 Alternating Voltage and Current

9.1 Generating an Alternating Waveform

The concept of alternating voltage was introduced in chapter 1, and the reader will recall that its magnitude varies periodically about zero, being positive at one instant and negative the next.

Examples of alternating waveforms are shown in figure 9.1: diagram *a*) shows a **sinusoidal waveform** which follows a sine-law variation; diagram *b*) shows a **rectangular** (or **square**) **wave**; and diagram *c*) illustrates one form of **sawtooth waveform** (so named because of its shape). Note that in each case, **the area above the zero line is equal to the area below it**;

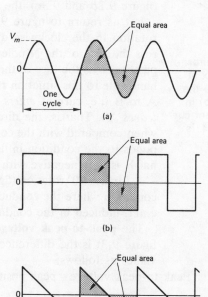

Fig. 9.1 Examples of alternating waveform: (*a*) sinusoidal, (*b*) rectangular, (*c*) sawtooth

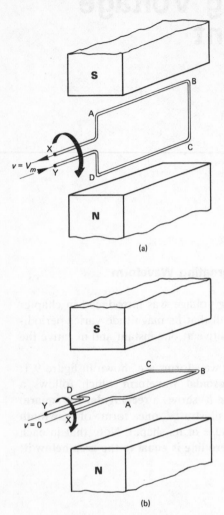

(a)

(b)

Fig. 9.2 A single loop alternator: (*a*) conductors cutting the flux at the maximum rate to produce the maximum induced voltage, (*b*) in this case the conductors do not cut the flux and the induced e.m.f. is zero

this is an important relationship which we often use when defining an alternating waveform.

One simple form of alternating voltage generator (known as an **alternator**) is shown in figure 9.2. The generator consists of a single loop of wire which is rotated in a magnetic field. From the work in chapter 6, the e.m.f. induced in a conductor moving in a magnetic field is proportional to the rate at which it cuts magnetic flux. In figure 9.2*a*, the conductors AB and CD cut the magnetic field at right-angles, and therefore the maximum value of voltage V_m is induced in the coil (see the waveform diagram in figure 9.1*a*); the maximum voltage is also known as the **peak voltage** (see also figure 9.3). Fleming's right-hand rule can be applied to verify not only the direction of the induced current in figure 9.2*a* but also that the e.m.f. induced in conductor AB adds to that induced in conductor CD. The two e.m.f.s. combine to cause current to flow out of terminal X and into terminal Y. So far as the external circuit is concerned, terminal X is instantaneously positive with respect to Y.

When the conductor loop has rotated through one-quarter of a revolution (see figure 9.2*b*), both conductors momentarily move parallel to the flux. That is, the *conductors are not cutting the flux*. Consequently, neither conductor has an e.m.f. induced in it at the instant illustrated in figure 9.2*b*.

The above conditions are also illustrated in figure 9.3. When the conductor loop is perpendicular (figure 9.2*a*), it corresponds to the condition in figure 9.3*b* (when V_m is induced in the loop of wire). When the coil has rotated through 90° (figure 9.2*b* and 9.3*c*), the induced e.m.f. is zero.

Let us return to figure 9.2 once more. After a further 90° rotation in the clockwise direction, conductor AB passes across the face of the N-pole of the magnet and conductor CD passes across the face of the S-pole. Applying Fleming's right-hand rule to this situation reveals that current now flows from A to B (i.e. current *enters* X) and from C to D (i.e. current *leaves* Y). That is, the direction of the current has reversed when compared with the conditions in figure 9.2*a* (this corresponds to the condition in figure 9.3*d*); the potential of terminal X is now negative with respect to Y.

A further 90° rotation (figure 9.3*e* and *a*) produces a second condition where the conductors no longer cut flux, so that the e.m.f. induced in the conductors is zero once more.

The **peak-to-peak voltage** of an alternating waveform (see figure 9.3) is the difference in voltage between the two peak values as follows:

Peak-to-peak voltage = peak positive voltage − peak negative voltage

$$= V_m - (-V_m) = 2V_m$$

$$= 2 \times \text{peak voltage}$$

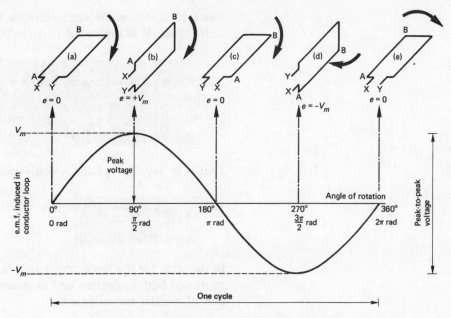

Fig. 9.3 One complete cycle of a sinusoidal waveform

If $V_m = 300$ V, then the peak-to-peak voltage is 600 V.

In one complete revolution of the conductor loop in figure 9.3, **one cycle** of alternating voltage waveform is generated.

In the above we have considered the method by which alternating voltage is generated in a loop of wire rotating in a stationary magnetic field; it is also possible to generate an alternating e.m.f. using the inverse of this mechanism. That is, the field winding is stationary, and the magnetic field rotates inside the fixed coil.

9.2 Angular Measure—the Degree and the Radian

Every reader will be familiar with the angular measure of the **degree**, in which the circle is divided into 360 equal parts; this subdivision of the circle can be traced back to Babylonian times.

The **radian** (abbreviated to rad) is another form of angular measure, and is the angle subtended at the centre of a circle by an arc whose length is equal to the radius (see figure 9.4). The radian is thought to have been invented by the mathematician James Thompson for a mathematics examination in Belfast in

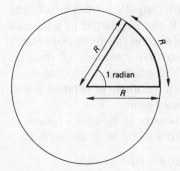

Fig. 9.4 The radian

about 1870. Since the circumference of a circle is equal to $2\pi R$, where R is the radius of a circle, then

$$\text{Number of radians in a circle} = \frac{\text{circumference}}{\text{radius}}$$

$$= \frac{2\pi R}{R} = 2\pi$$

That is to say, 2π radians is equivalent to $360°$, or

$$1 \text{ rad} = \frac{360°}{2\pi} = 57.3° \tag{9.1}$$

In the scale for the angle of rotation in figure 9.3, the angle is expressed both in degrees and in radians. The radian is the SI unit of angular measurement.

EXAMPLE 9.1

Convert *a*) $23.6°$ into radians and *b*) 3.2 radians into degrees.

Solution   *a*) From eqn. (9.1), $1° = 1/57.3$ rad, hence

   $23.6° = 23.6/57.3 \text{ rad} = 0.4119 \text{ rad}$ (*Ans.*)

b) From eqn. (9.1), 1 rad $= 57.3°$, hence

   $3.2 \text{ rad} = 3.2 \times 57.3° = 183.36°$ (*Ans.*)

9.3 The Sine Wave

The waveform most frequently associated with electrical and electronic engineering is the **sinusoidal wave** or **sine wave** (see figure 9.5). A sine wave can be plotted either to a base of angular rotation (based on the angular rotation of the generator loop in figure 9.3), or it can be plotted to a base of time (on the basis that the loop of wire in the generator rotates at a constant angular velocity, so that the angle of rotation depends on the time for which the conductor loop has been rotating). The relationship between the **angle of rotation** θ and the time t of rotation is developed below.

If the conductor loop of the generator in figure 9.3 rotates at speed ω rad/s, then in time t it rotates through an angle of

$\theta = \text{rotational speed (rad/s)} \times \text{time (s)} = \omega t \text{ rad}.$

If the frequency of the generated voltage is f Hz (or cycles

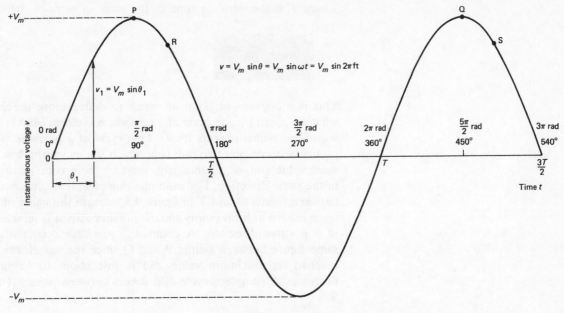

Fig. 9.5 A sine wave having a periodic time T seconds

per second), then the **angular frequency** ω in rad/s is

$$\omega = 2\pi f \text{ rad/s} \tag{9.2}$$

That is

$$\theta = \omega t = 2\pi f t \text{ rad} \tag{9.3}$$

The **instantaneous value** v of the sinusoidal voltage waveform in figure 9.5 is

$$v = V_m \sin \theta = V_m \sin \omega t = V_m \sin 2\pi f t \tag{9.4}$$

where V_m is the peak value of the voltage, ω is the angular velocity in rad/s, t is time in s, and f is the frequency in Hz.

It was shown in chapter 1 that the **frequency** f of the waveform is given by

$$f = 1/T \text{ Hz}$$

where T is the periodic time of the wave in seconds, hence

$$v = V_m \sin \frac{2\pi t}{T} \qquad (9.5)$$

This is a convenient point at which to define more precisely what we mean by one cycle of a **periodic waveform** (that is of a waveform which repeats itself). **One cycle of a periodic wave** occurs between any two points at which the waveform has the same value and, simultaneously, at which the wave is changing in the same direction. For example, one complete cycle occurs between points O and T in figure 9.5 because the value of the wave is zero at both points and, simultaneously, it is increasing in a positive direction. A complete cycle also occurs in the same figure between points P and Q since the waveform has reached its maximum value and is just about to begin to decrease. A complete cycle also occurs between points R and S.

EXAMPLE 9.2

Calculate the instantaneous value of a sinusoidal voltage waveform whose peak value is 10 V and whose frequency is 100 Hz when a) $\theta = 10°$, b) $\theta = 170°$, c) $\theta = 1$ rad, d) $\theta = 270°$, e) $\theta = 3.5$ rad, f) $\theta = 400°$, g) $t = 0.002$ s, h) $t = 0.009$ s.

Solution   For convenience, each condition is converted into its equivalent angle in degrees.

$\quad a)$ $\theta = 10°$: $v = V_m \sin \theta = 10 \sin 10° = 1.736$ V   (*Ans.*)

$\quad b)$ $\theta = 170°$: $v = V_m \sin \theta = 10 \sin 170° = 1.736$ V   (*Ans.*)

Note that during *each half-cycle* there are two angles which give the same voltage (see solutions a) and b) above); these angles are symmetrical about either 90° or 270°. The angles 90° and 270° are special cases, where the peak positive value and the peak negative value, respectively, occur.

$c)$ $\theta = 1$ rad $= 57.3°$:

$\quad v = V_m \sin \theta = 10 \sin 57.3° = 8.415$ V   (*Ans.*)

$d)$ $\theta = 270°$: $v = V_m \sin \theta = 10 \sin 270° = -10$ V   (*Ans.*)

Refer to figure 9.5, where it will be seen that the e.m.f. is $-V_m$ when $\theta = 270°$.

$e)$ $\theta = 3.5$ rad $= 200.5°$:

$\quad v = V_m \sin \theta = 10 \sin 200.5° = -3.508$ V   (*Ans.*)

$f)$ $\theta = 400° = 360° + 40°$

In this case we have entered 40° into the second cycle.

$\quad v = V_m \sin \theta = 10 \sin 400° \equiv 10 \sin 40° = 6.43$ V   (*Ans.*)

$g)$ $\omega = 2\pi f = 2\pi \times 100 = 628.3$ rad/s

Now $\theta = \omega t = 628.3 \times 0.002 = 1.257$ rad $= 72.02°$

$\quad v = V_m \sin \theta = 10 \sin 72.02° = 9.51$ V(*Ans.*)

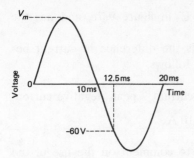

Fig. 9.6

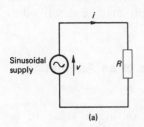

(a)

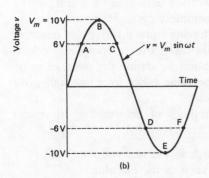

(b)

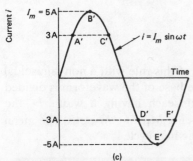

(c)

Fig. 9.7 The current flowing in a pure resistor with a sinusoidal applied voltage

h) $\theta = \omega t = 628.3 \times 0.009 = 5.655 \text{ rad} = 324°$:

$$v = V_m \sin \theta = 10 \sin 324° = -5.88 \text{ V} \quad (Ans.)$$

EXAMPLE 9.3

If the periodic time of a sinusoidal waveform is 20 ms, determine *a)* the frequency of the waveform and *b)* its peak value if its instantaneous value is -60 V after a time interval of 12.5 ms from the commencement of the wave.

Solution $T = 20 \times 10^{-3}$ s, $v = -60$ V at $t = 12.5 \times 10^{-3}$ s.

a) $f = 1/T = 1/20 \times 10^{-3} = 50 \text{ Hz}$ (*Ans.*)

b) The conditions relating to the problem are shown in figure 9.6. Since the periodic time is 20 ms, the second half-cycle commences 10 ms from the start of the cycle; consequently, at 12.5 ms the wave is in its negative half-cycle. From eqn. (9.5)

$$v = V_m \sin \frac{2\pi t}{T}$$

or

$$-60 = V_m \sin \left(\frac{2\pi \times 12.5 \times 10^{-3}}{20 \times 10^{-3}} \text{ rad} \right) = V_m \sin (3.927 \text{ rad})$$

$$= V_m \sin 225° = -0.707 \, V_m$$

therefore

$$V_m = -60/(-0.707) = 84.86 \text{ V} \quad (Ans.)$$

9.4 Current in a Resistive Circuit

When a pure resistance (i.e. a resistance which does not possess either inductance or capacitance) is connected to a sinusoidal supply voltage, then the current waveform is also sinusoidal. A resistive circuit together with its voltage and current waveforms is shown in figure 9.7.

If the circuit resistance is 2 Ω, then when the instantaneous value of the supply voltage is 6 V (see points A and C in figure 9.7*b*), the instantaneous value of the current is 6 V/2 Ω = 3 A (see A′ and C′ in figure 9.7*c*). When the supply voltage reaches its peak value (10 V) at point B in figure 9.7*b*, the instantaneous current is 10 V/2 Ω = 5 A (see point B′ in figure 9.7*c*). The value of the current at B′ is the **maximum current** I_m (which is also known as the **peak current**), and in an a.c. circuit containing only a pure resistor it occurs at the same instant of time as the peak voltage.

When the instantaneous value of the supply voltage reaches -6 V on the negative half-cycle (see points D and F in figure 9.7*b*), the instantaneous current in the circuit is -3 A (see points D′ and F′ in figure 9.7*c*). The peak current in the negative half-cycle occurs at E′ in figure 9.7c, and has the value $-10\,V/2\,\Omega = -5\,A$.

The **peak-to-peak current** is the difference in current between the two peak values as follows.

Peak-to-peak current = peak positive current − peak negative current

$$= 5 - (-5) = 10\,A$$

It is worthwhile at this point to comment on the use of the abbreviation **a.c.** It is usual to use this abbreviation to mean "alternating current", but it is also used as a descriptive adjective when describing any alternating waveform or alternating current operated device. Thus we may refer to an "a.c. current" or an "a.c. voltage" when describing an alternating current or alternating voltage, respectively. A machine which operates only from an alternating supply may be described as an "a.c. machine".

9.5 Average Value or Mean Value of an Alternating Waveform

Strictly speaking, the average value or mean value of an alternating waveform is the average area under a graph plotted for the waveform over one complete cycle. However, since an alternating waveform is one having equal positive and negative areas, then the average value taken over a complete cycle is zero! In an engineering situation we define the average value or **mean value** as **the average value taken over one half-cycle** (usually the positive half-cycle).

There are two general methods of determining the mean value of a waveform, which are

1 A graphical method such as the mid-ordinate rule.
2 An analytical method such as the calculus.

The mid-ordinate rule

First we will consider the use of this rule with a non-sinusoidal waveform (see figure 9.8). The base of the waveform is divided into a number of equal parts each having a width D, the length of the mid-ordinates being M_1, M_2, M_3, etc. The mean value of the waveform over one half-cycle is

$$\text{Mean value} = \frac{\text{sum of the values of the mid-ordinates}}{\text{number of mid-ordinates}}$$

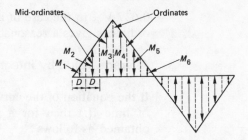

Fig. 9.8 Illustrating the mid-ordinate rule

In figure 9.8 there are six mid-ordinates, so that

$$\text{Mean value} = \frac{M_1 + M_2 + M_3 + M_4 + M_5 + M_6}{6}.$$

The reader will realize that, since we are only taking a small number of "spot" values over the half-cycle, the final result will be an approximate solution. However, the accuracy is improved by taking a large number of mid-ordinates (when the number of mid-ordinates is very large, the accuracy approaches that of the calculus method). However, as will be seen later when we compare mid-ordinate solutions with calculus solutions, reasonably accurate solutions can be obtained by the graphical method.

Average value of a sine wave using the mid-ordinate rule

Suppose that we split the positive half-cycle of a sinewave of maximum value 1.0 into six consecutive intervals of 30°. The first mid-ordinate is at 15°, the second is at 15° + 30° = 45°, the third at 75°, etc. The values of the mid-ordinates for a sinewave of peak value 1.0 are given in Table 9.1. The mean value is given by

$$\text{Mean value} = \frac{\text{sum of the mid-ordinates}}{\text{number of mid-ordinates}}$$

$$= \frac{3.8636}{6} = 0.6439$$

If the sinewave is that of a voltage of peak value V_m, then each mid-ordinate in Table 8.1 must be multiplied by V_m. Thus the mid-ordinate for 15° is 0.2588 V_m, etc. Hence we may say that, based on the 6-ordinate calculation, that the average value of a sinusoidal voltage waveform is 0.6439 V_m. If the number of mid-ordinates is increased to twelve, we find that the average value is 0.6384 V_m. If an infinite number of mid-ordinates is used, then the mean value is found to be

Table 9.1 Mean value of a sine wave of peak value 1.0

Angle θ	$\sin \theta$
15°	0.2588
45°	0.7071
75°	0.9659
105°	0.9659
135°	0.7071
165°	0.2588
	Sum=3.8636

0.637 V_m. In the case of a sine wave, it is evident that twelve ordinates gives a reasonably accurate answer.

Average value by integration

If the equation of the curve can be written down as a function of time f(t) then for a voltage wave the average value is obtained as follows

$$\text{Average value } V_{av} = \frac{\text{area under the curve (i.e. over } T/2)}{\text{time period for one half-cycle } (T/2)}$$

$$= \frac{1}{T/2} \int_0^{T/2} f(t) \cdot dt \qquad (9.6)$$

Alternatively, if the equation for the voltage is given in terms of angle θ, i.e. f(θ), then

$$V_{av} = \frac{\text{area of curve in one half-cycle (i.e. over } \pi \text{ rad)}}{\text{angle corresponding to one half-cycle } (\pi \text{ rad})}$$

$$= \frac{1}{\pi} \int_0^{\pi} f(\theta) \cdot d\theta \qquad (9.7)$$

Average value of a sine wave using the calculus

If the equation to the curve is expressed in terms of the angular displacement θ, then $v = V_m \sin \theta$. Applying eqn. (9.7)

$$V_{av} = \frac{1}{\pi} \int_0^{\pi} V_m \sin \theta \cdot d\theta = \frac{1}{\pi} \left[-V_m \cos \theta \right]_0^{\pi}$$

$$= -\frac{V_m}{\pi} [\cos \pi - \cos 0] = -\frac{V_m}{\pi} [-1 - (+1)]$$

$$V_{av} = \frac{2V_m}{\pi} = 0.637 V_m \qquad (9.8)$$

The above value should be compared with 0.638 V_m obtained by the twelve-ordinate method. Applying the above method to a sinusoidal current waveform (whose equation is $i = I_m \sin \theta$) gives an average value of

$$I_{av} = 0.637 I_m \qquad (9.9)$$

The average value of a square wave

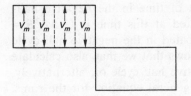

Fig. 9.9 The mean value of a square wave

For simplicity, the mid-ordinate method is applied in this case. As shown in figure 9.9, the value of each mid-ordinate for the wave is equal to the peak value. Using four mid-ordinates, the average value of the wave is

$$V_{av} = \frac{V_m + V_m + V_m + V_m}{4} = V_m$$

Since each mid-ordinate is equal to V_m, then even if we took one thousand mid-ordinates, the average value would remain equal to V_m.

9.6 The Effective Value or Root Mean Square (r.m.s.) Value of an Alternating Waveform

Whenever current flows in a resistor, power is dissipated (lost) in it. This applies both in the positive and negative half-cycles. Since we are concerned in electrical engineering with the efficient use of electrical power, we define the effective value of either a current or a voltage in terms of the heat it generates in a resistance.

If the waveform in figure 9.8 is that of a current which flows through a resistor R, then the heating produced by current M_1 is $M_1^2 R$, the heating produced by M_2 is $M_2^2 R$, etc. The average heating effect in the resistor is

$$\frac{\text{Sum of } i^2 R}{\text{Number of samples}} = \frac{M_1^2 R + M_2^2 R + M_3^2 R + M_4^2 R + M_5^2 R + M_6^2 R}{6}$$

If I is the effective value of the current which gives rise to the same heating effect, then

$$I^2 R = \frac{M_1^2 + M_2^2 R + \cdots + M_6^2 R}{6}$$

that is the **effective value of the current** is

$$I = \sqrt{\left(\frac{M_1^2 + M_2^2 + \cdots + M_6^2}{6} \right)} \qquad (9.10)$$

Effective current = the square **root** of the **mean** of the sum of the **squares** of the current values

= **root mean square (r.m.s.)** value

In the above, we have determined the r.m.s. value of the positive half-cycle of the waveform. However, if the current is $-M$ amperes at some instant of time in the negative half-cycle, then the power dissipated at this time is $(-M)^2R = M^2R$; that is, the power dissipated in the negative half-cycle also has a positive sign. It follows that we may also calculate the r.m.s. value over the negative half-cycle or, alternatively, over the complete cycle. The general equation for the r.m.s. value of a waveform having n mid-ordinates is

$$\text{r.m.s. value} = \sqrt{\left(\frac{M_1^2 + M_2^2 + \cdots + M_n^2}{n}\right)}$$

where n is the number of mid-ordinates (taken over the complete cycle), and $M_1, M_2, \ldots, M_n$ are the mid-ordinate values.

R.m.s. value of a sine wave using the mid-ordinate rule

Let us divide the 360° of the sine wave into twelve equal parts of 30°. The first mid-ordinate occurs at 15°, the second at 45°, etc., and the final one at 345°. The values of the mid-ordinates for a current waveform of peak value I_m are listed in Table 9.2.

From the results of Table 9.2

R.m.s. value of current $I = \sqrt{(6I_m^2/12)} = I_m/\sqrt{2}$

i.e.

$$\boxed{\text{R.m.s. value of current} = 0.7071 I_m} \qquad (9.11)$$

Applying the above technique to a sinusoidal voltage waveform of peak value V_m yields

R.m.s. value of voltage $V = V_m/\sqrt{2} = 0.7071 V_m$ (9.12)

That is to say, a sinusoidal supply voltage of 250 V r.m.s. has a peak value of

$V_m = \sqrt{2} \times \text{r.m.s. value} = \sqrt{2} \times 240 = 353.4 \text{ V}$

and its peak-to-peak value is

Peak-to-peak value $= 2V_m = 706.8 \text{ V}$

Table 9.2 R.m.s. value of a sine-wave of peak value I_m

Angle	Mid-ordinate	(Mid-ord)^2
15°	$0.2588I_m$	$0.067I_m^2$
45°	$0.7071I_m$	$0.5I_m^2$
75°	$0.9659I_m$	$0.933I_m^2$
105°	$0.9659I_m$	$0.933I_m^2$
135°	$0.7071I_m$	$0.5I_m^2$
165°	$0.2588I_m$	$0.067I_m^2$
195°	$-0.2588I_m$	$0.067I_m^2$
225°	$-0.7071I_m$	$0.5I_m^2$
255°	$-0.9659I_m$	$0.933I_m^2$
285°	$-0.9659I_m$	$0.933I_m^2$
315°	$-0.7071I_m$	$0.5I_m^2$
345°	$-0.2588I_m$	$0.067I_m^2$

Sum of (mid-ordinates)$^2 = 6I_m^2$

At this point the reader is reminded about the symbols used in this chapter as follows:

i or v	instantaneous value
I_m or V_m	peak (maximum) value
I_{av} or V_{av}	average (mean) value
I or V	r.m.s. value

R.m.s. value of a square wave using the mid-ordinate rule

With reference to figure 9.9, for the square wave, each mid-ordinate of the voltage waveform has the value V_m. For a square wave having four mid-ordinates in each half-cycle, then

R.m.s. value =

$$\sqrt{\left(\frac{V_m^2 + V_m^2 + V_m^2 + V_m^2 + (-V_m)^2 + (-V_m)^2 + (-V_m)^2 + (-V_m)^2}{8}\right)}$$

$$= V_m$$

In the case of the square wave, the result would remain the same even if one thousand mid-ordinates were used in each half-cycle.

9.7 Form Factor and Peak Factor of an Alternating Waveform

The **form factor** and the **peak factor** give the relationship between the peak value, the r.m.s. value and the mean value of an alternating waveform as follows.

$$\text{Form factor} = \frac{\text{r.m.s. value}}{\text{mean value}} \qquad (9.13)$$

$$\text{Peak factor} = \frac{\text{peak value}}{\text{r.m.s. value}} \qquad (9.14)$$

The peak factor is also known as the **crest factor**. The above factors give some information about the shape of the wave. For example, although widely differing waveshapes may have, for example, the same value of peak factor, they will not simultaneously have the same value of form factor *and* peak factor, because if it were the case, then the waveshapes would be identical. We may therefore use the form factor and the peak factor as a form of "fingerprint" which describes the shape of the wave.

Form factor and peak factor of a sine wave

In this case

R.m.s. voltage $V = V_m/\sqrt{2}$

Mean value $V_{av} = 2V_m/\pi$

hence

$$\text{Form factor} = \frac{V}{V_{av}} = \frac{V_m/\sqrt{2}}{2V_m/\pi} = \frac{\pi}{2\sqrt{2}} = 1.11 \qquad (9.15)$$

and

$$\text{Peak factor} = \frac{V_m}{V} = \frac{V_m}{V_m/\sqrt{2}} = \sqrt{2} = 1.414$$

Form factor and peak factor of a square wave

In this case

R.m.s. value $= V_m$ and   Mean value $= V_m$

hence

Form factor $= V/V_{av} = V_m/V_m = 1.0$

Peak factor $= V_m/V = V_m/V_m = 1.0$

EXAMPLE 9.4

The six equi-distant mid-ordinates of the positive half-cycle of a voltage waveform are given below. Estimate for the waveform, a) its mean value, b) its r.m.s. value, c) its form factor, and d) its peak factor.

Number of mid-ordinate	1	2	3	4	5	6
Voltage (V)	2	2	2	2	4	4

Solution

a) Mean value $V_{av} = \dfrac{2+2+2+2+4+4}{6} = 2.667\ \text{V}$ (*Ans.*)

b) R.m.s. value $V = \sqrt{\left(\dfrac{2^2+2^2+2^2+2^2+4^2+4^2}{6}\right)} = 2.828\ \text{V}$ (*Ans.*)

c) Form factor $= V/V_{av} = 2.828/2.667 = 1.06$ (*Ans.*)

d) Peak factor $= V_m/V = 4/2.828 = 1.414$ (*Ans.*)

9.8 Fundamental Frequency and Harmonics

Electronic music synthesizers (synthesis means "putting together") can produce music by utilizing a number of sine waves which have been added together to form complex waves. It is therefore possible to synthesize a complex waveform to simulate the sound of, say, an acoustic guitar or a flute, simply by adding together a variety of sine waves. The resulting waveform depends not only on the magnitude of the waveforms added together, but also on their frequency and on their relative "position" in time with respect to one another (this is described later in terms of the "phase angle" between the waves—see section 9.10).

Let us consider the addition of the two waves in figure 9.10 *a*) and *b*). The waveform in *a*) has the lowest frequency of the two waves ($f = 1/T$) and is known as the **fundamental frequency**. Waveform *b*) has a frequency three times greater than the fundamental frequency, and is known as a **third harmonic frequency**. The result of adding waveforms *a*) and *b*) together gives the **complex waveform** in *c*).

The shape of waveform *c*) depends on a number of factors including i) the amplitude of the two waveforms and ii) the relative "time" or "angle" relationship between the waves. It is a useful exercise to verify this by

1) doubling the amplitude of the third harmonic and adding it to waveform *a*), and
2) leaving the magnitude of the third harmonic unchanged, but "shifting" waveform *b*) so that it passes through zero at point X (see figure 9.10*b*), and then adding it to the fundamental waveform.

Remember that one cycle is measured between two points, which not only have the same value but also at which the waveform is changing in the same direction. Thus one cycle of the waveform in figure 9.10*a* occurs between, for example, P and Q, whilst one cycle of the waveform in figure 9.10*b* occurs between, say, R and S.

It can be shown that every cyclic complex wave (that is a complex wave which repeats itself periodically) can be built up from a fundamental frequency and a number of harmonic frequencies. A **harmonic frequency** is one whose frequency is an integral [whole number] multiple of the fundamental frequency. If the fundamental frequency is f_1, then

fundamental frequency = f_1 Hz

second harmonic frequency = $2f_1$ Hz

third harmonic frequency = $3f_1$ Hz

fourth harmonic frequency = $4f_1$ Hz

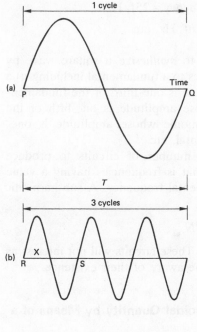

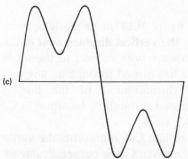

Fig. 9.10 Waveform (*c*) is synthesized from a fundamental frequency (*a*) and a third harmonic (*b*)

etc. and

twenty-fifth harmonic frequency $= 25f_1$ Hz

nth harmonic frequency $= nf_1$ Hz, etc.

It is, for instance, possible to *synthesize* a square wave by adding a number of harmonics to a fundamental including *a*) a 3rd harmonic whose amplitude is one-third of the fundamental, *b*) a 5th harmonic whose amplitude is one-fifth of the fundamental, *c*) a 7th harmonic whose amplitude is one-seventh that of the fundamental, etc.

It is also possible for a number of circuits to produce **sub-harmonic frequencies**, that is frequencies having a value less than that of the fundamental frequency. A sub-harmonic frequency has the value of

Fundamental frequency/N

where N is a whole number. These circuits will not interest us further, but it is as well to be aware of their existence.

9.9 Representing a Sinusoidal Quantity by Means of a Phasor

If we rotate the line OX in figure 9.11 in an anticlockwise direction at a speed of ω rad/s, the **vertical displacement** of the tip of the line traces out a sinewave with respect to the angle of displacement. When the line has turned through an angle θ_1 (position OX$_1$) the vertical displacement of the line is $(V_m \sin \theta_1)$, and when it has turned through θ_2 (position OX$_2$) the vertical displacement is $(V_m \sin \theta_2)$.

If the vertical displacement of line OX represents the variation of a voltage waveform, then when OX is perpendicular we see that OX $= V_m$.

However, it is usual to represent a sinusoidally varying quantity by a line described as a **phasor**, the length of the phasor representing the r.m.s. value of the sinewave. In the case of figure 9.11, the phasor is represented by the line on the right-hand side of the diagram whose length is V, where V is scaled to represent the r.m.s. value of the voltage. The angle of the phasor with respect to the horizontal represents the angle of rotation of the line OX (see figure 9.11) *at the instant when* $t = 0$ (in this case, it corresponds to $\theta = 0$).

Applying the above principle to the waveforms in figure 9.12*a*, we see that the peak values of waveforms v_1, v_2 and v_3 are V_{m1}, V_{m2} and V_{m3}, respectively. Note that the length of each phasor in figure 9.12*b* is drawn to represent the r.m.s. value of the respective waveform. Thus V_1 represents the

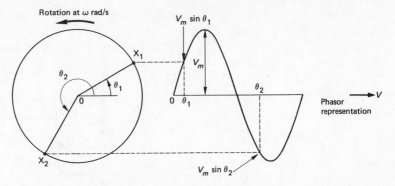

Fig. 9.11 Representation of a sinusoidal waveform by means of a rotating line

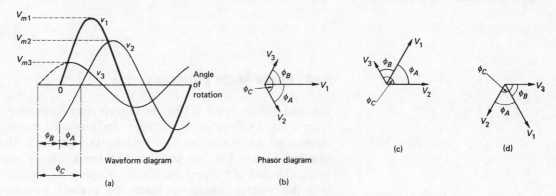

Fig. 9.12 The waveforms in (a) are represented by phasor diagram (b). Phasor diagrams (c) and (d) are alternative methods of representation (see page 170)

r.m.s. value of v_1 (that is, its length is $V_1 = 0.7071\,V_{m1}$), V_2 represents the r.m.s. value of v_2, and V_3 represents the r.m.s. value of v_3.

The **phase angle** of each phasor corresponds to the "starting" angle of the line which causes the sinewave to be traced out (refer once more to figure 9.12). Thus V_3 is shown at angle ϕ_B in an anticlockwise direction from V_1, and V_2 is at angle ϕ_A in a clockwise direction from V_1.

When discussing phasors, it is normal to describe the horizontal direction as the **reference direction**. In figure 9.12b, phasor V_1 is described as the **reference phasor** since it points in the horizontal direction. We will return to figure 9.12 in section 9.10 when diagrams c) and d) are discussed.

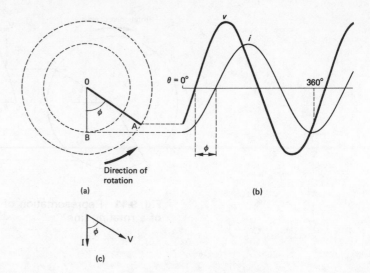

Fig. 9.13 Phase angle difference

9.10 Phase Angle Difference

OA and OB in figure 9.13a are two rotating lines whose tips trace out the sinewaves of voltage v and current i respectively in diagram b). Since line OA rotates through the horizontal axis before line OB, we say that OA **leads** OB by angle ϕ. Since OA and OB represent v and i, respectively, we also say that **the voltage waveform leads the current waveform by angle ϕ**. Angle ϕ is known as the **phase angle difference**, or simply as the **phase angle** between the waveforms.

The phasors in figure 9.13c are drawn to represent r.m.s. values of voltage and current. From the phasor diagram, note that V leads I by angle ϕ.

Alternatively, since OB passes through the horizontal after OA has passed through it, then we may say that I **lags behind** V by angle ϕ.

Applying the above description of "lag" and "lead" to the phasor diagram in figure 9.12b, we see that

1 V_1 leads V_2 by ϕ_A

2 V_1 lags behind V_3 by ϕ_B

3 V_3 leads V_2 by ϕ_C

4 V_2 lags behind V_3 by ϕ_C

Descriptions 1 to 4 above also fit the phasor diagrams in figures 9.12c and d, since the latter phasors correspond to the phasors in figure 9.12a, but with phasor V_2 and phasor V_3, respectively, being on the reference axis.

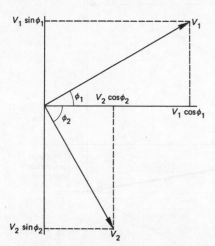

Fig. 9.14 Resolving phasors into horizontal and vertical (quadrature) components

9.11 Addition of Phasors

In alternating current circuits, quantities such as e.m.f.s or voltages which are connected in series with one another may not be in phase with one another. For example, the voltage phasors illustrated in figure 9.12 may be generated by separate generators, and in this section we deal with a method of determining the resultant voltage when the voltages are connected in series with one another. To determine the resultant of a number of voltages which are out of phase with one another, we must *add the voltage phasors together*; if we merely add the magnitude of the voltages, we get the wrong result.

The phasors can be added graphically or mathematically. Graphical methods are, at best, approximate; great care should be taken to draw each phasor to scale (always use the largest possible diagram, as this ensures a more accurate result). The general procedure for addition of phasors is outlined below.

When adding phasors it is first necessary to resolve the phasors into their horizontal and vertical components (see figure 9.14). The horizontal component is often described as the "real" component, and the vertical component as the "imaginary" or "quadrature" component. The terms "real" and "imaginary" come from a historical background, and the vertical component is no more "imaginary" than the component in the horizontal direction.

The horizontal component of phasor V_1 is ($V_1 \cos \phi_1$), and of phasor V_2 is ($V_2 \cos \phi_2$).

The vertical component of V_1 is ($V_1 \sin \phi_1$), and of V_2 is ($V_2 \sin \phi_2$).

For example, if $V_1 = 10$ V and $\phi_1 = 30°$, then

Horizontal component of V_1 is

$V_1 \cos \phi_1 = 10 \cos 30° = 8.66$ V

Vertical component of V_1 is

$V_1 \sin 30° = 10 \sin 30° = 5$ V

If $V_2 = 8$ V and $\phi_2 = -60°$, then

Horizontal component of V_2 is

$V_2 \cos \phi_2 = 8 \cos (-60°) = 4$ V

Vertical component of V_2 is

$V_2 \sin \phi_2 = 8 \sin (-60°) = -6.93$ V

The phasors V_1 and V_2 in figure 9.14 are added together as shown in figure 9.15. The resultant voltage V has a horizontal component of

$$V \cos \phi = V_1 \cos \phi_1 + V_2 \cos \phi_2$$

$$= 8.66 + 4 = 12.66 \text{ V}$$

Fig. 9.15 Addition of two phasors

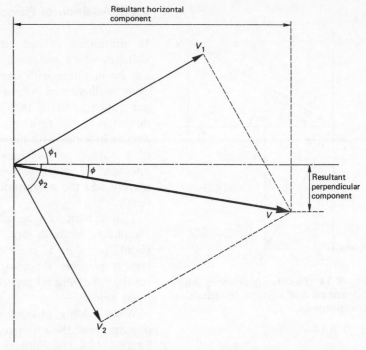

where ϕ is the phase angle with respect to the reference axis of the resultant voltage V. The vertical component of V is

$$V \sin \phi = V_1 \sin \phi_1 + V_2 \sin \phi_2$$

$$= 5 + (-6.93) = -1.93 \, \text{V}$$

The **magnitude** or **modulus** of the **resultant voltage** V is

$$V = \sqrt{[(\text{horizontal component})^2 + (\text{vertical component})^2]}$$

$$= \sqrt{[12.66^2 + (-1.93)^2]} = 12.81 \, \text{V}$$

The **phase angle** or **argument** ϕ of the resultant voltage can be calculated from

$$\tan \phi = \frac{\text{vertical component}}{\text{horizontal component}}$$

$$= \frac{-1.93}{12.66} = -0.1524$$

ϕ = angle whose tangent is $(-0.1524) = \tan^{-1}(-0.1524)$
$$= -8.67° \text{ (or } -0.151 \, \text{rad)}$$

Fig. 9.16 Subtraction of phasors

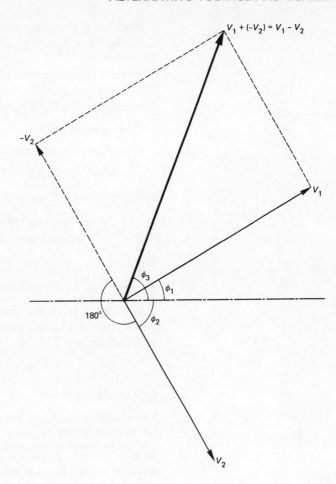

9.12 Subtraction of Phasors

To subtract one phasor from another, we must *add the "negative" value of the phasor to be subtracted.* Thus

$$V_1 - V_2 = V_1 + (-V_2)$$

This is illustrated in figure 9.16. Here the phasor V_2 is reversed to give $-V_2$; this phasor is added to phasor V_1 to give the phasor difference $(V_1 - V_2)$.

If $V_1 = 10\,\text{V}$ and $\phi_1 = 30°$, and $V_2 = 8\,\text{V}$ and $\phi_2 = -60°$, then from the above values the horizontal component of V_1 is $8.66\,\text{V}$ and the vertical component of V_1 is $5\,\text{V}$. Also, the horizontal component of V_2 is $4\,\text{V}$ and its vertical component is $-6.93\,\text{V}$. Hence

Horizontal component of $(-V_2) = -4\,\text{V}$
Vertical component of $(-V_2) = -(-6.93) = 6.93\,\text{V}$
Therefore
Horizontal component of $(V_1 - V_2) = 8.66 + (-4) = 4.66\,\text{V}$
Vertical component of $(V_1 - V_2) = 5 + 6.93 = 11.93\,\text{V}$
The magnitude of the resultant voltage is given by

Magnitude of $(V_1 - V_2)$

$= \sqrt{[(\text{horizontal component})^2 + (\text{vertical component})^2]}$

$= \sqrt{[4.66^2 + 11.93^2]} = 12.81\,\text{V}$

and

$$\tan \phi_3 = \frac{\text{vertical component}}{\text{horizontal component}} = \frac{11.93}{4.66} = 2.56$$

or

$$\phi_3 = \tan^{-1} 2.56 = 68.66° \quad (\text{or } 1.198\,\text{rad})$$

It is an interesting exercise to verify, using the values for V_1 and V_2 above, that the modulus of $(V_2 - V_1)$ is 12.81 V and its phase angle is $-111.34°$.

EXAMPLE 9.5

Two sources of e.m.f., V_1 and V_2, are connected in series, the sum of the two voltages being V_T.

 a) If V_1 has a r.m.s. value of 220 V, and V_2 is 180 V r.m.s. and leads V_1 by 25°, determine the magnitude and phase angle of V_T (take V_1 as the reference voltage).

 b) If V_T is the reference voltage and has an r.m.s. value of 28 V, and if V_1 is 20 V r.m.s. and leads V_T by 30°, determine the r.m.s. value of V_2 and also its phase angle with respect to V_T.

Solution Both sections of the problem can be solved either graphically or by calculation. Both methods of solution are illustrated here.

a) GRAPHICAL SOLUTION

Phasors V_1 and V_2 are drawn to scale in figure 9.17a, phasor V_1 being drawn in the horizontal (reference) direction. The magnitude and phase angle of V_T can be measured from the scale diagram and is approximately

$V_T = 390.7\,\text{V} \qquad \phi = 11.5° \text{ (leading } V_1) \quad (Ans.)$

Remember that the results using any graphical method are, at best, approximate, and considerable care should be taken in constructing the scale drawing if accurate results are to be obtained.

MATHEMATICAL SOLUTION

Since $V_1 = 220\,\text{V}$ and $\phi_1 = 0°$, then
Horizontal component of $V_1 = V_1 \cos \phi_1 = 220 \cos 0° = 220\,\text{V}$
Vertical component of $V_1 = V_1 \sin \phi_1 = 220 \sin 0° = 0\,\text{V}$

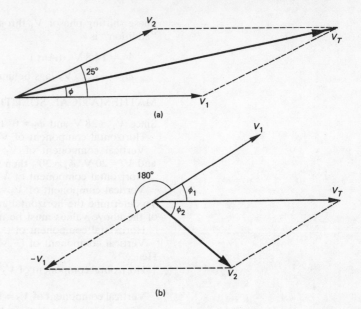

Fig. 9.17

and $V_2 = 180$ V, $\phi_2 = 25°$, hence

Horizontal component of $V_2 = V_2 \cos \phi_2 = 180 \cos 25° = 163.14$ V

Vertical component of $V_2 = V_2 \sin \phi_2 = 180 \sin 25° = 76.07$ V

Since V_T is the phasor sum of V_1 and V_2, then

Horizontal component of $V_T = V_1 \cos \phi_1 + V_2 \cos \phi_2$

$$= 220 + 163.14 = 383.14 \text{ V}$$

Vertical component of $V_T = V_1 \sin \phi_1 + V_2 \sin \phi_2$

$$= 0 + 76.07 = 76.07 \text{ V}$$

Hence

Magnitude of $V_T = \sqrt{(383.14^2 + 76.07^2)} = 390.62$ V   (*Ans.*)

and

$$\tan \phi = \frac{\text{vertical component of } V_T}{\text{horizontal component of } V_T} = \frac{76.07}{383.14} = 0.1985$$

therefore

$$\phi = \tan^{-1} 0.1985 = 11.23° \ (V_T \text{ leading } V_1 \text{ by } \phi) \quad (Ans.)$$

b) GRAPHICAL SOLUTION

Referring to figure 9.17*b*

Phasor V_T = phasor V_1 + phasor V_2

hence

Phasor V_2 = phasor V_T – phasor V_1

$$= \text{phasor } V_T + (-\text{phasor } V_1)$$

In figure 9.17*b*, the phasor corresponding to $(-V_1)$ is obtained by phase shifting phasor V_1 through 180°. The graphical solution to the "addition" is

$V_2 = 14.8$ V   (*Ans.*)

$\phi_2 = -42°$ (V_2 lags behind V_T by 42°)   (*Ans.*)

MATHEMATICAL SOLUTION

Since $V_T = 28$ V and $\phi_T = 0°$ (V_T is the reference voltage), then
  Horizontal component of $V_T = V_T \cos \phi_T = 28 \cos 0° = 28$ V
  Vertical component of $V_T = V_T \sin \phi_T = 28 \sin 0° = 0$ V
and $V_1 = 20$ V, $\phi_1 = 30°$, then
  Horizontal component of $V_1 = V_1 \cos \phi_1 = 20 \cos 30° = 17.32$ V
  Vertical component of $V_1 = V_1 \sin \phi_1 = 20 \sin 30° = 10$ V
To determine the horizontal and vertical components of $(-V_1)$, both of the above values must be multiplied by (-1), to give
  Horizontal component of $(-V_1) = -17.32$ V
  Vertical component of $(-V_1) = -10$ V
Hence
  Horizontal component of $V_2 = V_T \cos \phi_T + (-V_1 \cos \phi_1)$
    $= 28 + (-17.32) = 10.68$ V
  Vertical component of $V_2 = V_T \sin \phi_T + (-V_1 \sin \phi_1)$
    $= 0 + (-10) = -10$ V
From the above results we deduce that

Magnitude of $V_2 = \sqrt{(10.68^2 + [-10]^2)} = 14.63$ V   (*Ans.*)

and

$\tan \phi_2 = $ vertical component/horizontal component

$= -10/10.68 = -0.9363$

$\phi_2 = \tan^{-1}(-0.9363)$

$= -43.12°$ (V_2 lags behind V_T by ϕ_2)   (*Ans.*)

9.13 Three-phase Systems

A **balanced three-phase supply system** is one which has three sets of voltages, each voltage being phase displaced from the other two voltages by 120°. Moreover, each voltage has the same magnitude.

Advantages of the three-phase system over three separate single-phase systems to supply the same amount of electrical power include

1 The resulting alternator is smaller.
2 The cables used to supply the current require a smaller volume of conductor material (i.e. less copper or aluminium is required).
3 The motors are smaller and they produce a more uniform torque.

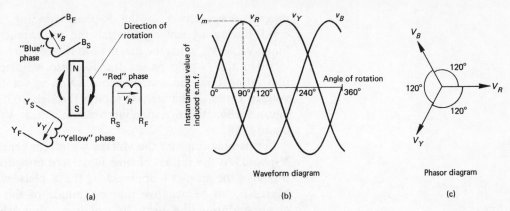

Fig. 9.18 Generating a three-phase supply

Although our discussions are restricted to three-phase systems, there are a number of reasons why some installations use six-, twelve- and even twenty four-phase systems. The general name used to describe multiphase systems (including three-phase) is **poly-phase systems**.

During the discussion on the simple a.c. generator, it was stated that in a single-phase generator the coil could be stationary whilst the magnetic field is rotated inside the coil. This arrangement has a number of advantages, and is the most common method of generating an alternating supply; a rudimentary three-phase alternator using this principle is shown in figure 9.18a. The generator has three independent windings fixed to its frame (which is known as the **stator** of the machine); the three windings are known respectively as the **red phase** (R-phase), the **yellow phase** (Y-phase), and the **blue phase** (B-phase). Each winding has a "start" point and a "finish" point. The start of the red phase is designated R_S in figure 9.18a and its finish as R_F. The start and finish of the yellow phase are Y_S and Y_F, respectively; similarly for blue. Note that in this case the windings are physically displaced from one another by 120°.

The rotating part of the machine (which carries the field system) is known as the **rotor**. In the following we will assume that when a N-pole of the rotor magnet approaches a winding, the voltage induced in the winding has a positive potential; when a S-pole approaches the same winding, a negative voltage is induced in it.

Under the conditions shown in figure 9.18a, the red phase winding is at right angles to the magnet; hence the instantaneous e.m.f. induced in the red phase is zero (in figure 9.18b this point is shown as 0° on the angle of rotation axis). As the magnet rotates in a clockwise directions, so the N-pole of the magnet draws closer to the R-phase winding, inducing an e.m.f. having a positive potential; the e.m.f. reaches its maximum value V_m when the magnet has rotated through 90° (that is when the N-pole passes the R-phase winding). A graph illustrating how the instantaneous value v_R of the R-phase voltage varies as the magnet rotates through 360° is shown in figure 9.18b; the corresponding voltage phasor V_R appears in figure 9.18c.

Let us now consider the voltage waveform generated in the Y-phase. At the instant of time illustrated in figure 9.18a, the S-pole of the magnet is approaching the Y-phase winding. This causes v_Y to be negative, the magnitude of this voltage increasing during the next 30° rotation, after which time it reaches its peak negative value (when the S-pole is in line with the Y-phase winding). It is an interesting exercise to verify the shape of the remainder of the waveform for v_Y. Using the notation developed earlier, we see that phasor V_Y (figure 9.18c) lags behind V_R by 120° or, alternatively, it leads V_R by 240°. By a similar argument it can be shown that phasor V_B leads V_R by 120° (see figure 9.18c) or, alternatively, it lags behind V_R by 240°.

9.14 Star-connected Three-phase Systems

If the three start points of the windings in figure 9.18a are connected together, the result is known as the **star connection** (see figure 9.19a). The common connecting point S is known as the **star point** or the **neutral point** of the system; the expression "neutral point" arises from the fact that, in a power supply system, this point is often connected to earth potential so that it is electrically "neutral".

Referring to figure 9.18, we see that the r.m.s. voltage induced in the R-phase is V_R and the associated current in that phase is I_R. Similarly, V_Y and I_Y are associated with the Y-phase, and V_B and I_B with the B-phase. The magnitude of the individual voltage induced in each phase is known as the **phase voltage** V_P and the individual current in each phase is known as the **phase current** I_P. In a *balanced three-phase system*, each voltage has the same value, that is

$$V_P = \text{magnitude of } V_R = \text{magnitude of } V_Y$$
$$= \text{magnitude of } V_B$$

The phasor diagram for the voltages of the star-connected system is shown in figure 9.19b. Since the start points of the windings are connected together, the potential difference V_{RY} between the finish points of the R and Y phases is determined from

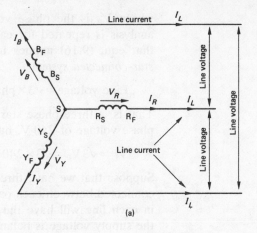

(a)

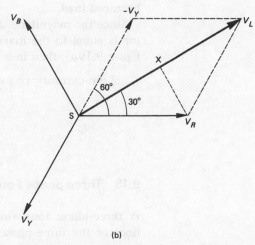

(b)

Fig. 9.19 (*a*) Star connection of three-phase windings, (*b*) phasor diagram of the voltages for a balanced system

$$V_{RY} = \text{phasor } V_R - \text{phasor } V_Y$$
$$= \text{phasor } V_R + (-\text{phasor } V_Y)$$

This subtraction is performed in figure 9.19*b*. The magnitude of the resulting voltage is known as the **line-to-line voltage** (or simply as the **line voltage**) V_L of the system and is calculated as follows.

$$\text{Magnitude of } V_L = 2 \times SX \qquad \text{(see figure 9.19}b\text{)}$$
$$= 2 \times V_R \cos 30° = 2 \times V_P \cos 30°$$
$$= 2 \times V_P \times \frac{\sqrt{3}}{2}$$
$$= \sqrt{3} V_P \qquad\qquad (9.16)$$

where V_P is the phase voltage of the system. If the above analysis is repeated for each pair of phase voltages, we find that eqn. (9.16) applies to each line voltage. That is, in a *star-connected system*

Line voltage $= \sqrt{3} \times$ phase voltage

That is, a three-phase star-connected supply system having a phase voltage of 240 V, has a line voltage of

$$V_L = \sqrt{3} V_P = \sqrt{3} \times 240 = 415.7 \text{ V}$$

Suppose that we have three resistors of equal value; if one is connected between each pair of lines, then the current flowing in each line will have the same numerical value (remember, the supply voltage is balanced). Such a load is described as a **balanced load**.

Since the magnitude of the current leaving the phase winding is equal to the magnitude of the current in the line (see figure 9.19*a*), then in a star-connected system

Line current $=$ phase current

or

$$I_L = I_P \tag{9.17}$$

9.15 Three-phase Four-wire System

A **three-phase four-wire supply** comprises the R, Y and B lines of the three-phase system together with a fourth wire known as the **neutral wire** (see figure 9.20).

Using this system, three separate loads (or groups of loads) can be supplied, each being supplied by one phase of the generator. A typical application of this type of supply is to a housing estate. For example, a number of houses in one street would obtain electricity from one phase of the supply (say the red-to-neutral phase), whilst a second group of houses would be supplied from another phase of the supply (say the yellow-to-neutral), and a third group of houses would be supplied from the remaining phase (the blue-to-neutral phase).

The supply voltage depends on the standard adopted by the supply authority. For example, the phase voltage for the domestic supply in the United Kingdom is 240 V, 50 Hz (corresponding to a three-phase line voltage of 415.7 V), and in the United States of America is 120 V, 60 Hz (corresponding to a three-phase line voltage of 207.8 V).

It is difficult to guarantee that each group of loads connected to a three-phase four-wire system consumes the same power, so that, in general, the current in any one line has a value

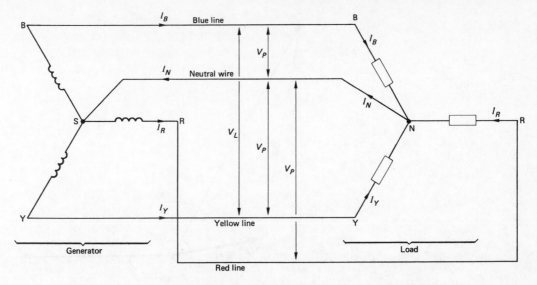

Fig. 9.20 A three-phase four-wire supply system

which differs from that in another line. The equation relating the line currents and the neutral wire current is obtained by applying Kirchhoff's first law to the **neutral point** N of the load (or, for that matter, to the star point S of the generator) as follows:

$$\textbf{Phasor sum of } (I_R + I_Y + I_B) = I_N \tag{9.18}$$

Note the emphasis on the phasor sum in the above expression; the reason is that, in the general case, the three line currents are at some phase angle to one another. An application of eqn. (9.18) is considered below.

EXAMPLE 9.6

The line currents in a three-phase four-wire system are as follows:

$I_R = 10$ A on the reference axis

$I_Y = 15$ A lagging I_R by 120°

$I_B = 16$ A leading I_R by 120°

Determine the magnitude of I_N and also its phase angle with respect to I_R.

Solution The solution can be obtained either graphically or mathematically. Both methods are used here.

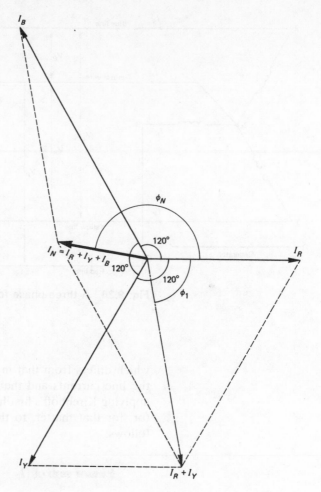

Fig. 9.21

GRAPHICAL SOLUTION

It is first necessary to draw the three current phasors I_R, I_Y and I_B to scale (see figure 9.21). Next, any two of the phasors are added together; in figure 9.21 the phasors I_R and I_Y are added to give the phasor $(I_R + I_Y)$ which lags behind I_R by ϕ_1. Phasor I_B is then added to this phasor to give the neutral current phasor I_N. The estimated solution is

$$I_N = 5.5 \text{ A leading } I_R \text{ by } 171.5° \ (\phi_N) \quad (Ans.)$$

The value of ϕ_N could, alternatively, be specified as 51.5° leading with respect to I_B, or 68.5° lagging with respect to I_Y.

It is a useful exercise to repeat the above procedure, but first add together, say, I_Y and I_B, after which I_R should be added to the resultant. The outcome should be the same (or very close to) the above result.

MATHEMATICAL SOLUTION

The horizontal and vertical components of the three line currents are determined as follows.

For I_R
  Horizontal component $= I_R \cos \phi_R = 10 \cos 0° = 10$ A
  Vertical component $= I_R \sin \phi_R = 10 \sin 0° = 0$ A
For I_Y
  Horizontal component $= I_Y \cos \phi_Y = 15 \cos (-120°) = -7.5$ A
  Vertical component $= I_Y \sin \phi_Y = 15 \sin (-120°) = -13.0$ A
For I_B
  Horizontal component $= I_B \cos \phi_B = 16 \cos 120° = -8.0$ A
  Vertical component $= I_B \sin \phi_B = 16 \sin 120° = 13.86$ A

The horizontal and vertical components of I_N are evaluated as follows.

Horizontal component $=$ sum of horizontal comps. of I_R, I_Y and I_B

$$= I_R \cos \phi_R + I_Y \cos \phi_Y + I_B \cos \phi_B$$

$$= 10 + (-7.5) + (-8) = -5.5 \text{ A}$$

Vertical component $=$ sum of vertical components of I_R, I_Y and I_B

$$= I_R \sin \phi_R + I_Y \sin \phi_Y + I_B \sin \phi_B$$

$$= 0 + (-13) + 13.86 = 0.86 \text{ A}$$

hence

Magnitude of $I_N = \sqrt{[(\text{horizontal comp.})^2 + (\text{vertical comp.})^2]}$

$$= \sqrt{[(-5.5)^2 + 0.86^2]} = 5.57 \text{ A} \quad (Ans.)$$

and

$$\tan \phi_N = \frac{\text{vertical component}}{\text{horizontal component}} = \frac{0.86}{-5.5} = -0.1564$$

CAUTION is advised when using an electronic calculator to determine the value of ϕ_N from the above values, since there is a trap for the unwary. The calculator will provide the principal angle, that is it gives the angle which satisfies the relationship

$$\phi_N = \tan^{-1}(-0.1564)$$

which lies in the range $\pm 90°$ (i.e. an angle which lies either in the first or fourth quadrants). Clearly, when we look at the mathematical signs of the horizontal and vertical components of I_N (or look at the phasor diagram), I_N lies in the second quadrant. Using an electronic calculator, the correct solution is obtained as follows.

$$\phi = \tan^{-1}(-0.1564) = -8.89°$$

hence

$$\phi_N = 180° + \phi = 180° + (-8.89°) = 171.11° \quad (Ans.)$$

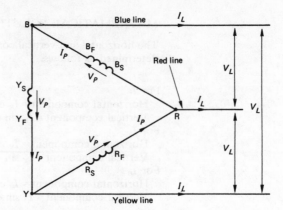

Fig. 9.22 A delta connected or mesh connected supply system (balanced load assumed)

9.16 Delta Connection or Mesh Connection

In the **delta connection** or **mesh connection**, the three windings of the generator in figure 9.18a are connected so that the finish of one winding is connected to the start of the next winding in the manner shown in figure 9.22.

Since the voltage V_P developed in each winding of the generator is connected between a pair of lines, then in a delta-connected system

Line voltage V_L = phase voltage V_P (9.19)

It can also be shown that with a balanced load

Line current $I_L = \sqrt{3} \times$ phase current I_P (9.20)

EXAMPLE 9.7

If the line current drawn by a balanced load from a mesh-connected generator is 173.2 A, determine the current in each phase of the load.

Solution $I_L = 173.2$ A

From eqn. (9.20)

Phase current $I_P = I_L/\sqrt{3} = 173.2/\sqrt{3} = 100$ A   (*Ans.*)

9.17 Summary of the Current and Voltage Relationships in Star-connected and Delta-connected Systems

The relationships in balanced star-connected and in delta-connected systems are summarized in Table 9.3.

Table 9.3

	Phase voltage	Phase current	Line voltage	Line current
Star connection	V_P	I_P	$V_L = \sqrt{3}V_P$	$I_L = I_P$
Delta connection	V_P	I_P	$V_L = V_P$	$I_L = \sqrt{3}I_P$

In an unbalanced three-phase four-wire star-connected system the neutral current is given by

$$I_N = \text{phasor sum of } (I_R + I_Y + I_B)$$

Exercises

9.1   Define an alternating current. Draw two sine waves which are displaced from one another by a) 90°, b) 180°, c) 270°.

9.2   A sinusoidal alternating voltage waveform has a peak value of 100 V. Determine the instantaneous voltage at the following angles in the waveform: 0°, 45°, 90°, 160°, 220°, 330°, 360°.

[0 V; 70.7 V; 100 V; 34.2 V; −64.3 V; −86.6 V; 0 V]

9.3   Determine the periodic time corresponding to the following frequencies: 50 Hz, 52 kHz, 6 MHz, 8 GHz.

[0.02 s; 19.23 μs; 0.1667 μs; 0.125 ns]

9.4   Calculate the frequency corresponding to the following periodic times: 2 ms, 5 μs, 10 ns, 5 ps.

[500 Hz; 200 kHz; 100 MHz; 200 GHz]

9.5   Determine the mean value, the r.m.s. value and the form factor of the following current waveform which changes linearly between the points given.

Current (A)	0	3.6	8.4	14	19.4	22.5	25	25.2
Angle (deg)	0	15	30	45	60	75	90	105

Current (A)	23	15.6	9.4	4.2	0
Angle (deg)	120	135	150	165	180

[14.2; 16.4; 1.155]

9.6   An alternating current waveform has a periodic time T. The instantaneous value of current between zero and $T/6$ is 50 A, its value between $T/6$ and $T/4$ is 20 A, and between $T/4$ and $T/2$ is zero. This waveshape is inverted between $T/2$ and T. Determine the r.m.s. value and the average value of the waveform.

[30 A; 20 A]

9.7   The following voltages are connected in series

$$v_1 = 100 \sin \theta \qquad v_2 = 50 \sin (\theta + 60°)$$

$$v_3 = 60 \sin (\theta - \tfrac{1}{4}\pi \text{ rad}) \qquad v_4 = 80 \sin (\theta + \tfrac{1}{2}\pi \text{ rad})$$

Express the resultant voltage in a similar form.

[$v = 188 \sin (\theta + 25°)$]

9.8 An alternating waveform has a peak value of 500 V. If the form factor of the waveform is 1.16 and the peak factor is 1.6, calculate the r.m.s. value and the mean value of the waveform.

[312.5 V; 269.4 V]

9.9 A circuit contains two parallel branches and draws a r.m.s. current of 50 A. If the current in one branch is given by

$$i_1 = 70.7 \sin (314.2t - \tfrac{1}{3}\pi \text{ rad}) \text{ A}$$

determine the expression for the current in the other branch. Calculate also the supply frequency.

[70.7 sin (314.2t + $\tfrac{1}{3}\pi$ rad); 50 Hz]

9.10 Two branches A and B are connected in parallel. The current drawn by circuit A is 12 A r.m.s. in the reference direction, and the current drawn by circuit B is 20 A lagging behind the current in branch A by 30°. Determine the magnitude of the current drawn by the parallel circuit, and also its phase angle with respect to the reference phasor.

[31 A; 18.8° lagging]

9.11 Three circuits X, Y and Z are connected in series to a 200 V a.c. supply. The voltage across circuit X is 100 V leading the supply voltage by 30°, and the voltage across circuit Y is 50 V lagging the supply voltage by 45°. Determine the magnitude and the phase angle associated with circuit Z.

[79.4 V; 10.6° lagging]

9.12 A balanced three-phase load takes a line current of 40 A at a line voltage of 11 kV. Determine the line and phase values of voltage and current if the load is a) star connected, b) delta connected.

[a $I_L = 40$ A, $I_P = 40$ A, $V_L = 11$ kV, $V_P = 6.35$ kV; b) $I_L =$ 40 A, $I_P = 23.1$ A, $V_L = 11$ kV, $V_P = 11$ kV]

9.13 If the phase voltage of a three-phase alternator is 250 V, determine the line voltage. If the connections to one of the phases are reversed, what will be the value of the line voltages?

[433 V; 433 V, 250 V, 250 V]

9.14 The three line currents taken by a 3-phase 4-wire load are as follows:

red line: 25.4 A in the reference direction.
yellow line: 16.93 A lagging I_R by 150°.
blue line: 25.4 A leading I_R by 150°.

Calculate the magnitude of the current in the neutral wire and also its phase angle with respect to I_R.

[12.03 A; 159.4° leading]

10 The Single-phase Transformer

10.1 What is the Function of a Transformer?

A **transformer** is an electro-magnetic device which "transforms" one alternating voltage level to another. Transformers are used both in power systems and in electronics. For example, in a power supply system, a transformer is used at the generating station to increase the value at which it is generated (say 25 kV) to the voltage at which it is transmitted by the overhead line system (say 275 kV). At the receiving end of the transmission system, the voltage is transformed "down" to a value at which it can be utilized by factories (say 33 kV or 11 kV) and homes (say 240 V or 100 V). In electronics, transformers are used to step the mains supply voltage down to one which is suitable for semiconductor devices (say 5 V or 15 V). Transformers are also used in t.v. receivers to develop the extra high tension (e.h.t.) supply in the range 6 kV to 25 kV required to supply some of the electrodes in the t.v. picture tube. In other electronic circuits, a transformer may be used to make a loudspeaker having a resistance of, say, 8 Ω "look" as though it has a much higher resistance.

In general it can be said that transformer windings carry only alternating current. There are, however, special cases in which one of the windings of the transformer must carry direct current as well as alternating current. Examples of this kind occur in a number of electronic amplifier circuits.

10.2 Transformer Operation

The transformer depends for its operation on the mutual inductance between two magnetically coupled coils. The supply voltage is connected to the **primary winding** of the transformer (see figure 10.1), and the load is connected to the

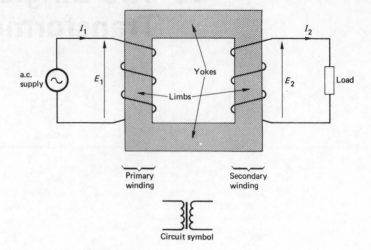

Fig. 10.1 A double-wound
transformer

secondary winding of the transformer. Some transformers have
more than one secondary winding; this occurs, for example,
where the transformer must provide a number of different
values of voltage.

The majority of **power transformers** (that is a transformer
which supplies more than about 1 W of power to the load)
have independent windings on an **iron circuit** which is common
to both windings (see figure 10.1). Such a transformer is said
to be **double-wound**. The magnetic circuit is made of iron to
provide an efficient flux path with very little magnetic leakage;
that is to say, the magnetic coupling coefficient between the
two windings is practically unity. The majority of this chapter
is devoted to this type of transformer.

Certain types of double-wound transformer have an air-
core; the magnetic coupling coefficient between the two windings in this case has a very low value. This type of transformer
is dealt with in more specialized texts.

When an alternating supply is connected to a transformer,
the current in the primary winding produces an alternating
magnetic flux in the iron circuit. The iron circuit comprises two
limbs which physically support the coils, and two **yokes** which
connect the limbs. The mutual magnetic flux which links the
windings induces an e.m.f. in the secondary winding; this
alternating e.m.f. causes current to flow in the load.

10.3 Basic Theory for an "Ideal" Transformer

In the following, it is assumed that we are dealing with an
"ideal" transformer. That is, a transformer in which all the flux

produced by one winding links with the other winding, and one in which all the windings are assumed to be resistanceless.

In chapter 6 it was shown that the e.m.f. induced in a coil of N turns is given by

Induced e.m.f. $= N \times$ rate of change of flux in the coil

or

$$e = N \, d\Phi/dt$$

hence

$$\frac{d\Phi}{dt} = \frac{e}{N}$$

The above relationship applies to both coils on the magnetic circuit (i.e. both the primary and the secondary windings), since the *same flux* cuts both coils. If the supply voltage is sinusoidal and has an r.m.s. value E_1, then the secondary voltage waveform is also sinusoidal and has an r.m.s. value E_2. It follows from the above relationship that

$$\frac{E_1}{N_1} = \frac{E_2}{N_2} \qquad\qquad (10.1)$$

or

$$\frac{\text{Supply voltage}}{\text{Number of turns on primary winding } (N_1)} = \frac{\text{Secondary voltage}}{\text{Number of turns on secondary winding } (N_2)}$$

Re-writing eqn. (10.1) gives

$$\frac{E_1}{E_2} = \frac{N_1}{N_2} \qquad\qquad (10.2)$$

If the value of E_2 is GREATER than E_1, the transformer is said to have a **step-up voltage ratio**.

If E_2 is LESS than E_1, it has a **step-down voltage ratio**.

Since we are dealing with an "ideal" transformer, the power loss in it is zero, so that

Volt-amperes supplied to the primary winding

= volt-amperes supplied to the load

that is

$$E_1 I_1 = E_2 I_2 \tag{10.3}$$

where I_1 and I_2 are the r.m.s. values of the primary current and the secondary current, respectively. From equations (10.2) and (10.3) we conclude that

$$\frac{E_1}{E_2} = \frac{I_2}{I_1} \tag{10.4}$$

Arising from eqn. (10.4), we see that a transformer which has a step-up voltage ratio has a step-down current ratio and vice versa. Thus

1 the **"high" voltage winding** of a transformer is associated with a **"low" current,** and
2 the **"low" voltage winding** is associated with a **"high" current**.

Combining eqns. (10.2) and (10.4) gives

$$\frac{E_1}{E_2} = \frac{N_1}{N_2} = \frac{I_2}{I_1} \tag{10.5}$$

From the centre and right-hand terms of eqn. (10.5) it is possible to deduce that

$$I_1 N_1 = I_2 N_2 \tag{10.6}$$

The effort of recalling the above equations can be reduced simply by remembering eqns. (10.1) and (10.6) in the following form.

1 The volts per turn is the same for each winding.
2 Ampere-turn balance is maintained between the windings.

EXAMPLE 10.1

An ideal transformer has a step-up voltage ratio of 7 : 1, its secondary voltage being 2800 V. If the primary current is 21 A, calculate *a*) the primary winding voltage, *b*) the secondary winding current.

Solution $E_2 = 2800$ V, $I_1 = 21$ A.
a) Since the transformer has a 7:1 step-up voltage ratio, then $E_2 = 7E_1$, hence

$$E_1 = E_2/7 = 2800/7 = 400 \text{ V} \quad (Ans.)$$

b) From eqn. (10.5)

$$I_2 = I_1 E_1/E_2 = 21/7 = 3 \text{ A} \quad (Ans.)$$

EXAMPLE 10.2

An ideal single-phase transformer has a step-down voltage ratio of 240/6 V. If there are 200 turns of wire on the primary winding, and the secondary current is 100 A, determine *a*) the number of turns on the secondary winding and *b*) the primary winding current.

Solution $E_1 = 240$ V, $E_2 = 6$ V, $N_1 = 200$, $I_2 = 100$ A.
a) Since each winding supports the same number of volts/turn, then $E_1/N_1 = E_2/N_2$, hence

$$N_2 = E_2 N_1/E_1 = 6 \times 200/240 = 5 \quad (Ans.)$$

b) To maintain ampere-turn balance between the windings,

$$I_1 N_1 = I_2 N_2$$
$$I_1 = I_2 N_2/N_1 = 100 \times 5/200 = 2.5 \text{ A} \quad (Ans.)$$

10.4 Transformer Construction

The two basic types of magnetic circuit construction used for double-wound single-phase transformers are illustrated in figure 10.2. In the **core-type construction** (figure 10.2*a*), the transformer has two limbs each having a uniform cross-sectional area, and in the case shown each limb carries a separate winding. In practice, it is often the case that each limb carries part of the primary winding and part of the secondary winding.

A transformer with a **shell-type construction** is shown in figure 10.2*b*. This type has three limbs. The centre limb carries both windings and has twice the cross-sectional area of each of the outer limbs; the reason for the reduced cross-sectional area of the outer limbs is that they carry only one-half of the flux in the centre limb.

10.5 Power Loss in a Transformer with an Iron Core

The power loss in a transformer with an iron core can be divided into two main headings, namely *iron loss* and *copper loss*.

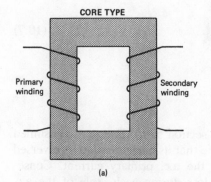

CORE TYPE

Primary winding

Secondary winding

(a)

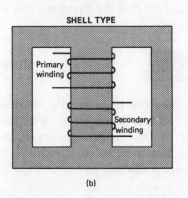

SHELL TYPE

Primary winding

Secondary winding

(b)

Fig. 10.2 Transformer construction: (*a*) core-type, (*b*) shell-type

Iron loss

The **iron loss** is the power dissipated in the magnetic material in the magnetic (iron) circuit. At a constant supply voltage and frequency, the iron loss is more-or-less constant, and is independent of the current flowing through the transformer due to the load; the iron loss is sometimes described as the *constant loss*. Since the iron loss takes place in the iron core, it is also known as the *core loss*. Moreover, since the iron loss occurs when the secondary load is disconnected, it is also known as the *no-load loss*. The iron loss can be subdivided into two types of loss, namely the **hysteresis loss**, P_h, and the **eddy current loss** P_e. The iron loss P_0 is therefore given by the expression

$$\text{Iron loss } P_0 = P_h + P_e \tag{10.7}$$

Hysteresis loss

(This was first described in section 5.19.) Energy is consumed by the iron circuit every time that its magnetic state is reversed in alternate half-cycles of the a.c. primary current. Consequently, there is a power loss during each cycle of the a.c. supply. It was shown in section 5.19 that the hysteresis loss is given by

$$\text{Hysteresis loss } P_h = kvfB_m^n \text{ W} \tag{10.8}$$

where k is the hysteresis coefficient of the magnetic material whose value is typically 100–200 for silicon steel, v is the volume of the magnetic circuit, f is the supply frequency, B_m is the maximum value of the flux density in the core, and n is a number known as the **Steinmetz coefficient** having a value in the range 1.6–2.2.

Energy loss due to the hysteresis effect appears as heat in the magnetic core; the hysteresis loss is reduced by using steel having a low reluctance.

EXAMPLE 10.3

The hysteresis loss in a transformer at a frequency of 50 Hz is 250 W. If the maximum flux density in the core is unchanged, but the supply frequency is increased to 60 Hz, determine the new value of hysteresis loss.

Solution $f_1 = 50$ Hz, $f_2 = 60$ Hz, $P_{h1} = 250$ W.

From eqn. (10.8) we see that the hysteresis loss is proportional to frequency, so that

$$P_{h1} \propto f_1 \qquad (10.9)$$

$$P_{h2} \propto f_2 \qquad (10.10)$$

where P_{h1} and P_{h2} are the hysteresis losses at frequency f_1 and f_2, respectively. Dividing eqn. (10.10) by eqn. (10.9) gives

$$\frac{P_{h2}}{P_{h1}} = \frac{f_2}{f_1}$$

or

$$P_{h2} = P_{h1}f_2/f_1 = 250 \times 60/50 = 300 \text{ W} \quad (Ans.)$$

Eddy current loss

When the magnetic flux linking with a conductor changes, an e.m.f. is induced in the conductor (Faraday's law of electromagnetic induction). This e.m.f. acts to set up a current which opposes the change of magnetic flux producing the e.m.f. (Lenz's law). Suppose that the flux Φ_1 passing through the iron block in figure 10.3a is increasing in the direction shown. The direction of the induced current (known as an **eddy current**) in the iron circulates in a direction which produces a flux which opposes Φ_1. Thus flux Φ_2, which is produced by the eddy current, opposes Φ_1. Since iron is a good conductor of electricity, the value of the induced eddy current in a solid conductor is large; the associated power loss (the I^2R loss)—known as the **eddy current loss**—is also large.

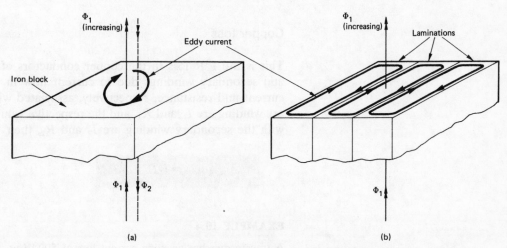

Fig. 10.3 (a) Eddy current path in a block of iron, (b) eddy current flow in a laminated iron path

By dividing the iron circuit into a number of thin **laminations** (see figure 10.3*b*) which are insulated from one another by a layer of varnish or of oxide, the main eddy current path is broken down into many paths. If, say, ten laminations replace the solid iron path, then the e.m.f. induced in each lamination is only about one-tenth of the e.m.f. induced in the solid iron; this reduces the value of the eddy current. Moreover, the cross-sectional area of each conducting path in the iron is reduced, so that the effective resistance to current flow is increased. It can be shown that in the case where a solid piece of iron is replaced by n laminations, then the power loss in the laminations due to eddy current is about $1/n^2$ of the loss in the solid iron. If $n = 10$, the loss in the laminated material is about 1/100th of the loss in the solid iron. Thus, if T is the thickness of the laminations, then

$$\text{Eddy current loss } P_e \propto T^2 \qquad (10.11)$$

In practice the thickness of the laminations is not reduced below about 0.4 mm, since thinner laminations do not justify the cost of assembling them in the core. Eddy current losses are also reduced by the use of a steel with a high resistivity, such as a steel with a 4 per cent silicon content. It can be shown that the eddy current loss is related to frequency f and maximum flux density B_m as follows

$$P_e \propto f^2 B_m^2 \qquad (10.12)$$

Copper loss

This is the I^2R loss in the copper conductors of the primary and secondary windings due to current flow in them. If the current and resistance, respectively, associated with the primary winding are I_1 and R_1, and the respective values associated with the secondary winding are I_2 and R_2, then

$$\text{Copper loss} = I_1^2 R_1 + I_2^2 R_2 \qquad (10.13)$$

EXAMPLE 10.4

A transformer has an eddy current loss of 500 W at a frequency of 50 Hz. Calculate the eddy current loss if *a*) the frequency was increased to 60 Hz, *b*) if the frequency was 50 Hz, but double the number of laminations having one-half the original thickness were used in the iron circuit.

Solution $P_{e1} = 500$ W, $f_1 = 50$ Hz, $f_2 = 60$ Hz.

a) From eqn. (10.12), the eddy current power loss is proportional to (frequency)^2, hence

$$P_{e1} \propto f_1^2 \quad \text{and} \quad P_{e2} \propto f_2^2$$

where P_{e1} is the eddy current power loss at frequency f_1, and P_{e2} is the corresponding power loss at frequency f_2. Dividing the expression for P_{e2} by that for P_{e1} gives

$$\frac{P_{e2}}{P_{e1}} = \frac{f_2^2}{f_1^2}$$

or

$$P_{e2} = P_{e1}f_2^2/f_1^2 = 500 \times 50^2/60^2 = 347.2 \text{ W} \quad (Ans.)$$

b) From eqn. (10.11)

$$P_{e1} \propto T_1^2 \quad \text{and} \quad P_{e2} \propto T_2^2$$

where P_{e1} is the eddy current power loss with lamination thickness T_1, and P_{e2} is the eddy current power loss with lamination thickness T_2. Hence

$$\frac{P_{e2}}{P_{e1}} = \frac{T_2^2}{T_1^2} = \frac{(\frac{1}{2}T_1)^2}{T_1^2} = \frac{1}{4}$$

therefore

$$P_{e2} = P_{e1}/4 = 500/4 = 125 \text{ W} \quad (Ans.)$$

Note that the eddy current power loss cannot be reduced indefinitely simply by reducing the lamination thickness, because the economic law of diminishing returns applies when a very large number of laminations have to be assembled to construct the magnetic circuit.

10.6 Transformer Efficiency

The transformer efficiency η (pronounced eta) is given by

$$\text{Efficiency } \eta = \frac{\text{output power}}{\text{input power}} \text{ per unit (p.u.)} \qquad (10.14)$$

Alternatively, it may be expressed as a per cent (%) value as follows

$$\text{Efficiency} = \frac{\text{output power}}{\text{input power}} \times 100 \text{ per cent (\%)} \qquad (10.15)$$

Now

$$\text{Input power} = \text{output power} + \text{power loss in transformer}$$

$$(10.16)$$

where

> Power loss in the transformer = iron loss + copper loss

then

$$\text{Efficiency } \eta = \frac{\text{output power}}{\text{output power} + \text{iron loss} + \text{copper loss}} \text{ p.u.}$$

(10.17)

$$\eta = \frac{\text{output power}}{\text{output power} + P_h + P_e + I_1^2 R_1 + I_2^2 R_2} \text{ p.u.}$$

EXAMPLE 10.3

A transformer delivers 4 kW of power to a load, and under this condition the copper loss is 80 W and the iron loss is 65 W. Determine the efficiency of the transformer.

Solution   Output power = 4000 W.

$$P_C = (I_1^2 R_1 + I_2^2 R_2) = 80 \text{ W}$$
$$P_0 = (P_h + P_e) = 65 \text{ W}$$

From eqn. (10.17)

$$\eta = \text{output power/(output power + losses)}$$
$$= 4000/(4000 + 65 + 80) = 0.965 \text{ p.u. or } 96.5\% \quad (Ans.)$$

10.7 The Auto-transformer

An **auto-transformer** has a single winding, the primary and secondary windings being obtained by "taps" or connections on to the common winding (see figure 10.4). However, since the two parts of the winding carry different values of current, the conductor section alters at the junction of the two windings.

The equations of the ideal auto-transformer are identical to those of an ideal double-wound transformer, namely that each winding has the same number of volts per turn, and that ampere-turn balance is maintained between the windings. That is

$$\frac{E_1}{N_1} = \frac{E_2}{N_2} \quad \text{and} \quad I_1 N_1 = I_2 N_2$$

or

$$\frac{E_1}{E_2} = \frac{N_1}{N_2} = \frac{I_2}{I_1}$$

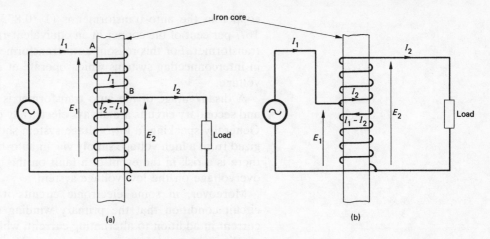

Fig. 10.4 Autotransformer giving (a) a step-down voltage
ratio, (b) a step-up voltage ratio

where (see figure 10.4a) N_1 = number of turns between A and
C, and N_2 = number of turns between B and C. Inspecting
figure 10.4 shows that the current in the part of the winding
which is common to both the supply and the load is equal to
the difference between I_1 and I_2. In the case of the voltage
step-down transformer (current step-up) in figure 10.4a, I_2 is
greater that I_1; in the case of the voltage step-up transformer
(figure 10.4b), I_1 is greater than I_2.

Suppose that an auto-transformer has a step-down voltage
ratio of 1.2:1; if the primary current is, say, 12 A, then the
secondary current is $12 \times 1.2 = 14.4$ A. That is to say, the
current in the upper part of the winding (see figure 10.4a) is
12 A, and the current in the "common" part of the winding is
the difference between the two values of current, i.e. it is
$(14.4 - 12) = 2.4$ A. Thus 16.7 per cent of the winding carries
12 A, and 83.3 per cent of it carries only 2.4 A. Since the
current in the common part of the winding has a small value,
then the conductor area (and therefore the volume of copper)
needed for this part of the winding is also small. This gives the
auto-transformer a cost saving over an otherwise equivalent
two-winding transformer. It can be shown that for an auto-
transformer

$$\frac{\text{Volume of copper in an auto-transformer}}{\text{Volume of copper in a two-winding transformer}} = 1 - n$$

where n is the value of the ratio (smaller voltage/larger
voltage). In the above case, $n = 1/1.2 = 0.833$; the volume of

copper in the auto-transformer is $(1-0.833) = 0.167$ p.u. or 16.7 per cent of the copper in an equivalent-rated two-winding transformer. For this reason, auto-transformers are often used in interconnecting systems which operate at roughly the same voltage.

A disadvantage of the auto-transformer is that the primary and secondary circuits are always electrically coupled together. Generally speaking, a low voltage system should not be energized from a high voltage supply via an auto-transformer, since there is a risk in the event of a fault on the transformer of an overvoltage on the low voltage system.

Moreover, in some electronic circuits it is sometimes a circuit condition that the primary winding may carry direct current in addition to alternating current, whilst the secondary winding must not carry direct current. The auto-transformer does not provide this form of isolation, and if d.c. flows in one winding then it also flows in the other winding. A two-winding transformer is required in this type of application.

10.8 Instrument Transformers

It is impractical to directly operate electrical measuring instruments (i.e. ammeters, voltmeters and wattmeters) at the very high voltage and current associated with many a.c. power systems such as the grid system. It is therefore necessary to use transformers to reduce the voltage and current to values which are realistic for instruments. The standard secondary voltage of a **voltage transformer** or **potential transformer** (abbreviated VT and PT, respectively) is 110 V in the UK and 115 V in America.

A **current transformer** (abbreviated CT) is used to reduce the line current in the supply system to 5 A r.m.s., so that it can be indicated on a simple ammeter. An important feature to note is that *the secondary winding of a CT must never be open-circuited when the transformer is connected in circuit*; if the ammeter is disconnected from the secondary winding, it is necessary to short-circuit the terminals of the secondary winding. The reason is that ampere-turn balance must be maintained between the windings; in the event that the secondary of a CT is open-circuited (i.e. the secondary winding current is zero), it is equivalent to open-circuiting the primary winding. This results in a very high voltage appearing across the secondary winding terminals, which may result in the electrical breakdown of the secondary winding. Moreover, if the secondary winding is open-circuited the flux in the iron circuit rises to a very high value (since the secondary no longer produces opposing ampere-turns); this results in a large amount of energy being dissipated in the iron circuit, leading to the CT becoming very hot.

Exercises

10.1 A single-phase transformer has a rating of 600/240 V, 15 kVA. Determine the full-load value of the primary current and the secondary current. Neglect the effects of power loss in the transformer.

[25 A; 62.5 A]

10.2 If the rated secondary voltage of a 25 kVA transformer is 3.3 kV, calculate the full-load value of the secondary current.

[7.58 A]

10.3 A 415/250 V single-phase transformer is supplied at 250 V and draws a current of 10 A when fully loaded. Neglecting the effects of power loss in the transformer, determine a) the rating of the transformer in kVA, b) the full-load secondary current.

[a) 2.4 kVA; b) 5.78 A]

10.4 A single-phase transformer supplies a load current of 16 A. If the primary-to-secondary turns ratio is 160:20, determine the value of the primary current if the effects of power loss can be ignored.

[2 A]

10.5 The induced e.m.f. per turn on a transformer is 0.8 V. Determine the number of turns on each winding if the transformer has a step-down voltage ratio of 3.3 kV/240 V.

[4125; 300]

10.6 A 5 kVA transformer supplies a lighting load comprising a number of parallel-connected 240 V, 100 W tungsten filament lamps. If the transformer is rated at 3.3 kV/240 V, calculate a) the number of lamps that may be connected without overloading the transformer, b) the full-load secondary current, and c) the full-load primary current. Neglect the effects of power loss.

[a) 50; b) 20.83 A; c) 1.52 A]

10.7 A single-phase transformer has an iron loss of 40 W at a supply frequency of 40 Hz, and an iron loss of 80 W at 60 Hz, the r.m.s. value of the applied voltage being the same in each case. Assuming the same value of peak flux density in both cases, calculate the hysteresis loss and the eddy current loss for a supply frequency of 50 Hz.

[16.6 W; 41.75 W]

10.8 The power loss in a transformer amounts to 5 kW when it supplies a load of 160 kW. Determine the efficiency of the transformer.

[0.97 p.u.]

10.9 A 5 kVA, single-phase transformer has an iron loss of 80 W and a full-load copper loss of 100 W. Determine the full-load efficiency if the power factor of the load is a) unity, b) 0.8 lagging.

[a) 0.965 p.u.; b) 0.957 p.u.]

10.10 The output power supplied by a single-phase transformer is 10 kW. If the total copper loss at this load is 200 W and the efficiency is 0.97 p.u., determine the iron loss.

[109.3 W]

10.11 The primary and secondary voltages of an auto-transformer are 500 V and 450 V, respectively. Determine the value of the current flowing in each section of the transformer winding if the secondary load current is 50 A. Neglect losses in the transformer.

[45 A; 5 A]

10.12 An auto-transformer is used to step a voltage up from 240 V to 260 V. If the total number of turns on the transformer is 1300, determine a) the position of the tapping point, b) the current in each part of the winding when the connected load is 5 kVA. Neglect losses in the transformer.

[50 turns from one end; 19.23 A; 1.6 A]

11 Measuring Instruments

11.1 Types of Measuring Instrument

Instruments may be categorized not only by the quantity measured (i.e. voltage, current, power, etc.), but also by the way in which the measured quantity is displayed (i.e. in analogue or in digital form—more about this below). It is also possible to distinguish between instruments in terms of whether they are d.c. (mean) reading or r.m.s. reading.

Instruments are also categorized according to their application, i.e. as panel meters or as laboratory instruments, etc., and they are further sub-divided by the accuracy of the displayed result.

An instrument is described as an **analogue instrument** if the indication is given by the position of a pointer above the face of the instrument scale (see figure 11.1). A **digital instrument** is one whose display is presented in the form of a series of decimal values (see figure 11.2). The choice between an analogue instrument and a digital instrument involves many factors including the required overall accuracy, its reliability (which includes the reliability of the power supply in digital instruments), its maintainability, etc.

11.2 Analogue Instruments

Many analogue instruments depend for their **deflecting torque** on the force acting on a current-carrying conductor which is situated in a magnetic field; this torque causes the pointer to deflect from zero. Instruments in this category include *permanent-magnet moving-coil meters* (*galvanometers*) and *electrodynamic* (*dynamometer*) *instruments*.

Another popular range of instruments known as *moving-iron instruments*, depend for their deflecting force on the

Fig. 11.1 An analogue multimeter (*Courtesy of Salford Electrical Instruments Ltd.*)

attraction between or repulsion between pieces of magnetized iron.

Once the instrument has developed a deflecting force, it is necessary to ensure that the pointer moves to a specific point on the scale which indicates the value of the measured quantity. That is, the result must be **repeatable** when the measured quantity next has the same value. Repeatability is ensured by the **controlling force** of the instrument. This is provided in many instruments by **spring control**; in the case where two control springs are used (figure 11.3), movement of the instrument shaft increases the tension in one spring and reduces it in the other.

An additional (and essential) feature of practical measuring instruments is a means of **damping** the movement. The damping system ensures that the pointer comes quickly to its final position without excessive oscillation. There are two principal methods of damping instruments, namely *a*) air vane damping and *b*) eddy-current damping.

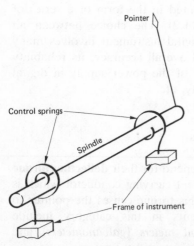

Fig. 11.3 Control springs (deflecting system omitted for simplicity)

Fig. 11.2 A digital multimeter (*Courtesy of AVO Limited*)

One form of **air vane damping system** is shown in figure 11.4*a*; in this case the movement is damped by the movement of a light vane or piston (usually made of aluminium) inside a cylinder. A gap is left between the vane and the cylinder so that the damping force is not excessive. When the vane moves into the cylinder, energy is taken up in compressing the air in the cylinder; when the vane moves out of the cylinder the air pressure inside the cylinder is reduced, and energy is taken up in pulling against the reduced pressure. This type of damping is widely used in moving-iron and electrodynamic instruments.

In **eddy-current damping systems**, the movement of the instrument spindle causes a light conductor (usually aluminium) to move between the poles of a permanent magnet. The eddy current which is induced in the conductor dissipates energy, causing the movement of the instrument to be damped. One form of eddy-current damping is shown in figure 11.4*b*. Eddy-current damping is used in moving-coil instruments (galvanometers), but in this case the eddy-current damping element is the aluminium former on which the coil of the instrument is wound (see figure 11.5).

Certain types of instrument use what is known as **oil damping**. In this type of damping system, the movement of the instrument is connected to a vane which is enclosed in an oil-filled container. Rotation of the instrument spindle causes the vane to move through the oil; the net result is that the movement of the instrument is damped.

11.3 Permanent-magnet Moving-coil Instrument or Galvanometer

The permanent-magnet moving-coil instrument is a **direct current milliammeter** (or a microammeter) and, for reasons given below, requires additional electrical circuits to enable it to measure alternating current. Since the instrument can measure in its normal form only direct current and voltage, the manufacturer supplies the user with information about the polarity of the meter terminals.

In general, the terminal where the current enters the meter is either marked with a "plus" (+) sign or it is a red terminal; the terminal where the current leaves the meter is either marked with a "minus" (−) sign or it is a black terminal.

The basis of one form of moving-coil instrument is shown in figure 11.5. The design shown is known as an **internal magnet instrument**, in which the coil (for simplicity a single-turn coil is shown, but in practice it would be a multi-turn coil) is wound on an aluminium former which can rotate about a cylindrical permanent magnet; the coil former provides eddy-current damping, in the manner outlined earlier.

The movement is surrounded by a soft iron cylinder. The function of this cylinder is twofold: firstly, it ensures that the magnetic field between the magnet and the ring is radial and, secondly, it provides a magnetic screen for the instrument; the latter has the effect of reducing errors which may arise from stray magnetic fields. Since the magnetic field is radial at all points, the force on the conductors is uniform; this feature permits the instrument to have a linear scale calibration.

Other types of moving-coil instrument use **external magnets**, in which the position of the magnet and the soft iron are interchanged.

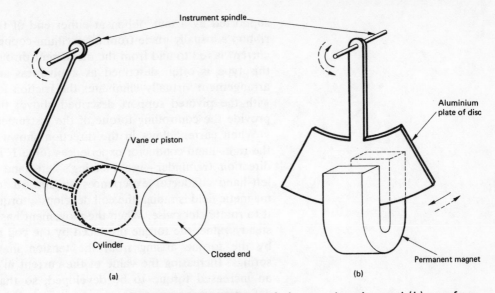

Fig. 11.4 (a) One form of air vane damping and (b) one form of eddy-current damping

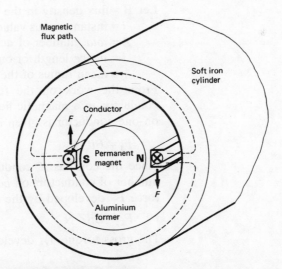

Fig. 11.5 The basis of an "internal" magnet moving-coil instrument

In instruments in which the spindle of the instrument is supported by jewelled bearings, the current is fed both to and from the coil by two contra-wound springs (see also figure 11.3); these springs provide the controlling torque of the instrument. In some other instruments, the spindle (and coil) is supported by a taut ribbon at either end of the spindle. The ribbon is usually made from a beryllium-copper material, and current is fed to and from the movement through the ribbons; this type is often described as a **pivotless suspension**. This arrangement virtually eliminates the friction losses associated with the pivoted support described above; the taut ribbons provide the controlling torque of the instrument.

When current flows in the direction shown in figure 11.5, the right-hand conductor experiences force F in a downwards direction (reminder—use Fleming's left-hand rule), and the left-hand conductor experiences an upward force. Since the magnetic field is radial, the coil develops a torque which causes it to rotate clockwise. When the movement has deflected to its steady value, the torque produced by the coil is just balanced by the torque arising from the tension in the controlling springs. Increasing the value of the current in the coil causes an increased torque to be developed, so that the angle of deflection increases further until it is balanced once more against the torque of the controlling springs.

Equation of the moving-coil system

Let B = flux density in the air gap (T)
i = instantaneous value of the current in the coil (A)
Z = *total* number of *active* conductors on the coil
l = *active* length of one conductor (m)
r = mean radius of the coil (m)

From the work on the force acting on a current-carrying conductor in a magnetic field (chapter 6), the force F_1 acting on one conductor is given by

$$F_1 = Bil \text{ N}$$

Since the coil has Z conductors (remember, this is the total number of conductors on *both* sides of the coil), then the total force F_T developed by the coil is

$$F_T = BilZ \text{ N}$$

The gross torque T_G developed by the coil is

$$\text{Torque } T_G = F_T \times \text{radius} = BilZr \text{ Nm} \tag{11.1}$$

The controlling torque T_C developed by the controlling springs is proportional to the angular deflection θ of the spring. That is

$$T_C = k\theta \text{ Nm} \tag{11.2}$$

where k is a constant of the spring having dimensions of Nm/rad (or Nm/deg).

Under steady operating conditions when the meter gives a steady deflection, the gross torque developed by the movement is balanced by the controlling torque. That is

$$T_C = T_G$$

or

$$k\theta = BilZr$$

hence

$$\theta = \frac{BlZr}{k} \times i \qquad (11.3)$$

In any given moving-coil instrument, the quantities B, l, Z, r and k are constant, so that

$$\theta \propto i$$

That is, the angle of deflection of the movement is proportional to the current flowing through the coil. For this reason the scale of a moving-coil meter is uniformly (linearly) calibrated.

Although not apparent from the above analysis, the moving-coil instrument gives improved accuracy at high deflection. Thus if a 2 A and a 1 A instrument are available, and we wish to measure 0.8 A, the 1 A meter should be selected since this instrument gives a larger deflecting angle at the measured current.

A disadvantage of the moving-coil instrument is that the meter indicates zero when an alternating current with a frequency greater than about 10 Hz flows through it. The reason is as follows. During the positive half-cycle of the alternating waveform, the direction of the current through the coil is, say, in the direction shown in figure 11.5; this produces a clockwise torque on the movement. In the negative half-cycle the direction of the current is reversed, which causes the torque to reverse. As a result the torque developed pulsates, the average torque over the complete cycle being zero. For frequencies between zero (d.c.) and about 5 Hz, the needle of the instrument tries to follow the instantaneous current in the coil (that is, the reading is alternately positive and negative). At frequencies in the range 5–10 Hz, the needle vibrates about zero, the amplitude of the deflection diminishing as the frequency increases. Above about 10 Hz the reading is zero.

The moving-coil instrument can be modified to enable it to measure a.c. quantities by using it in conjunction with a **rectifier**. A rectifier is an electronic device which converts an alternating current into a unidirectional (direct) current. The meter is calibrated so that the rectified (d.c.) current indicates the r.m.s. value of the alternating current. The calibration is usually carried out with a sinusoidal waveform, and for accurate results the form factor of the measured a.c. waveform must be 1.11.

EXAMPLE 11.1

The flux density in the air gap of a moving-coil instrument is 0.26 T and the coil has $48\frac{1}{2}$* turns. The effective length of each conductor is 15 mm and the mean radius of the coil is 7 mm. If the constant of the control spring is 1.375×10^{-6} Nm/rad, and the current in the coil is 0.8 mA, determine the steady angular deflection of the coil in degrees.

Solution $B = 0.26$ T, $l = 15 \times 10^{-3}$ m, $Z = 48\frac{1}{2} \times 2 = 97$, $r = 7 \times 10^{-3}$ m, $i = 0.8 \times 10^{-3}$ A, $k = 1.375 \times 10^{-6}$ Nm/rad

From eqn. (11.3)

$$\theta = BlZri/k = \frac{0.26 \times (15 \times 10^{-3}) \times 97 \times (7 \times 10^{-3}) \times (0.8 \times 10^{-3})}{1.375 \times 10^{-6}}$$

$$= 1.54 \text{ rad or } 88.3° \quad (Ans.)$$

11.4 Dynamometer (Electrodynamic) Instruments

A **dynamometer instrument** (see figure 11.6) is a form of moving-coil instrument which does not have a permanent magnet, the magnetic field being provided by means of current I_1 which flows through a pair of coils which are fixed to the frame of the instrument (the so-called **fixed coils**). When current I_2 flows through the third coil (the **moving coil**) which is pivoted about its centre, the interaction between the two magnetic fields produces a torque which results in the moving coil rotating about its axis.

The controlling torque is produced by springs (which are also the means of supplying current to the moving coil) attached to the spindle of the moving coil. Damping is provided by means of an air vane arrangement attached to the spindle of the moving coil. It can be shown for this instrument that

$$\text{Mean value of the deflecting torque} \propto I_1 \times I_2$$

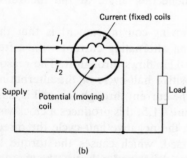

Fig. 11.6 (*a*) The basis of a dynamometer instrument and (*b*) connection diagram for use as a wattmeter

---

* *Note*: Since the current enters the coil via a spring at one end of the spindle and leaves it via a spring at the other end, then the coil has an odd half-turn of wire.

In addition to measuring d.c. quantities, the dynamometer instrument can also be used to measure a.c. quantities as follows. In this case both sets of coils are energized by alternating current, so that when the current in one coil reverses so does the current in the other coil. It is an interesting exercise to verify that reversal of both currents results in an unchanged direction of torque. Consequently, the dynamometer instrument is an a.c./d.c. instrument.

The most popular application of the dynamometer instrument is as a *wattmeter* (for connections see figure 11.6b). In this case the fixed coils are wound with a few turns of large-section wire and carry the load current. The moving-coil circuit is arranged to have a very high resistance, the coil being wound with many turns of fine wire. The supply voltage is connected to the moving coil, so that current I_2 is proportional to the applied voltage V. Hence

Deflecting torque $\propto I_1 \times I_2 \propto I \times V$

$\propto$ load current $\times$ load voltage

$\propto$ power

That is, the deflecting torque is proportional to the *average power* consumed by the load.

11.5 Moving-iron Instruments

The majority of moving-iron instruments have a **repulsion-type movement** (see figure 11.7), in which the force of repulsion between two similarly magnetized iron rods or vanes causes the pointer to move. One of the vanes is fixed to the

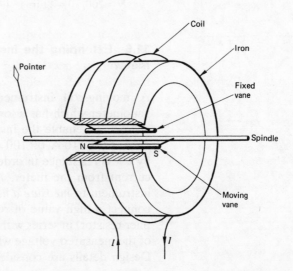

Fig. 11.7 The basis of a repulsion-type moving-iron instrument

frame of the instrument, and the other vane is attached to the spindle of the instrument. When a current passes through the coil, the two iron vanes are similarly magnetized and repel one another.

The controlling force of the instrument is provided by a spring, and since current does not flow in the moving member, only one spring is necessary. Damping is usually provided by means of an air vane system.

In a simple instrument of this kind, it can be shown that the deflecting torque is proportional to the square of the current in the coil. As a result the scale calibration is non-linear, being very cramped at the lower end of the scale. However, by using a wedge-shaped fixed vane, the scale calibration can be made almost linear over the majority of the scale.

The flux in a magnetic circuit is related to the number of ampere-turns produced by the coil. Provided that the number of ampere-turns to give **full-scale deflection** (f.s.d.) is known for a particular design, then we can calculate the number of turns required to give f.s.d. for a particular current.

EXAMPLE 11.2

A moving-iron instrument requires an m.m.f. of 200 ampere-turns to give f.s.d. Determine the number of turns on the coil to give f.s.d. for a current of a) 0.5 A and b) 50 A.

Solution $NI = 200$ A or AT
a) $I = 0.5$ A, hence

$$N = 200/I = 200/0.5 = 400 \text{ turns}   (Ans.)$$

b) $I = 50$ A, hence

$$N = 200/50 = 4 \text{ turns}   (Ans.)$$

11.6 Extending the Instrument Range of a Moving-coil Meter

A moving-coil instrument is basically a low-current galvanometer which has a low value of p.d. between its terminals at f.s.d. To enable the instrument to *measure a large value of current* (say 10 A or 100 A), the instrument must be shunted by a low resistance in order to shunt or to by-pass most of the current from the meter. Alternatively, if we need to use the instrument to *measure a high value of voltage*, it is necessary to connect a high value of resistance (known as a voltage multiplier resistor) in series with the meter; this "drops" the majority of the measured voltage when current flows through the meter. Design details are considered below.

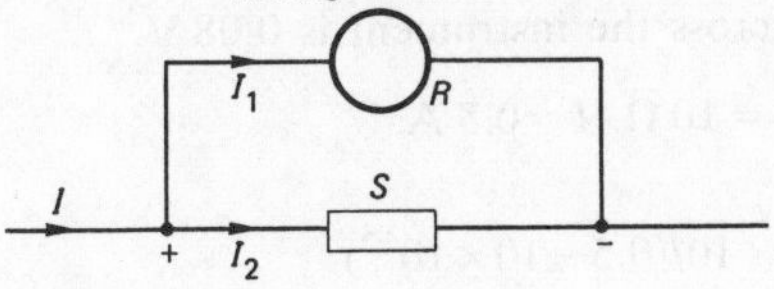

Fig. 11.8 The moving-coil instrument as an ammeter

Extending the current range

As mentioned above, the moving-coil instrument has a delicate construction and is capable of handling only a small value of current. When a large value of current has to be measured, a **shunt resistor** S (see figure 11.8), of low resistance, is connected between the meter terminals. Note in figure 11.8 that the terminal where the current enters the meter is marked with a + sign, and the terminal where the current leaves is marked with a − sign. The following notation is adopted in figure 11.8.

I = current in the external circuit when the meter gives f.s.d.

I_1 = current in the meter to give f.s.d.

I_2 = current in the shunt when the meter gives f.s.d.

R = resistance of the meter

S = resistance of the shunt

Applying Kirchhoff's first law to one terminal of the meter gives

$$I = I_1 + I_2 \qquad (11.4)$$

Also, since the meter and the shunt are in parallel with one another, the same p.d. appears across both of them, hence

$$I_1 R = I_2 S \qquad (11.5)$$

The resistance of the shunt S can be determined from eqns. (11.4) and (11.5) as follows

$$S = \frac{I_1 R}{I_2} = \frac{I_1 R}{I - I_1} \qquad (11.6)$$

Note: The shunt resistor must be manufactured to a very high degree of precision and must ideally have a very low temperature coefficient of resistance; the latter ensures that the resistance of the shunt does alter significantly with temperature change. However, the coil of the meter is wound with copper wire and its resistance does vary with temperature. The variation in the meter resistance with temperature affects the shunt "current multiplying" ratio, leading to variation in the accuracy of the meter. To reduce error from this cause as much as possible, a resistor known as a **swamp resistor** (see figure 11.9) is connected in series with the meter; the resistance of the swamp resistor is typically three times the resistance of the meter.

EXAMPLE 11.3

A moving-coil instrument gives f.s.d. for a current of 10 mA and has a resistance of $10\,\Omega$. Calculate *a*) the resistance of the shunt resistor which enables the meter to be used to give a f.s.d. of 0.5 A, *b*) the power consumed by the combination at f.s.d., and *c*) the current in the main circuit when the p.d. across the instrument is 0.08 V.

Solution   *a*) $I_1 = 10 \times 10^{-3}$ A, $R = 10\,\Omega$, $I = 0.5$ A.
From eqn. (11.6)

$$S = I_1 R / (I - I_1) = (10 \times 10^{-3}) \times 10 / (0.5 - 10 \times 10^{-3})$$
$$= 0.2041\,\Omega \quad (Ans.)$$

b) The power consumed can be calculated in any one of several ways. One method is to calculate the power consumed when 0.5 A flows in the equivalent resistance R_T of the instrument (this comprises R in parallel with S). Another method is to determine the sum of the power lost in the meter and in the shunt. Yet another method is to determine the p.d. V_T across the instrument at f.s.d., from which the total power loss V^2 / R_T can be calculated. The first method is used here.

$$R_T = RS / (R + S) = 10 \times 0.2041 / (10 + 0.2041) = 0.2\,\Omega$$
$$\text{Power consumed} = I^2 R_T = 0.5^2 \times 0.2 = 0.05 \text{ W} \quad (Ans.)$$

c) The p.d. across the instrument is 0.08 V. Now

$$V = I_g R$$

where I_g is the current through the instrument to give a p.d. of 0.08 V across it, hence

$$I_g = V/R = 0.08/10 = 0.008 \text{ A}$$

The meter current I_1 to give f.s.d. is 10 mA or 0.01 A, and since

$$\text{Deflection} \propto \text{current}$$

then

$$\frac{\text{Deflection for } I_g}{\text{Deflection for } I_1 \text{ (f.s.d.)}} = \frac{I_g}{I_1}$$

or

$$\text{Deflection for } I_g = \frac{I_g}{I_1} \times \text{f.s.d.} = \frac{0.008}{0.01} \times \text{f.s.d.}$$
$$= 0.8 \times \text{f.s.d.} = 0.8 \times 0.5 = 0.4 \text{ A} \quad (Ans.)$$

The universal shunt

When measuring the current in a circuit using a multi-range ammeter (see figure 11.1) it is advisable to switch the meter to its highest current range, and then to reduce the current range until the meter gives the largest possible readable deflection. The switching arrangement should enable the user to change the current range

   a) without interrupting the current and
   b) without momentarily causing an excessive current to pass
       through the meter.

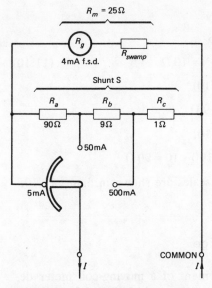

Fig. 11.9 A multi-range ammeter incorporating a universal shunt

The **universal shunt** in figure 11.9 satisfies these conditions.

In the following, we consider the design of a universal shunt suitable for use with a moving-coil meter having a f.s.d. of 4 mA. The ranges on the resulting multi-range meter are to be 5 mA, 50 mA and 500 mA, respectively, the meter scales being shown in figure 11.10.

In the circuit shown, the resistance R_m of the meter section is

$$R_m = R_g + R_{swamp}$$

where R_g is the resistance of the galvanometer itself and R_{swamp} is the resistance of the swamp resistor.

The meter section is shunted by shunt S which comprises resistors R_a, R_b and R_c connected in series. The current to give f.s.d. on the meter itself is usually fairly close to the most sensitive current range of the multi-range meter. For example, the current to give f.s.d. in the meter in figure 11.9 is 4 mA, and the most sensitive current range of the multi-range meter is to be 5 mA. If R_m $(= R_g + R_{swamp})$ is 25 Ω, then the p.d. across the meter at f.s.d. is

$$4 \text{ mA} \times 25 \text{ } \Omega = 0.1 \text{ V}$$

Under this condition the current in the main circuit is 5 mA, so that the current in the shunt circuit is 1 mA. Hence

$$R_a + R_b + R_c = \frac{\text{p.d. across the shunt at f.s.d.}}{\text{shunt current at f.s.d.}}$$

$$= \frac{0.1}{10^{-3}} = 100 \text{ } \Omega \tag{11.7}$$

It can be shown that for this type of shunt that

Most sensitive range $\times (R_a + R_b + R_c)$
$= $ next least sensitive range $\times (R_b + R_c)$
$= $ least sensitive range $\times R_c$

That is

$$5 \text{ mA} \times (R_a + R_b + R_c) = 50 \text{ mA} \times (R_b + R_c) = 500 \text{ mA} \times R_c \tag{11.8}$$

Hence

$$5 \text{ mA} \times (R_a + R_b + R_c) = (5 \times 10^{-3}) \times 100 = 0.5 \text{ V}$$

From eqn. (11.8)

$$500 \text{ mA} \times R_c = 0.5$$

therefore

$$R_c = 0.5/(500 \times 10^{-3}) = 1 \text{ } \Omega \tag{11.9}$$

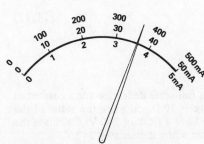

Fig. 11.10 Meter scale for the multi-range ammeter in figure 11.9

Also from eqn. (11.8)

$$50 \text{ mA} \times (R_b + R_c) = 0.5$$

or $R_b + R_c = 0.5/(50 \times 10^{-3}) = 10 \, \Omega$ (11.10)

From eqns. (11.9) and (11.10)

$$R_b = 10 - R_c = 10 - 1 = 9 \, \Omega$$

From eqns. (11.7) and (11.10)

$$R_a = 100 - (R_b + R_c) = 100 - 10 = 90 \, \Omega$$

The corresponding current scales are shown in figure 11.10.

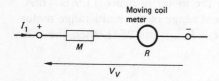

Fig. 11.11 The moving-coil instrument as a voltmeter

Extending the voltage range

The deflection of the movement of a moving-coil meter depends on the value of the current which flows through the meter; at f.s.d., the p.d. across the instrument is normally only a fraction of a volt. In order to measure a high value of voltage, a resistor M (see figure 11.11) known as a **voltage multiplier resistor**, is connected in series with the instrument. Once again, in order to cause the pointer to deflect in the correct direction, the positive polarity supply lead must be connected to the + terminal of the instrument. The following notation is adopted in figure 11.11.

V_V = voltage applied to the terminals of the voltmeter to produce f.s.d.

I_1 = current to give f.s.d.

R = resistance of the galvanometer

M = resistance of the multiplier resistor

Applying Kirchhoff's second law to figure 11.11 gives

$$V_V = I_1(M + R) \tag{11.11}$$

hence

$$M = \frac{V_V}{I_1} - R \tag{11.12}$$

EXAMPLE 11.4

A moving-coil instrument gives a full-scale deflection for a current of 1 mA. If the instrument resistance is 10 Ω, calculate the value of the multiplier resistor to enable it to have a f.s.d. of 300 V. Calculate the power consumed by the voltmeter when it indicates 240 V.

Solution $V_V = 300 \text{ V}$, $I_1 = 10^{-3}$ A, $R = 10 \, \Omega$.
  From eqn. (11.12)

$$M = \frac{V_V}{I_1} - R = \frac{300}{10^{-3}} - 10 = 300\,000 - 10 = 299\,990\,\Omega \quad (Ans.)$$

The total resistance R_V of the voltmeter is

$$R_V = M + R = 300\,000\,\Omega$$

The power consumed by the voltmeter when 240 V is applied is

$$P = V^2/R_V = 240^2/300\,000 = 0.192\,W \quad (Ans.)$$

Voltmeter sensitivity

The sensitivity of a voltmeter is often quoted in **ohms per volt** (o.p.v.). This is defined as follows.

$$\frac{\text{Sensitivity in}}{\text{ohms per volt}} = \frac{\text{total resistance of the voltmeter}}{\text{voltage required to give f.s.d.}}$$

$$= \frac{M + R}{V_V} = \frac{R_V}{V_V}$$

The voltmeter in example 11.4 has a sensitivity of

$$300\,000\,\Omega/300\,V = 1000\,\Omega/V$$

The resistance of the instrument can also be calculated from the equation as follows

$$R_V = (\Omega/V) \times \text{f.s.d. in volts}$$

From eqn. (11.11)

$$\frac{1}{I_1} = \frac{1}{\text{current to give f.s.d.}} = \frac{M + R}{V_V}$$

$$= \text{voltmeter sensitivity in o.p.v.}$$

Applying this expression to the voltmeter in example 11.4 shows that it has a sensitivity of

$$1/1\,\text{mA} = 1/10^{-3}\,A = 1000\,\Omega/V$$

The "goodness" of a voltmeter is indicated by its sensitivity, and a "good" voltmeter has a high ohms per volt sensitivity. A high-quality multi-range test instrument may typically have a sensitivity of 20 000 Ω/V (corresponding to an instrument giving f.s.d. at 50 μA).

A multi-range voltmeter

A typical circuit of a voltmeter having three ranges is shown in figure 11.12a. Using an instrument which gives f.s.d. at a

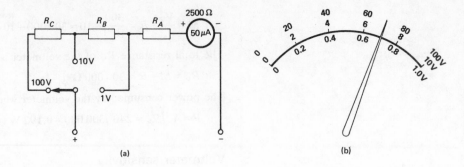

Fig. 11.12 (*a*) Typical multi-range voltmeter circuit and (*b*) instrument scales

current of 50 μA and which has a resistance of 2500 Ω, then applying eqn. (11.12) we find that, when the voltmeter is switched to its 1 V range, the required value of multiplier resistor is $R_A = 17\,500\,\Omega$. When switched to the 10 V range, an additional resistance $R_B = 180\,000\,\Omega$ is needed. When switched to the 100 V range, a further resistance $R_C = 1.8\,M\Omega$ is needed.

Consequently, the total resistance on the 1 V range is 20 000 Ω, on the 10 V range is 200 000 Ω, and on the 100 V is 2 MΩ. The voltmeter therefore has a sensitivity on all ranges of 20 000 Ω/V (corresponding to a f.s.d. current of $1/20\,000\,\Omega/V = 50\,\mu$A.)

11.7 The Moving-coil Instrument as an Ohmmeter

The resistance of a resistor can be determined by measuring the current flowing in it when a known voltage is applied to the resistor. This is the basis of many ohmmeters.

A simple ohmmeter circuit is shown in figure 11.13*a*, and comprises a moving-coil meter in series with a battery (which is part of the ohmmeter) and a current limiting resistor R_L (which is the "set zero" control of the ohmmeter). The value of R_L is adjusted to a value that allows the maximum current (i.e. f.s.d.) to flow through the meter when the test leads are short-circuited (1 mA in the case considered here).

A point worth noting is that the polarity of the 1.5 V "internal" battery results in the + terminal of the instrument being negative with respect to the − terminal. This fact is of importance when testing many types of semiconductor device such as diodes and transistors.

When the resistance of the unknown resistor R_U is zero (corresponding to the case where the test leads are short-circuited together), the meter current is a maximum. Thus *full-scale deflection corresponds to zero ohms*. When the value

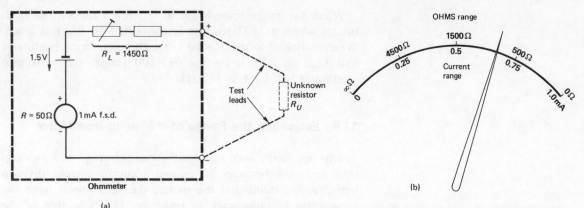

Fig. 11.13 (a) Simple ohmmeter circuit and (b) its scale calibration

of R_U is infinity (corresponding to the test leads being open-circuited), the current is zero. Thus *zero deflection corresponds to infinite resistance* (see figure 11.13b).

With the values given in figure 11.13a, the current in the meter when $R_U = 1500\,\Omega$ is

$$I = 1.5\,\text{V}/(R + R_L + R_U) = 1.5/(50 + 1450 + 1500)$$
$$= 0.5 \times 10^{-3}\,\text{A or 0.5 mA}$$

that is, the deflection is one-half f.s.d. (see figure 11.13b). It is the case in ohmmeters of this type that *the resistance indicated at one-half f.s.d. is equal to the total internal resistance of the meter*. Note from figure 11.13b that the resistance scale calibration is non-linear, being open at the low-resistance (high current) end and cramped at the high-resistance (low current) end.

Resistance values used in both electrical and electronic circuits range from very low to very high values; practical instruments must therefore be capable of measuring a very wide range of resistance values. The circuit of a practical multi-range ohmmeter differs from that in figure 11.13a, one basic circuit being illustrated in figure 11.14. The instrument is manually adjusted by means of the 10 kΩ SET ZERO control to give f.s.d. when the test leads are short-circuited. The SET ZERO control must be adjusted a) if the internal battery voltage changes (which it will do with age and use) or b) if the ohmmeter is switched to a different range, since this alters the resistance values in the circuit; the SET ZERO control must, of course, be adjusted with the test leads short-circuited.

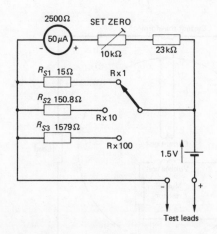

Fig. 11.14 Typical ohmmeter circuit

When the range scale is set to the $R \times 1$ range, half f.s.d. occurs when a $15\,\Omega$ resistor is connected to the test leads. When switched to the $R \times 10$ range, the resistance reading at half f.s.d. is $150\,\Omega$; on the $R \times 100$ range, the resistance reading at half f.s.d. is $1500\,\Omega$.

11.8 Extending the Range of a Moving-iron Meter

Shunts are rarely used to alter the current range of a moving-iron ammeter because, to ensure accurate current division between the shunt and the meter, the shunt must have the same ratio of inductance to resistance (L/R) as that of the meter. One method of obtaining different ranges of current is by having a number of coils with a different number of turns on them (see also section 11.5).

Multi-range moving-iron ammeters usually have a number of coils wound on the iron circuit, the coils being connected in various series-parallel combinations to give differing current ranges.

To measure a high value of alternating current, it is usual to use either a 0–1 A meter or a 0–5 A meter in conjunction with a current transformer.

Moving-iron instruments used as voltmeters have high resistance windings consisting of many turns of fine wire; the current required to give f.s.d. usually being in the range 0.05–0.1 A. In all but low-voltage meters, a voltage multiplier resistor is included in series with the instrument. To measure a high value of alternating voltage, a 0–110 V meter is used in conjunction with a potential transformer.

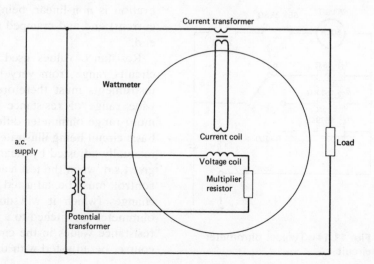

Fig. 11.15 Extending the instrument range of a dynamometer wattmeter

11.9 Extending the Range of a Dynamometer Wattmeter

When a dynamometer wattmeter is to be used to measure the power in a high-voltage high-current circuit, it is usual to use the instrument in association with a potential transformer and a current transformer, as shown in figure 11.15. The rating of the voltage and current coils, respectively, of the meter are usually 0–110 V and 0–1 A or 0–5 A. The power consumed by the load is

Wattmeter reading × p.t. ratio × c.t. ratio

11.10 The D.C. Potentiometer

The **d.c. potentiometer** is an instrument designed primarily for the **comparison of direct voltages**. The usual measuring range is about 0–1.5 V. It can be adapted for other functions such as the measurement of current and resistance, and also for the calibration of ammeters and voltmeters.

The basic circuit of a d.c. potentiometer is shown in figure 11.16; it consists of a length l_1 of resistance wire, an adjustable slider being in contact with the wire. When e.m.f. E_1 is connected to the wire, a current I_1 flows along the resistance wire. *Provided that the current is the same at every point along the wire, then the p.d. per unit length along the wire is constant. This implies that current must neither flow into the slider nor out of it.* A grasp of this fact is critical in understanding the operation of the d.c. potentiometer.

A sensitive galvanometer G is connected in series with the slider; this permits the user to detect when the slider current is zero. The galvanometer has a centre-zero scale. The potentiometer is said to be **balanced** when the current through the galvanometer is zero.

When the potentiometer is balanced, the p.d. per unit length of the slide wire is E_1/l_1 V/m. Since current neither flows into nor out of the slider at balance, then if balance is obtained when the slider is at length l_2 away from the left-hand end of the slide wire (see figure 11.16), then

$$E_2 = \text{p.d. per unit length of the slide wire} \times l_2$$
$$= \frac{E_1}{l_1} \times l_2$$

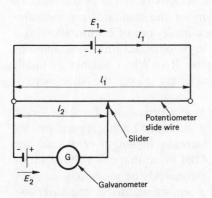

Fig. 11.16 Basic circuit of a d.c. potentiometer

$$\boxed{\frac{E_1}{l_1} = \frac{E_2}{l_2}}$$

(11.13)

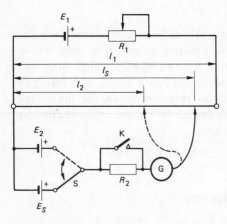

Fig. 11.17 Comparison of e.m.f.s using a d.c. potentiometer

Measuring the e.m.f. of a cell

The method adopted for the determination of the e.m.f. of a cell is illustrated in figure 11.17; in this figure E_1 is a cell which supplies electricity to the slide wire, E_2 is the unknown value of e.m.f., and E_S is a "standard" value of e.m.f. Normally the value of E_1 is also unknown, but its value is relatively unimportant (it may, for example, be a 2 V cell). It is first necessary to calibrate the p.d. per unit length of the slide wire by means of the standard source of e.m.f. E_S (this is obtained from a **standard cell**). This process is known as **standardization**, and is described in principle below.

The standard cell E_S is connected to the slider via resistor R_2, and the slider is set at a point corresponding to the voltage of the standard cell. If the standard cell voltage is 1.018 V, then the slider is set at 1.018 metres from the left-hand end of the slide wire. The value of the variable resistor R_1 is adjusted until the galvanometer gives zero deflection. At this point in time, resistor R_2 is connected in series with the galvanometer, its effect being to reduce the sensitivity of the instrument. To increase the overall sensitivity of the standardizing measurement, key K is pressed; this cuts R_2 out of circuit, allowing a more precise null condition to be obtained (this is obtained by making a small adjustment to R_1). When balance is finally obtained, the p.d. per unit length along the slide wire is standardized to 1 V/m.

In practice, the slide wire is a combination of a short length of slide wire and a tapped resistor. Each tapping on the resistor gives an effective increase in length of 0.1 m, and the slide wire has a length of 0.1 m, so that any voltage within the range of the instrument can quickly be measured.

Once the slide wire has been standardized, the unknown e.m.f. E_2 can be measured. (Note: E_2 must have a lower value than E_1.) To measure E_2, the blade of switch S (figure 11.17) is moved so that E_2 is connected to the slider via R_2. The position of the slider is then adjusted until balance is obtained on the galvanometer. (Note: the setting of R_1 must not be altered.) The process is repeated with key K depressed; this provides a more accurate balance point. The value of E_2 is obtained by replacing E_1/l'_1 in eqn. (11.13) by E_S/l_S, where E_S and l_S are the e.m.f. of the standard cell and the position of the slider at balance when the standard cell is connected, respectively. That is

$$E_2 = \frac{E_S}{l_S} \times l_2$$

(11.14)

but since $E_S/l_S = 1$ V/m, then

$$E_2 = 1 \times l_2 = l_2 \text{ V}$$

In the event that the ratio E_S/l_S cannot be arranged to be 1 V/m, then E_2 is calculated from eqn. (11.14)

EXAMPLE 11.5

A d.c. potentiometer is calibrated against a cell of e.m.f. 1.2 V; balance is obtained against a length of 99 cm of slide wire. An unknown e.m.f. is next balanced by the potentiometer, when balance is obtained against 66 cm of slide wire. Determine the value of the unknown e.m.f.

Solution $E_1 = 1.2$ V, $l_1 = 99$ cm, $l_2 = 66$ cm.
  From eqn. (11.13)

$$E_1/l_1 = E_2/l_2$$

$$E_2 = E_1 l_2/l_1 = 1.2 \times 66/99 = 0.8 \text{ V} \quad (Ans.)$$

EXAMPLE 11.6

A cell is balanced against the p.d. across 120 cm of a potentiometer wire. An accurate moving-coil voltmeter of resistance 100 Ω is connected across the terminals of the cell, and it is found that the potentiometer is no longer balanced. The potentiometer is rebalanced whilst the voltmeter remains connected, this time against 110 cm of the wire. The reading on the voltmeter is now 1.21 V. Determine the e.m.f. of the cell and its internal resistance.

Solution   Since the voltmeter is an accurate instrument, then the p.d. across 110 cm (1.1 m) of wire is 1.21 V. Hence the p.d. per unit length is 1.21 V/1.1 m = 1.1 V/m.

The difference in balance lengths under the two sets of conditions in the problem are accounted for as follows. Under the first set of conditions (for a balance length of 1.2 m), no current is drawn from the cell, so that we balance the e.m.f. E of the cell against the p.d. along the wire. Hence

$$E = \text{balance length} \times \text{p.d. per unit length}$$
$$= 1.2 \text{ m} \times 1.1 \text{ V/m} = 1.32 \text{ V} \quad (Ans.)$$

In the second case, when the voltmeter of internal resistance 100 Ω is connected to the cell (see figure 11.18), current I is drawn from the cell. This current flows through the internal resistance r of the cell; the voltmeter therefore indicates the **terminal voltage** of the cell under this loading condition. That is

$$\text{Terminal voltage} = \text{e.m.f.} - Ir \text{ (p.d. in } r)$$

Substituting values gives

$$1.21 = 1.32 - Ir \tag{11.15}$$

Now, since a p.d. of 1.21 V appears between the terminals of the voltmeter, then the current I flowing through the voltmeter is

$$I = 1.21 \text{ V}/100 \ \Omega = 0.0121 \text{ A}$$

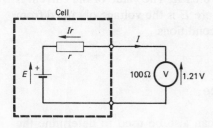

Fig. 11.18

Substituting the above value in eqn. (11.15) gives

$$r = (1.32 - 1.21)/0.0121 = 9.9091 \ \Omega \quad (Ans.)$$

11.11 Extending the Range of the D.C. Potentiometer

Measurement of a high value of direct voltage

To accommodate voltages higher than about 1.5 V, we make use of a **resistance potential divider** or **voltage ratio box** (also known as volt box) shown in figure 11.19. The unknown voltage is connected to the terminals on the left-hand side of the potential divider. The two lower terminals on the right-hand side are connected to the points on the potentiometer where the unknown voltage is connected. Assuming that the potentiometer gives balance in the range 0–1.5 V, then the resistances in the potential divider are arranged to give multiplication factors of 10, 100 and 200 at the 0–15 V, 0–150 V and 0–300 V terminals, respectively.

The value of resistors R_1–R_4, inclusive, must have a reasonably high value, otherwise the current drawn from the measured voltage may give rise to an error in the measured voltage.

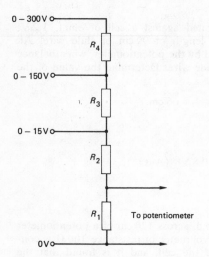

Fig. 11.19 A potential divider or voltage ratio box

Measurement of direct current

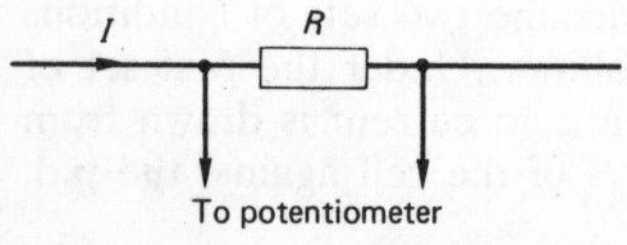

The value of an unknown current I can be determined by measuring the p.d. it produces across a standard resistor R (see figure 11.20). The value of the standard resistor depends on the value of the current being measured; the p.d. developed by the current must be large enough to give a measurable voltage on the potentiometer. The value of R in a high current circuit may, for example, be 0.01 Ω. The value of the current is calculated from $I = E/R$, where E is the voltage obtained from the potentiometer balance conditions.

Fig. 11.20 Basic circuit for current and resistance measurement with a d.c. potentiometer

Measurement of resistance

The circuit in figure 11.20 can also be used to determine the value of an unknown resistor R. In this case, a known value of direct current I is passed through the resistor. The value of R is calculated from $R = E/I$, where E is the voltage determined from the potentiometer balance conditions.

11.12 The Wheatstone Bridge

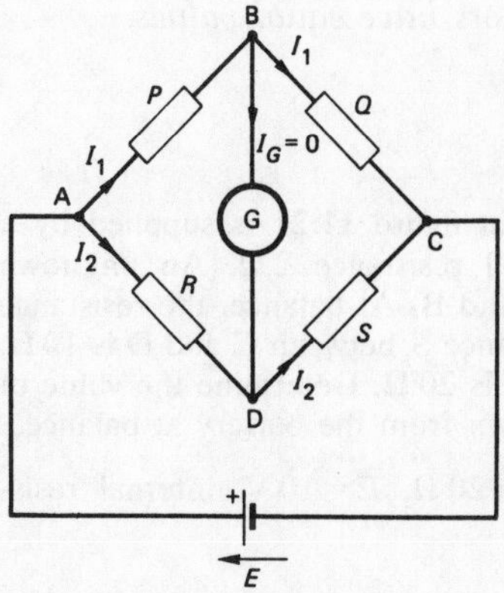

The Wheatstone bridge is a set of resistors which are interconnected as shown in figure 11.21, and is used to determine the value of one of the resistors.

A source of e.m.f. (whose value need not be known) is connected between points A and C, and a sensitive galvanometer G is connected between points B and D. In order to determine the value of one of the resistors, say P, we need to **balance** the bridge; the bridge is said to be balanced when the galvanometer deflection is zero. Balance is obtained by adjusting one or more of the resistors Q, R and S. When the bridge is balanced, the value of the unknown resistor P can be calculated either from the value of one other resistor, say Q, and the value of the ratio between the remaining two resistors (say the ratio R/S), or alternatively it can be calculated from the value of all three of the resistors Q, R and S. When we know only the value of one resistor and the ratio of the remaining resistors, the latter two arms of the bridge are known as the **ratio arms**; in the above case we have nominated R and S to be the ratio arms, but any pair of arms would do equally well.

When the bridge is balanced (see figure 11.21), the galvanometer current I_G is zero; current I_1 flows in P and Q, and I_2 flows in R and S. Since no current flows in the galvanometer, the p.d. across it is zero and, hence

P.d. across resistor P = p.d. across resistor R

that is

$$I_1 P = I_2 R \tag{11.16}$$

also

P.d. across resistor Q = p.d. across resistor S

or

$$I_1 Q = I_2 S \tag{11.17}$$

Dividing eqn. (11.16) by eqn. (11.17) gives

$$\frac{P}{Q} = \frac{R}{S} \tag{11.18}$$

The above equation can be re-written in the form

$$PS = RQ \tag{11.19}$$

Fig. 11.21 The Wheatstone bridge network at balance

Equation (11.19) is often a more convenient form to remember than eqn. (11.18) since *at balance the product of diagonally opposed pairs of resistors have equal values.*

EXAMPLE 11.7

A Wheatstone bridge of the type in figure 11.21 is supplied by a battery of e.m.f. 10 V and internal resistance 2 Ω. An unknown resistor P is connected between A and B. At balance, the resistance Q between B and C is 200 Ω, resistance S between C and D is 10 Ω, and resistance R between D and A is 20 Ω. Determine the value of resistor P and the total current drawn from the battery at balance.

Solution $Q = 200\,\Omega$, $S = 10\,\Omega$, $R = 20\,\Omega$, $E = 10\,V$, internal resistance of the battery = 2 Ω.

From eqn. (11.19)

$$PS = RQ$$

hence

$$P = RQ/S = 20 \times 200/10 = 400\,\Omega \quad (Ans.)$$

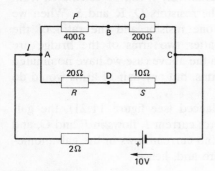

Fig. 11.22

The equivalent electrical circuit of the bridge at balance is given in figure 11.22. (Note: since no current flows in the galvanometer, we can regard the path BD as an open-circuit.) The resistance of the bridge circuit between points A and C is

$$R_{AC} = \frac{(400 + 200) \cdot (20 + 10)}{(400 + 200) + (20 + 10)} = 28.57\,\Omega$$

The current drawn from the battery when the bridge is at balance is

$$I = E/(R_{AC} + 2) = 10/(28.57 + 2) = 0.327\,A \quad (Ans.)$$

EXAMPLE 11.8

A resistance thermometer is in the form of the Wheatstone bridge circuit in figure 11.23. The resistance thermometer element has a resistance of 65 Ω at a temperature of 25° C. When the thermometer element is heated, the resistance of the variable resistor R is increased by 10 Ω in order to restore the bridge to the balance condition. If the temperature coefficient of resistance referred to 0° C of the thermometer element is 0.001 (°C)$^{-1}$, calculate the temperature to which the element has been heated.

Solution $Q = 80\,\Omega$, $S = 160\,\Omega$, $P = 65\,\Omega$ at 25° C.

At 25° C

$$PS = RQ$$

$$R = PS/Q = 65 \times 160/80 = 130\,\Omega$$

In order to maintain balance at the elevated temperature θ_2, the value of R is increased to $(130 + 10) = 140\,\Omega$. From eqn. (1.8) on page 9,

$$\frac{R_{P1}}{R_{P2}} = \frac{1 + \alpha_0 \theta_1}{1 + \alpha_0 \theta_2}$$

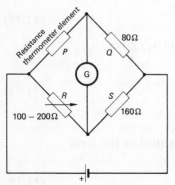

Fig. 11.23

where R_{P1} = resistance of element P at temperature θ_1, R_{P2} = resistance of element P at temperature θ_2, and α_0 is the temperature coefficient of resistance of the element referred to 0° C. We solve for θ_2 as follows. Re-writing the above equation gives

$$1 + \alpha_0 \theta_2 = \frac{R_{P2}}{R_{P1}}(1 + \alpha_0 \theta_1)$$

hence

$$\theta_2 = \left[\frac{R_{P2}}{R_{P1}}(1 + \alpha_0 \theta_1) - 1\right] \Big/ \alpha_0$$

$$= \left[\frac{140}{130}(1 + [0.001 \times 25]) - 1\right] \Big/ 0.001 = 103.8° \text{ C} \quad (Ans.)$$

11.13 Digital Multimeters

Digital multimeters are basically **digital voltmeters** (DVM) with circuit modifications which allow them to measure current and resistance. Whilst the reader will appreciate that discussion on the operating principle of digital voltmeters is beyond the scope of this volume, it is not out of place to describe how a DVM can be modified to measure current and resistance.

Measurement of current

The basis of current measurement is illustrated in figure 11.24. The method involves the measurement of the voltage across a known value of resistance S, through which the unknown value of current flows. The current is determined from the equation $I = V/R$. In practice, resistance S is incorporated in the digital multimeter, enabling the instrument reading to be calibrated in terms of current.

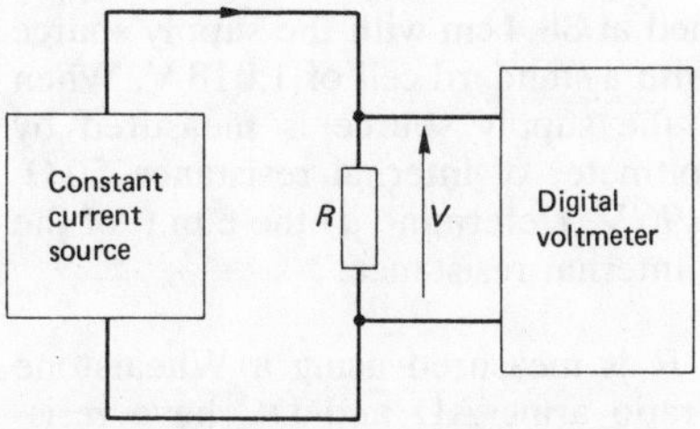

Measurement of resistance

When the digital multimeter is switched to the OHMS range, the internal circuitry is as shown in figure 11.25, where R is the unknown resistance connected to the terminals of the instrument.

The constant current source is an electronic circuit which delivers a constant value of direct current I to the unknown resistor R. The resistance is determined from the equation $R = V/I$, where V is the reading of the DVM. The constant current source is incorporated in the multimeter, enabling the instrument to be calibrated directly in terms of resistance.

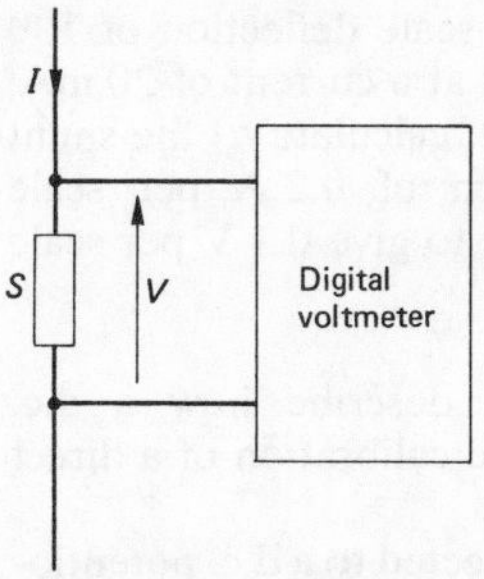

Fig. 11.24 Measurement of current using a digital voltmeter and a shunt

Fig. 11.25 Measurement of resistance by means of a digital voltmeter

Exercises

11.1 A moving-coil milliammeter is wound with $35\frac{1}{2}$ turns of wire. The effective radius of the coil is 1.0 cm and the effective length of each coil side in the magnetic field is 2 cm. If the flux density in the air gap is 0.15 T and the controlling torque produced by the hairsprings is 0.75×10^{-6} Nm/degree of deflection, calculate the current required to give a deflection of 90°.

[31.7 mA]

11.2 A moving-iron meter is wound with 50 turns and gives a full-scale deflection with a current of 5 A. If the instrument is to be rewound to give full-scale deflection with a current of 12.5 A, how many turns of wire are required?

[20]

11.3 A moving-coil instrument gives full-scale deflection with a current of 20 mA and has a resistance of 10 Ω. Calculate a) the shunt resistance required so that the meter may be used as a 5 A ammeter, b) the resistance of a voltage multiplier which allows the meter to be used as a 0–100 V meter.

[0.0402 Ω; 4990 Ω]

11.4 A moving-coil instrument gives full-scale deflection when the current is 10 mA, the terminal voltage of the meter being 70 mV. Calculate the value of the voltage multiplier resistor needed to allow the instrument to be used as a 0–50 V meter.

[4993 Ω]

11.5 A moving-coil meter has a maximum scale deflection of 100 divisions. If full-scale deflection occurs at a current of 20 mA, and the resistance of the meter is 10 Ω, calculate a) the shunt resistor required to give a deflection of 0.2 A per scale division, b) the series resistor required to give 0.1 V per scale division.

[a) 0.01 Ω; b) 490 Ω]

11.6 With the aid of a circuit diagram, describe how a d.c. potentiometer can be used to check the calibration of a direct current ammeter.

When a cell of e.m.f. 1.018 V is connected to a d.c. potentiometer, balance is obtained at 81 cm. A current is passed through an ammeter in series with a 0.2 Ω standard resistor, and the current is adjusted until the ammeter indicates 5 A. The p.d. across the standard resistor gives balance on the d.c. potentiometer at 78 cm. Calculate the percentage error in the reading of the instrument.

[2.0 per cent high]

11.7 A d.c. potentiometer is used to measure the e.m.f. of a supply source. Balance is obtained at 88.4 cm with the supply source in circuit, and at 45 cm with a standard cell of 1.018 V. When the terminal voltage of the supply source is measured by means of an accurate voltmeter of internal resistance 50 Ω, the voltmeter indicates 1.96 V. Determine a) the e.m.f. of the supply source and b) its internal resistance.

[a) 2 V; b) 1.02 Ω]

11.8 An unknown resistance R is measured using a Wheatstone bridge. At balance the ratio arms AD and DC have resistances of 1000 Ω and 10 Ω, respectively. The resistance in arm BC being 5.6 Ω. Determine the value of R, which is connected between points A and B.

[560 Ω]

11.9 Four resistors are connected together in the arms of a Wheatstone bridge, one each between points A and B, B and C, C and D, D and A. When the bridge is balanced, the value of the resistors between AB, BC and CD are 10.6 Ω, 10 Ω, and 21 Ω, respectively. Determine the value of the unknown resistor.

A cell of e.m.f. 3.0 V and internal resistance 1.04 Ω is connected between points A and C. Calculate the p.d. across the unknown resistor and also the power consumed by the 10 Ω resistor.

[22.26 Ω; 1.44 V; 0.184 W]

11.10 Derive the conditions of balance for a Wheatstone bridge. A Wheatstone bridge is used to measure the resistance of a 0–10 V moving-coil voltmeter. The resistances in the arms of the bridge are as follows: AB = 160 Ω, BC = voltmeter, CD = 1000 Ω, DA = 20 Ω. Calculate the resistance of the voltmeter.

If a 10 V d.c. supply is connected between points A and C, estimate the reading on the voltmeter when the bridge is at balance.

[8000 Ω; 9.8 V]

Index